☆ **THE BEST** ☆
FOOTBALL
PUB QUIZ
☆ **BOOK** ☆

Ever! **2**

CARLTON
BOOKS

☆ THE BEST ☆
FOOTBALL
PUB QUIZ
☆ BOOK ☆

CARLTON
BOOKS

Contents

INTRODUCTION

Over the past decade snugs and lounges in pubs the length and breadth of the country have become if not seats of learning, at least seats of intellect – which makes a change from seats of worn leatherette (although these still prevail in some areas). The pub quiz has transformed the bar into an arena of knowledge where beery brethren battle to the final bell. The format is simple: some friends, acquaintances, even complete strangers will do; a questioner; some paper; a collection of ragged Biros and a surfeit of beer and questions are all that is needed to create the perfect evening's entertainment. Wits are challenged, heads are huddled and patience is tested as teams try to outdo each other in their show of trivia retention. At these events you will learn that no fact is too small, no soccer star too obscure and no match too insignificant to test the pub crowds grey matter. In fact, the more obscure and wide-ranging the questions, the greater the chance of involving the entire bar room – nothing will gain the pub idiot greater respect than showing that they have the team line-up for every Preston North End game lodged in their head, except perhaps their switching from slip-ons to lace-ups. So take heart, and a copy of *The Best Football Pub Quiz Book Ever! (Volume 2)* to the boozer and have a few warm-up sessions and see if you can't organise your own pub quiz. You know it makes sense – it's the only way you'll know all the answers.

The main aim of *The Best Football Pub Quiz Book Ever! (Volume 2)* is to entertain, so it is important that you retain a sense of humour and sportsmanship as you play along, whether you are testing friends at home or setting a quiz for your local hostelry. That aside you also have to ensure that you are fully in control of your questions and players; remain calm, speak in a steady voice and constantly be unflapped when challenged by any one of the more heavily imbibed, as indeed you will be.

If the locals do get testy your best bet is to head for the door while throwing beer nuts in the air to confuse them, though this should happen in only the roughest pubs or on outings with the extended family – in which case you should attempt to rescue your spouse, if you can do so without spilling your drink and it isn't them causing the trouble.

The Best Football Pub Quiz Book Ever! (Volume 2) is divided into Easy, Medium and Hard questions. Giving Easy questions is bound to reveal some interesting answers, but it is possibly more interesting to tailor your questions so that the experts receive the brain-wracking Hard questions and the novices the stupefyingly Easy questions. Nothing hurts a fanatic more than being beaten on their specialist subject and the division of questions gives you the chance to employ a handicap system. Other handicap systems will also become apparent as you continue as quiz master, the team that wins the Sunday afternoon quiz will doubtless fail when it comes to Sunday night although if you want to set a quiz for Friday night you should check pupil dilation first, as on that evening of great relaxation you may find your teams asleep or brawling before calling the whole thing quits and joining them in a drink... or three.

In the interest of further clarification there follows a brief run down of each section:

Easy
In this primary round the main objective is to keep breathing and keep a pen in your hand. These questions are so easy that even the most docile pub idiot could gurgle his way through them in the time it takes to down a pint and still have time to knock over the stack of pennies on the bar. If you know what shape a football is, you shouldn't have too much difficulty.

Medium
On your toes people, things are getting tricky. By now the ringers on the out-of-towner's team will no longer be looking smug. These questions make for a challenge, but you are bound to get the odd soccer nut who will fancy his chances, for which you should continue on to section three.

Hard
Ask a full 20 of these questions and only the shrill wail of the pub cat fighting in the yard will be heard. Brows will be furrowed, glances exchanges and beer stared into.

All that is left to say is good luck with your testing and if you can't keep your spirits up at least try to keep them down.

The Easy Questions

If you don't know the difference between John Barnes and John Motson, then you will no doubt struggle through the next few questions. For the rest of us, though, these are the EASY questions, so called because if the quizzee falters on these they are either three sheets to the wind or far too young to be in the pub – either state rendering them toddling buffoons whose social graces will equal the depth of their knowledge.

These questions are perfect when used in the first round of an open entry quiz as they lull everyone into a false sense of security, although you must beware that contestants don't shout answers out because that creates a problematic precedent for the later, harder questions. Another way of placing these questions is to dot them throughout your quiz, thus making sure that on every team everyone should know the answer to at least one question, despite their age.

If you are running a league quiz then some of your team members may heap derision on such obvious questions but don't worry, even the cleverest quiz team member can come a cropper.

Quiz 1 **Who Did What?**

Answers – see page 11

1 Which team won the Premiership in 1999-2000?

2 Which team won the World Cup in 1998?

3 Which team won the FA Cup in 1999?

4 Which team won the European Super Cup in 1998?

5 Which team won the Worthington Cup in 2000?

6 Who was Footballer of the Year in 1999 in England?

7 Which team won Division One in 1999-2000?

8 Which team won Euro 96?

9 Which team finished bottom of the Premiership in 1999-2000?

10 Which team won the European Cup in 1999?

11 Which team won the World Cup in 1994?

12 Who scored the Premier League Goal of the Season for 1999-2000?

13 Who wrote *Fever Pitch*?

14 Which country hosted the World Cup in 1998?

15 Which countries staged Euro 2000?

16 Who scored the winning goal in the Euro 2000 final?

17 Which team won the Premiership in 1997-98?

18 Which team won the Scottish Premier League in 1997-98?

19 Who joined Real Madrid from Barcelona in summer 2000?

20 Which team won the UEFA Cup in 1999?

Answers

The Premier League (see Quiz 3)
1 Robbie Fowler. **2** Three. **3** Ipswich Town. **4** West Ham United.
5 Tottenham Hotspur. **6** Manchester United. **7** Newcastle United.
8 Leicester City. **9** Kevin Phillips **10** Charlton Athletic. **11** Arsenal.
12 Sunderland. **13** Everton. **14** The referee. **15** Dennis Bergkamp.
16 Aston Villa. **17** West Ham and Aston Villa. **18** Chelsea.
19 Coventry City. **20** Chelsea and Leeds.

Quiz 2 Goals Galore

Answers – see page 12

1   What is the record score in English football?

2   What is the record home win in a Premier League game?

3   Who beat Bury 10-0 in a League Cup game in 1983?

4   What was the score in the quarter-final between Holland and Yugoslavia in Euro 2000?

5   What is Chelsea's record win?

6   What is the record score in British football?

7   Who holds the record for England goals?

8   How many goals did he score for England?

9   Who holds the record for most international goals?

10   How many goals did he score?

11   Who beat Sheffield Wednesday 7-1 in March 1995?

12   Who holds the record for goals scored in FA Cup finals?

13   Who holds the record for hat-tricks scored in one season?

14   Who beat Fulham 10-0 in a League Cup game in 1986?

15   Who scored 306 goals in 559 appearances for Wolves?

16   Who scored 27 goals for Glasgow Rangers during season 1998-99?

17   Who scored a hat-trick for Italy in a World Cup game against Brazil in 1982?

18   Which team has scored most goals in a Premier League season?

19   How many goals did they score?

20   Who scored four times in an international match for West Germany v Switzerland?

Quiz 3 **The Premier League**

Answers – see page 9   **LEVEL 1**

1   Which Liverpool player was fined after an alleged 'cocaine-sniffing' goal celebration?

2   How many teams are relegated from the Premier League each season?

3   Which East Anglian team gained promotion to the Premier League in 1999-2000?

4   Which team has Steve Potts, Trevor Sinclair and Rio Ferdinand in their squad?

5   Whose 1999-2000 leading scorer was Steffen Iversen?

6   Who has won the Premier League the most times?

7   Which Premier League team is managed by Bobby Robson?

8   Which team has Matt Elliott, Muzzy Izzett and Steve Guppy in their squad?

9   Which Sunderland player was the Premier League's top scorer in 99-2000?

10   Which Premier League team plays at The Valley?

11   Euro 2000 winners Robert Pires, Thierry Henry and Patrick Vieira play for which Premier League team?

12   Which team has Niall Quinn, Alex Rea and Steve Bould in their squad?

13   Whose 1999-2000 leading scorer was Kevin Campbell?

14   Who did Paulo Di Canio push over to earn a suspension in 1999?

15   Which Arsenal striker is frightened of flying?

16   Which Premier League team is managed by John Gregory?

17   Which two Premier League teams play in claret and blue?

18   Ken Bates is the chairman of which Premier League team?

19   Which Premier League team have Hadji and Chippo in their squad?

20   For which two Premier League teams has Jimmy Floyd Hasselbaink played?

Answers

Who Did What? (see Quiz 1)
1 Manchester United. 2 France. 3 Manchester United. 4 Chelsea.
5 Leicester City. 6 David Ginola. 7 Charlton Athletic. 8 Germany.
9 Watford. 10 Manchester United. 11 Brazil. 12 Paolo Di Canio.
13 Nick Hornby. 14 France. 15 Holland and Belgium. 16 David
Trezeguet. 17 Arsenal. 18 Celtic. 19 Luis Figo. 20 Parma.

Quiz 4 **Euro Football**
Answers – see page 10

1   Anderlecht have dominated which country's national league for the past 30 years?

2   Complete the Spanish League team name: Deportivo La... ?

3   Which two teams share Madrid's Bernabeu stadium?

4   Which Italian team played Liverpool in the tragic European Cup Final at Heysel Stadium?

5   For which Spanish team does England's Steve McManaman play?

6   Complete the German league team name: Eintracht... ?

7   What are the names of the two Rome teams?

8   The Bundesliga is the name of which country's highest league?

9   Which Italian club did Robbie Keane sign for in summer 2000?

10   Which Spanish club played Real Madrid in the 2000 Champions League final: Valencia, Atletico Madrid or Barcelona?

11   Which Spanish club have Terry Venables and Bobby Robson both managed?

12   Which Roberto is known in Italy as 'the divine ponytail'?

13   Complete the Spanish league team name: Celta... ?

14   What are the names of the two Milan teams?

15   Complete the Dutch league team name: PSV... ?

16   Which Italian team did Paul Gascoigne play for?

17   Partizan and Red Star are from which Eastern European country?

18   Glentoran and Crusaders play in which country's league?

19   Which English television channel broadcasts live Italian football?

20   Which Frenchman playing for Juventus was the 1998 European and World Footballer of the Year?

Answers

Goals Galore (see Quiz 2)
1 Preston North End 26 Hyde United 0. **2** Manchester United 9 Ipswich Town 0. **3** West Ham. **4** 6-1 to Holland. **5** 13-0 v Jeunesse Hautcharage, 1971. **6** Arbroath 36 Bon Accord 0. **7** Bobby Charlton. **8** 49. **9** Ferenc Puskas. **10** 83, for Hungary. **11** Blackburn Rovers. **12** Ian Rush. **13** Jimmy Greaves. **14** Liverpool. **15** Steve Bull. **16** Rod Wallace. **17** Paolo Rossi. **18** Manchester United. **19** 97. **20** Gerd Müller.

Quiz 5 Goalkeepers

Answers – see page 15   **LEVEL 1**

1   Who kept goal for England in the 1998 World Cup Finals?

2   Which French keeper did Manchester United buy in May 2000?

3   From whom did they buy him?

4   What nationality is Chelsea's Ed de Goey?

5   Who is the only English keeper with a World Cup winner's medal?

6   Which English keeper was beaten by Maradona's 'Hand of God' goal?

7   What number do keepers traditionally wear?

8   Who saved John Aldridge's penalty in the 1988 FA Cup final?

9   Which keeper was sent off after 12 seconds of his first match of a season?

10   Which Russian goalkeeper was known as the 'Black Panther'?

11   Which keeper was transferred from Wimbledon to Tottenham in 2000?

12   Who is Arsenal's Austrian keeper?

13   Who kept goal for England against Romania in Euro 2000?

14   Which club side does he play for?

15   Who did he play for before joining his present club?

16   Who does David James keep goal for?

17   Which keeper joined Manchester United from Villa in June 1999?

18   Name Liverpool's Dutch international keeper.

19   Who keeps goal for Manchester City?

20   Which former keeper managed Italy in Euro 2000?

Answers

Memorable Matches (see Quiz 7)
1 Manchester United. **2** Arsenal. **3** 7-3 to Real. **4** West Germany.
5 Socrates and Julio Cesar. **6** Zinedine Zidane. **7** Iran. **8** France.
9 Germany. **10** Wimbledon. **11** Manchester United and Barcelona.
12 Nayim. **13** 1979. **14** 3-2 to Argentina. **15** Roma. **16** Carlisle
United. **17** Cameroon. **18** 5-0. **19** Crystal Palace. **20** Argentina.

Quiz 6 Manchester United

Answers – see page 16

1   Where do Manchester United play home games?

2   What is Manchester United's nickname?

3   Who is Manchester United's most successful manager?

4   Who was Manchester United's regular captain at the end of the 90s?

5   Who was their top scorer in the 1999-2000 season?

6   How many goals did he score in total?

7   Who made the most appearances for United in that season?

8   Against whom was the biggest league crowd at Old Trafford of the 1999-2000 season?

9   Who kept goal in the championship-clinching match of the 1999-2000 season?

10 Against whom was that match played?

11 Who knocked Manchester United out of the Champions League in the 1999-2000 season?

12 In what round were they knocked out?

13 Who did Manchester United beat in the Toyota Inter-Continental Cup?

14 Where do they come from?

15 Who scored the winning goal in that match?

16 Who did Manchester United play in the UEFA Super Cup?

17 Where was that match played?

18 What was the final score?

19 By how many points did Manchester United win the Premiership in the 1999-2000 season?

20 Who were the runners-up?

Answers

Division One (see Quiz 8)
1 Charlton Athletic. 2 Manchester City. 3 Ipswich Town.
4 Bolton Wanderers. 5. 5 6 Jean Tigana. 7 Kent. 8 Prenton
Park. 9 Sheffield. 10 Burnley. 11 Preston North End.
12 Graeme Souness. 13 The Canaries. 14 Bolton Wanderers. 15
Walsall, Port Vale and Swindon Town. 16 1995. 17 The Endsleigh
League. 18 Barnsley. 19 West Bromwich Albion. 20 24.

Quiz 7 **Memorable Matches**

Answers – see page 13

LEVEL 1

1 Who beat Arsenal 2-1 in an FA Cup semi-final replay in April 1999?

2 Who won the First Division title in 1988-89 by beating Liverpool 2-0?

3 What was the score when Real Madrid met Eintracht Frankfurt in the European Cup final in 1960?

4 Who did Italy beat 4-3 after extra time in the 1970 World Cup semi-final?

5 Name the two Brazilians who missed a penalty in their shoot-out against France in a 1986 World Cup quarter-final.

6 A golden goal penalty settled the Euro 2000 semi-final between France and Portugal. Who scored it?

7 Who beat the USA 2-1 in a dramatic World Cup match in France in 1998?

8 Which team equalised in the 90th minute of the Euro 2000 final?

9 Who did England beat for the first time in 34 years during Euro 2000?

10 Who beat West Ham 4-3 at Upton Park in 1998 having been 3-0 down?

11 Which two teams drew 3-3 twice during the 1998-99 European Cup?

12 Whose goal sunk Arsenal in the 1995 European Cup Winners' Cup final?

13 In which year did Trevor Francis score the winner for Nottingham Forest in the European Cup final against Malmo?

14 What was the score in the 1986 World Cup final?

15 Who did Liverpool beat on penalties in the 1984 European Cup final?

16 Whose on-loan goalkeeper scored a last-minute winner to keep his temporary team in the football league in 1998-99?

17 Which team did England beat in the quarter-finals of the 1990 World Cup?

18 Chelsea thrashed Manchester United in October 1999 by what score?

19 After a 9-0 league loss, who beat Liverpool in the 1990 FA Cup semi-final?

20 Who beat England in Saint Etienne during the 1998 World Cup?

Quiz 8 **Division One**

Answers – see page 14

1   Who won the Division One title in 1999-2000?

2   Who were the runners-up?

3   Who were also promoted to the Premiership that season, via the play-offs?

4   Who did they beat in the play-off final?

5   How many London teams were there in Division One in 2000-01?

6   Which Fulham manager came from France?

7   In which county do Gillingham play their home games?

8   What is the name of Tranmere Rovers' ground?

9   Which city in Yorkshire had two teams in Division One in 2000-01?

10 Who plays at Turf Moor?

11 Who were promoted to Division One in 1999-2000 as champions of Division Two?

12 Who was the manager of Blackburn Rovers in 2000?

13 What is Norwich City's nickname?

14 Which Nationwide League team reached the semi-finals of the FA Cup in 1999-2000?

15 Which three clubs were relegated from Division One in 1999-2000?

16 When did the Nationwide League become the Nationwide League?

17 What was it previously called?

18 Who finished fourth in the league in 1999-2000?

19 Who escaped relegation by one place during 1999-2000?

20 How many teams are there in Division One?

Which temperamental Frenchman won the league with Leeds United and Manchester United?

Which former Chelsea player captained France to World Cup 98 and Euro 2000 glory?

Which West Ham United Italian pushed a referee to the ground when playing for Sheffield Wednesday?

Manchester United's Ole Gunnar Solskjaer hails from which country?

For which team does Ukrainian striker Sergei Rebrov play?

Chelsea's Gustavo Poyet is from which South American country?

American goalkeeper Kasey Keller plays for which Premier League club?

Which Premier League team fields Moroccans Hadji and Chippo?

Which Georgian has played for Manchester City and Derby County?

From which country does Leeds United's Harry Kewell come?

Germans Dietmar Hamaan and Markus Babbel appear for which Reds?

Middlesbrough's Christian Karembeu is from New Caledonia but plays international football for which country?

Peruvian Nolberto Solano appears in which team's striped shirts?

What is the surname of Southampton's Latvian Marian?

For which country does Chelsea's Jimmy Floyd Hasselbaink play?

French teammates Vieira and Pires play for which London club?

Which Romanian Dan went from Chelsea to Bradford City in the summer of 2000?

Which French exile went from Tottenham to Aston Villa in summer 2000?

What is the nationality of managers Arsene Wenger and Gerard Houllier?

For which country did Manchester United's legendary goalkeeper Peter Schmeichel play?

Quiz 10 Celebrity Fans

Answers – see page 20

1 Which absolutely fabulous celebrity is a Wimbledon fan?

2 Actress Catherine Zeta Jones shows a high fidelity to her home town Swans. Who are they?

3 Who would have a south bank show at Arsenal?

4 Des Lynam rarely sees his south coast favourites live on TV. Name them

5 Which East Anglian team cooks up a treat for TV's Delia Smith?

6 Former Prime Minister John Major supported the blues – which ones?

7 For which team does Nick Berry's heart beat like a hammer?

8 It's not difficult to guess professional Geordies Ant and Dec's team?

9 Who would athlete Steve Cram run to the North East to see?

10 Which club brought sunshine to the late great comedian Eric Morecambe?

11 It's nice to see Bruce Forsyth at White Hart Lane, watching which team

12 Which comedian takes his 'Funky Moped' to Birmingham City?

13 GMTV presenter Lorraine Kelly supports which orange-shirted Scottish side?

14 Home Secretary Jack Straw shares his first name with his team's steel magnate former chairman – which team?

15 Who has been framed watching the Gunners?

16 Boris Becker and Steffi Graf kick up a racket for which European side?

17 Of which team has disc jockey John Peel has been a long-time supporter?

18 Notting Hill isn't a million miles from Hugh Grant's favourite cottage.

19 Which London club do Jo Brand, Sean Hughes and Eddie Izzard go to for a laugh?

20 *A Question of Sport*'s John Parrott is true blue... but which club?

Answers

Transfers (see Quiz 12)
1 Luis Figo. **2** Real Madrid. **3** Jimmy Floyd Hasselbaink. **4** £15m.
5 Fabien Barthez. **6** Paulo Wanchope. **7** Christian Karembeu. **8** Paul
Gascoigne. **9** Gary McAllister. **10** The Bosman Ruling. **11** Trevor
Francis. **12** Johan Cruyff. **13** Ruud van Nistelrooy. **14** PSV Eindhoven.
15 Marseille. **16** Lyons. **17** Fiorentina. **18** Real Madrid. **19** £90m.
20 Emile Heskey.

Which Gary is a Manchester United and England defender?

Which Jamie's father manages West Ham?

Which Gary is a Newcastle and Wales midfielder?

Which Paul scored England's first goal in Euro 2000?

What are Gary McAllister's last three Premiership clubs?

Which Leeds Gary is a Republic of Ireland full-back?

Which Emile used to play for Leicester City?

Which Chris joined Celtic after disappointing at Chelsea?

Which Dennis is an Arsenal and Holland marksman?

Which Dennis is often the only Englishman in a Chelsea shirt?

Which Nicky swapped Everton Blue for Liverpool Red?

Which Dennis has been Manchester United and the Republic of Ireland's Mr Reliable?

Which David was England's No 1?

Which Kenny managed Blackburn's Premiership winning team?

Which Teddy helped Manchester United to European Cup glory?

Which Marcel was one of France's Euro 2000 stars?

Which Paul has played for Arsenal, Middlesbrough, Aston Villa and England?

Which Matthew is affectionately called 'Le God' at Southampton?

Which Michael is England's youngest ever goalscorer?

Which Ian is Leeds United's tough-tackling full-back?

Quiz 12 Transfers

Answers – see page 18

1   Who was the most expensive player in the world by the end of 200

2   Who did he join?

3   Who is Chelsea's record signing?

4   How much did he cost?

5   Who joined Manchester United from Monaco in May 2000?

6   Which striker joined West Ham in 1999 and left for Manchester Ci 2000?

7   Which Frenchman joined Middlesbrough from Real Madrid in 2000

8   Who left Middlesbrough for Everton in 2000?

9   Which veteran midfielder joined Liverpool from Coventry in 2000?

10 What is the name of the ruling that allows players to change clubs free when out of contract?

11 Who was Britain's first million-pound transfer?

12 Who was the world's first million-pound transfer?

13 Whose last-minute injury in training scuppered his proposed move Manchester United in summer 2000?

14 Who was he playing for at the time?

15 From whom did Robert Pires join Arsenal?

16 Mark Vivien-Foe left West Ham for which club in 2000?

17 Gabriel Batistuta joined Roma from which club in 2000?

18 Which European club spent the most money on transfers during th summer of 2000?

19 About how much did they spend in total?

20 Who left Leicester for Liverpool in 1999-2000?

Answers

Celebrity Fans (see Quiz 10)
1 June Whitfield. 2 Swansea City. 3 Melvyn Bragg. 4 Brighton and Hove Albion. 5 Norwich City. 6 Chelsea. 7 West Ham. 8 Newc United. 9 Sunderland. 10 Luton Town. 11 Spurs. 12 Jasper Carrott. 13 Dundee United. 14 Blackburn Rovers. 15 Jeremy Bead 16 Bayern Munich. 17 Liverpool. 18 Fulham. 19 Crystal Pala 20 Everton.

Quiz 13 **The North East**

nswers – see page 23

LEVEL 1

What stadium does the Sunderland team illuminate?

In what colour shirts do Middlesbrough play?

Which former England captain is Middlesbrough's manager?

'H'way the lads' is the rallying cry of which team?

With which North East lower league club did Brian Clough begin his managerial career?

Which club used to be spurred on by the 'Roker roar'?

Who did Sunderland beat to win the FA Cup in 1973?

Which north-east club was managed by Argentinian Osvaldo Ardiles?

Which Republic of Ireland manager had spells in charge of Newcastle and Middlesbrough?

0   What did Hartlepools lose in 1968?

1   Whose supporters are known as 'the Toon Army'?

2   Who are the Mackems ?

3   Which North East lower league side are known as the Quakers?

4   Peter Reid is the manager of which club?

5   Which diminutive Brazilian starred for Middlesbrough?

6   Whose chaiman resigned after making disparaging comments about the local womenfolk?

7   What colour shirts do Darlington and Newcastle United have in common?

8   Which Geordie left home to play for Spurs, Lazio, Rangers, Middlesbrough and Everton?

9   Who played for Liverpool, Hamburg, Southampton and Newcastle?

0   Which Geordie ex-sausage stuffer played for Newcastle, Tottenham, Marseille and Sheffield Wednesday?

Answers

Full-backs (see Quiz 15)
1 France. 2 Dixon. 3 Aston Villa. 4 Chelsea. 5 Republic of Ireland. 6 Phillip Neville. 7 Germany. 8 Missed a penalty in the shoot-out. 9 Brazil. 10 Ben Thatcher. 11 Stuart Pearce. 12 Liverpool. 13 Italy. 14 West Ham. 15 French. 16 George Burley. 17 Wing Backs. 18 Sir Alf Ramsey. 19 Graeme Le Saux. 20 Silvinho.

Quiz 14 **Euro Football 2**

LEVEL 1

1 Torino and which other Italian club are based in Turin?

2 Which Dutch team plays in white shirts with a wide red stripe?

3 Which Argentinian Gabriel was transferred from Fiorentina to Roma in May 2000?

4 Sparta and which other Dutch team are based in Rotterdam?

5 Which German team did Manchester United beat in the 1999 Champions League final?

6 In which country is the San Siro stadium?

7 Complete the German league team name: Hertha...?

8 Saint-Etienne and Lens play in which country's league?

9 In what colour shirts do Fiorentina play?

10 Which southern Italian team did Maradona inspire to the league and cup double in 1987?

11 In which city are French club PSG based?

12 2000 EUFA Cup winners Galatasary are from which county?

13 Which European city completes the names of Spartak, Lokomotiv and CSKA?

14 Olympiakos and Panathinaikos hail from which European country?

15 Benfica and Porto are two of the biggest teams in which country?

16 What is the name of the top Italian league?

17 Bayern and 1860 are based in which European city?

18 Bohemians and Finn Harps play in which country's league?

19 Fabien Barthez joined Manchester United from which classy French resort side?

20 Which Brazilian playing for Barcelona was the 1999 European and World Footballer of the Year?

Answers

The 70s (see Quiz 16)
1 Brazil. 2 George Best. 3 Bill Shankly. 4 Billy Bremner.
5 Sunderland. 6 Argentina. 7 Atkinson. 8 Arsenal. 9 Manchester City
10 Johan Cruyff. 11 Bobby Moore. 12 Alan Ball. 13 Kenny Dalglish.
14 Chelsea. 15 West Germany. 16 Germany. 17 Brady.
18 Goalkeeper. 19 Poland. 20 Andy Gray.

uiz 15 Full-Backs

LEVEL 1

Lillian Thuram scored two goals in the 1998 World Cup semi final for which country?

Which Lee is Arsenal's long serving full-back?

England's Gareth Barry plays for which Premier League team?

Spanish international Albert Ferrer defends for which Blues?

For which country do Leeds United's Ian Harte and Gary Kelly play?

Which Manchester United full-back gave away the penalty to send England home from Euro 2000?

Middlesbrough's Christian Ziege played for which Euro 2000 team?

What was Michael Gray of Sunderland's fatal error in the 1998 play-offs?

Carlos Alberto was captain of which World Cup winning team?

Which full-back signed for Tottenham from Wimbledon in the summer of 2000?

Which England international full-back missed a penalty against Germany in the 1990 World Cup semi-final shoot-out, but made amends in 1996?

Norwegian Vegard Heggem plays for which Premier League team?

Paolo Maldini has been the regular full-back for which country?

Frank Lampard's father (also Frank Lampard) played for which team?

What nationality is Manchester United's Mikael Silvestre?

Which Ipswich manager and former player was a Scottish international?

What name is given to attacking full-backs in a five-man midfield?

Which 50s Tottenham full-back went on to become England's greatest manager?

Which Chelsea and England full-back has had run-ins with David Batty and Robbie Fowler?

Who is Arsenal's Brazilian full-back?

Quiz 16 The 70s

Answers – see page 22

1   Jarzinho and Rivelino were among the stars of which country's 70s team

2   Which Belfast boy left Manchester United in 1975 for a life of champagne, girls and some football in Fulham and the USA?

3   Which Liverpool manager retired in 1974 having taken his team to the to

4   Which fiery Scotsman captained Leeds to FA Cup and League Championship success in the 70s?

5   Who sensationally beat Leeds in the 1973 FA Cup Final?

6   Ossie Ardiles and Ricardo Villa came from which country to Spurs?

7   Which Big Ron managed West Bromwich and Manchester Utd in the 70

8   For which club did Leeds manager David O'Leary play?

9   Lee, Bell and Summerbee were the stars of which top 70s English tean

10 Which great Dutch player helped Ajax win three European cups in the 70s before joining Barcelona?

11 Which legendary England captain joined Fulham in 1974 after nearly years at West Ham?

12 Which England World Cup winner took his white boots to Arsenal in 197

13 Which King Kenny did Liverpool sign from Celtic in 1977?

14 Charlie Cooke and Peter Osgood were stars of which cup-winning team

15 Gerd Müller scored the winner for who in the 1974 World Cup final?

16 In which foreign country did Kevin Keegan play during the 70s?

17 Which Liam was Arsenal and Ireland's creative force in the 70s?

18 In which position did Peter Shilton play for England during the 70s?

19 Which Eastern European country earned a draw at Wembley and prevented England from qualifying for the 1974 World Cup?

20 Which Sky pundit played for Dundee United, Aston Villa, Wolves and Everton?

LEVEL 1

1 What is the name of Liverpool's ground?
2 Which lager is advertised on the team's shirts?
3 Who did Liverpool sign for £11m from Leicester City in February 2000?
4 Liverpool's Patrick Berger plays for which national team?
5 Who was Liverpool's manager at the start of the 2000-01 season?
6 Which Liverpool striker scored a memorable goal for England against Argentina in the 1998 World Cup?
7 Which Scottish former Liverpool player was manager from 1985-91?
8 Which 80s Liverpool striker is Wales' record goalscorer?
9 Which Liverpool manager won six championships and three European Cups between 1974 and 1983?
10 Which player captained Liverpool, England and *A Question of Sport* teams?
11 Which Liverpool midfielder's has missed out on England duty for three major tournaments through injury?
12 What is written on the Liverpool club crest?
13 For which team did goalkeeper Sander Westerveld play in Euro 2000?
14 Which Red was named Footballer of the Year in 1988 and 1990?
15 Steve McManaman supported which team as a boy?
16 Which England midfielder joined Liverpool from Inter Milan in 1997?
17 Which former Liverpool player has been a manager of Newcastle United, Fulham and England?
18 Which former Liverpool midfielder scored for Real Madrid in the 2000 European Cup final?
19 Which Liverpool striker was fined for displaying a T-shirt supporting sacked Liverpool dockers?
20 What is the first name of Liverpool's African star Camara?

Who Did What 2? (see Quiz 19)
1 Manchester United. 2 Lee Martin. 3 Lazio. 4 Chelsea.
5 Real Madrid. 6 Rangers. 7 Tottenham Hotspur. 8 Chelsea.
9 Nottingham Forest. 10 Dwight Yorke. 11 Peter Shilton.
12 Inter Milan. 13 Andy Cole. 14 Coventry City. 15 Ryan Giggs.
16 Denmark. 17 Bobby Moore. 18 Roberto Di Matteo. 19 AS Monaco. 20 Wimbledon.

Quiz 18 European Cup

Answers – see page 28

LEVEL 1

1   Who won the Champions League in 2000?

2   Who did they beat in the final?

3   Which other Spanish club reached the semi-final stage?

4   Who were the last English club to win the Champions League?

5   The game was decided on a penalty shoot-out. True or false?

6   In which city did they win the final?

7   In what year did the European Cup start?

8   Who won the first competition?

9   Which English club has won the European Cup the most times?

10   How many times have they won it?

11   When did Manchester United win the European Cup for the first time?

12   Who did they beat in the final?

13   Where was the match played?

14   Which club has won the European Cup the most times?

15   How many times have they won it?

16   Who were the losing finalists in 1997 and 1998?

17   In which city do they play their home games?

18   Who were the last Dutch club to win the tournament?

19   When did they last win it?

20   Who were the last Eastern European team to win the tournament?

Answers

FA Cup Finals (see Quiz 20)
1 Chelsea. 2 Aston Villa. 3 Manchester United. 4 Ten times.
5 Arsenal. 6 Newcastle United. 7 Eric Cantona. 8 Roberto Di Matteo i
1997 after 43 seconds. 9 Sunderland. 10 Kevin Moran, Manchester
United. 11 Marc Overmars and Nicolas Anelka.
12 Everton. 13 1993 Arsenal v Sheffield Wednesday. 14 Manchester
United 4 Chelsea 0. 15 1994. 16 1923 17 Bolton Wanderers and
West Ham United. 18 2000. 19 1872. 20 1970.

Quiz 19 **Who Did What? 2**

Answers – see page 25

LEVEL 1

1 Who won the FA Cup in 1990?

2 Who scored the winning goal in that match?

3 Who won Serie A in 1999-2000?

4 Who won the European Cup Winners' Cup in 1998?

5 Who won the European Cup in 1998?

6 Who won the Tennent's Scottish Cup in 1999?

7 Who won the Worthington Cup in 1999?

8 Who won the Charity Shield in 2000?

9 Who finished bottom of the Premiership in 1998-99?

10 Who was the Premiership's leading scorer in 1998-99?

11 Who is the most capped England international?

12 Who won the UEFA Cup in 1998?

13 Who holds the record for number of goals scored in a Premiership match?

14 Who won the FA Cup in 1987?

15 Who scored a 'wonder goal' to defeat Arsenal in the 1999 FA Cup semi-final replay?

16 Who won the European Championships in 1992?

17 Who captained England to World Cup glory in 1966?

18 Who scored the winning goal in the 2000 FA Cup final?

19 Who won the French League in 1999-2000?

20 Who were relegated from the Premiership in 1999-2000 along with Watford and Sheffield Wednesday?

Answers

Liverpool (see Quiz 17)
1 Anfield. 2 Carlsberg. 3 Emile Heskey. 4 The Czech Republic.
5 Gerard Houllier. 6 Michael Owen. 7 Kenny Dalglish. 8 Ian Rush.
9 Bob Paisley. 10 Emlyn Hughes. 11 Jamie Redknapp. 12 'You'll Never Walk Alone'. 13 Holland. 14 John Barnes. 15 Everton.
16 Paul Ince. 17 Kevin Keegan. 18 Steve McManaman.
19 Robbie Fowler. 20 Titi.

Quiz 20 FA Cup Finals

Answers – see page 26

1 Who won the FA Cup in 2000?

2 Who did they beat in the final?

3 Which club has won the most FA Cups?

4 How many times have they won it?

5 Who won the competition in 1998?

6 Who were the losing finalists in both 1998 and 1999?

7 Who scored the winning goal in the 1996 final?

8 Who scored the quickest goal ever in an FA Cup final?

9 Which was the last Second Division club to appear in the FA Cup final?

10 Who was the first player ever to be sent off in an FA Cup final?

11 Who scored Arsenal's goals in the 1998 final?

12 Who beat Manchester United in the 1995 final?

13 Which was the last FA Cup final decided on a replay?

14 What was the biggest victory in a final during the nineties?

15 In which year did that match take place?

16 When was the first FA Cup final played at Wembley?

17 Who contested that match?

18 When was the last FA Cup final at the 'old' Wembley?

19 When was the first FA Cup final?

20 When was the first Wembley FA Cup final that went to a replay?

Answers

European Cup (see Quiz 18)
1 Real Madrid. 2 Valencia. 3 Barcelona. 4 Manchester United. 5 False
6 Barcelona. 7 1956. 8 Real Madrid. 9 Liverpool. 10 Four times.
11 1968. 12 Benfica. 13 Wembley. 14 Real Madrid. 15 Eight times.
16 Juventus. 17 Turin. 18 Ajax Amsterdam. 19 1995. 20 Red Star
Belgrade.

Quiz 21 Scottish Football

Answers – see page 31

LEVEL 1

1 Which team plays home games at Ibrox Stadium?

2 What are the names of the two Edinburgh Premier League clubs?

3 What colour shirts do Aberdeen play in?

4 Which Henrik is Celtic's Swedish international striker?

5 Which Glasgow team is a Thistle?

6 Where are Scottish FA Cup finals traditionally played?

7 What is the name of Celtic's stadium?

8 Which Scottish city has two teams whose grounds are 100 yards apart?

9 Which team won nine championships in a row in the 60s and 70s?

10 Which *Question of Sport* captain is Rangers' record scorer?

11 Which Scottish manager led Aberdeen to glory before taking over at Manchester United?

12 Liam Brady, Kenny Dalglish and John Barnes have all been managers of which Scottish club?

13 Which Scottish team won nine championships in a row in the 70s and 80s?

14 What colour shirts do Hearts wear?

15 Which Scottish team are known as 'the Hi-Bs' ?

16 Which Scottish club plays at Pittodrie?

17 Which name groups Celtic and Rangers?

18 What sets Berwick Rangers apart from all other Scottish league teams?

19 Which English striker did Celtic buy from Chelsea before the 2000-01 season?

20 Which former Rangers and Scotland centre-forward went to Newcastle and Everton?

Answers

Midlands Clubs (see Quiz 23)
1 West Bromwich Albion. 2 Molineux. 3 Aston Villa. 4 West Bromwich Albion and Aston Villa, 10 times. 5 Birmingham City. 6 Wolves. 7 Division Two. 8 Colin Lee. 9 Birmingham City. 10 The Hawthorns. 11 Birmingham. 12 Three: Birmingham, West Brom and Wolves. 13 Stoke. 14 Billy Wright. 15 Wolves. 16 Four: Aston Villa, Stoke, West Brom and Wolves. 17 Port Vale and Walsall. 18 Division Two. 19 Britannia Stadium. 20 Coventry City.

1   Which round did England get to in the 1990 World Cup?
2   Who scored in the first minute against France in the 1982 World Cup?
3   Whose two goals put England out of the 1986 World Cup?
4   Who won the Golden Boot for most goals in the 1986 World Cup?
5   Which England keeper was known as Shilts?
6   Which influential player did Sir Alf Ramsey substitute when England were winning 2-0 against West Germany in Mexico 70?
7   Which African nation did England beat to reach the semi-finals in 1990?
8   Who scored England's penalty against Argentina in the 1998 World Cup?
9   Which Premier League team boss was manager of England during the 1986 and 1990 World Cups?
10 From which World Cup did England exit after penalty misses by Stuart Pearce and Chris Waddle?
11 Who was accused of stealing a bracelet prior to Mexico 70?
12 Where did England play Argentina in France 98: St Etienne or Lens?
13 Who cried after being booked against Germany in 1990?
14 Who scored the disallowed 'golden goal' against Argentina in France 98?
15 Who did Sir Alf Ramsey label as 'animals' in 1966?
16 Which England goalkeeper made 'the save of the century' against Brazil in Mexico 70?
17 Which then-Chelsea player scored the winning goal for Romania against England in 1998?
18 Who scored with a last-minute volley against Belgium in 1990?
19 In which year did England play France, Czechoslovakia, Kuwait, West Germany and Spain?
20 Which England goal in the 1966 Final was confirmed by a linesman?

Answers

Memorable Matches 2 (see Quiz 24)
1 Argentina. 2 The European Championships. 3 Kenny Dalglish.
4 Dave Beasant. 5 Munich 1860. 6 Inter Milan. 7 4-1.
8 West Germany. 9 2-1 to Holland. 10 Germany. 11 Holland.
12 Juventus. 13 England. 14 Manchester United. 15 Peter
Shilton. 16 2-2. 17 West Germany. 18 Spain. 19 Charlie George.
20 Gillingham.

Quiz 23 Midlands Clubs

Answers – see page 29

LEVEL 1

1 Which club is known as 'The Baggies'?

2 Where do Wolves play?

3 Which Midlands club appeared in the 2000 FA Cup final?

4 Which Midlands clubs have appeared in the most FA Cup finals?

5 Who plays at St Andrews?

6 Which Midlands club won the FA Cup in 1960?

7 In which division do Walsall play?

8 Who is the manager of Wolves?

9 Which Midlands club finished highest in the Nationwide League in 1999-2000?

10 What is the name of West Brom's home ground?

11 In which city do Aston Villa play their home games?

12 How many Midlands clubs were there in Division One in the 2000-01 season?

13 In which city do Port Vale play their home games?

14 Which legendary Midlands player skippered England 70 times?

15 Which club did he play for?

16 How many Midlands clubs were original members of the Football League?

17 Which two Midlands clubs were relegated from the Nationwide League in 2000?

18 In which division do Stoke City play?

19 What is the name of their ground?

20 Which was the last Midlands club to win the FA Cup?

Answers

Scottish Football (see Quiz 21)
1 Rangers. 2 Hibernian (Hibs) and Heart of Midlothian (Hearts). 3 Red.
4 Larsson. 5 Partick Thistle. 6 Hampden Park. 7 Celtic Park.
8 Dundee. 9 Celtic. 10 Ally McCoist. 11 Alex Ferguson. 12 Celtic.
13 Rangers. 14 Maroon. 15 Hibernian. 16 Aberdeen. 17 The Old Firm.
18 Their ground is in England. 19 Chris Sutton. 20 Duncan Ferguson.

1 Who did England play in the notorious World Cup quarter-final in 1966?

2 In which tournament did France beat Portugal in a semi-final in 1984?

3 Who scored the winner for Liverpool in the 1978 European Cup final?

4 Who saved a penalty to help Wimbledon win the FA Cup final in 1988?

5 Who did Leeds beat to qualify for the Champions League proper in August 2000?

6 Celtic beat which Italian giants to win the European Cup in 1967?

7 What was the score when Manchester United beat Benfica in the 1968 European Cup final?

8 Who did Holland play in the European Championship semi-final in 1988?

9 What was the score in that match?

10 Who beat England in the 1990 World Cup semi-final?

11 Who did England beat 4-1 in the Euro 96 group stage?

12 Who did Manchester United defeat in the 1999 Champions League semi-final?

13 Who lost 3-2 to Romania in the group stages of Euro 2000?

14 Who beat Liverpool with a last-minute goal in the FA Cup fourth round in 1999?

15 Who kept goal for England in the 'Hand of God' World Cup match?

16 What was the score when Chelsea met Leeds in the 1970 FA Cup final at Wembley?

17 Who knocked England out of the 1970 World Cup?

18 Who did England beat in a penalty shoot-out in the quarter-finals of Euro 96?

19 Whose goal against Liverpool in 1971 won Arsenal the FA Cup?

20 Manchester City beat who in the 1998-99 First Division play-off final?

Answers

England's World Cups (see Quiz 22)
1 Semi-finals. **2** Bryan Robson. **3** Diego Maradona. **4** Gary Lineker. **5** Peter Shilton. **6** Bobby Charlton. **7** Cameroon. **8** Alan Shearer. **9** Bobby Robson. **10** 1990. **11** Bobby Moore. **12** St Etienne. **13** Paul Gascoigne. **14** Sol Campbell. **15** Argentina. **16** Gordon Banks. **17** Dan Petrescu. **18** David Platt. **19** 1982. **20** The third.

Quiz 25 **Grounds**

Answers – see page 35

1   Who does battle at Stamford Bridge?

2   Ibrox Stadium is home to which great champions?

3   Which country plays internationals at Windsor Park?

4   Who moved into the Stadium of Light in 1997?

5   Everton play their home games at which ground?

6   The Arsenal Stadium is commonly referred to as... ?

7   Who plays at Highfield Road?

8   In which city is Wales' Millennium Stadium?

9   Crystal Palace and Wimbledon both play at which Park?

10   Down which lane would you find Tottenham Hotspur?

11   Which Reds play at Anfield?

12   Where is Manchester United's theatre of dreams?

13   Who moved home from Ayresome Park to The Riverside?

14   Which country plays internationals at Hampden Park?

15   Which stadium was famous for its twin towers?

16   Who plays at The Dell?

17   Leeds United strut their stuff at which ground?

18   Hillsborough is home to which Yorkshire team?

19   Which team in green plays at Landsdowne Road?

20   Who plays at the Nou Camp: Barcelona, Real Madrid or AC Milan?

Quiz 26 **Newcastle United**

Answers – see page 36

LEVEL 1

1 At which stadium do Newcastle United play?

2 What is Newcastle's nickname?

3 Which England captain was Newcastle's leading scorer in 1999-2000?

4 Who is Newcastle United's manager?

5 Who was their dreadlocked Dutch manager?

6 Who beat Newcastle in the 1999 Cup final?

7 Which England manager took Newcastle into the top flight as player and later as manager?

8 Which Manchester Utd striker was once Newcastle's leading goalscorer?

9 What colour shirts do Newcastle play in?

10 Which Kieron did Newcastle United sign from Ipswich in 1999?

11 Which Les left Newcastle for Tottenham in 1997?

12 Which England under-21 striker did Newcastle United sign from Wimbledon for £7m?

13 Which Duncan partnered Alan Shearer in the Newcastle United attack?

14 What was the real name of 'Wor Jackie' who scored 179 League goals for Newcastle United?

15 What is the unofficial Newcastle supporters anthem?

16 Which classy England international returned to Newcastle as the inspiration of the Keegan era?

17 Who are Newcastle's arch-rivals?

18 Who beat Newcastle in the 1998 Cup Final?

19 Which Newcastle United Robert is an England international and is nicknamed 'Lurker'?

20 Which Sir John developed the Durham Metro Centre and Newcastle as Premier League outfit?

Quiz 27 The 80s

Answers – see page 33

LEVEL 1

1 Who is England's top-scoring midfielder?
2 Which Manchester Utd and AC Milan midfielder was sent off for throwing the ball at the referee in an England World Cup game in 1986?
3 Of which Tottenham and England midfielder did Jasper Carrott say 'I hear he's found God, that must have been one hell of a pass'?
4 Which 'Sparky' was at Manchester United and Barcelona in the 80s?
5 Which hod carrier turned footballer turned film star made his name at Wimbledon in the 80s?
6 Which team had Waddle, Keegan and Beardsley in their 80s line-up?
7 Which forward scored a hat-trick against Poland in the World Cup in 1986?
8 Who was Liverpool's ace striker throughout the 80s apart from one season he spent at Juventus?
9 Who was the Tottenham captain who lifted the UEFA Cup in 1984?
10 In which country was the 1985 European Cup Final between Liverpool and Juventus in which 39 people were killed?
11 Scotland's Paul McStay stayed with which club throughout the 80s?
12 Which Argentinian destroyed England in the 1986 World Cup?
13 Who had McGrath, Strachan and Whiteside in their line-up in the 80s?
14 Lawrenson and Hansen were at the heart of which defence in the 80s?
15 Which Dutch Marco was European Footballer of the Year in 88 and 89?
16 Which Premier League manager was then Manchester United's captain?
17 Who was Liverpool and Sampdoria's midfield hardman?
18 Neville Southall played for which FA Cup and championship-winning side?
19 Which south coast team reached the FA Cup final in 1983?
20 Gary Mabbutt and Tommy Hutchison did what in 80s FA Cup Finals?

Grounds   (see Quiz 25)
1 Chelsea. 2 Rangers. 3 Northern Ireland. 4 Sunderland.
5 Goodison Park. 6 Highbury. 7 Coventry City. 8 Cardiff.
9 Selhurst. 10 White Hart. 11 Liverpool. 12 Old Trafford.
13 Middlesbrough. 14 Scotland. 15 Wembley. 16 Southampton.
17 Elland Road. 18 Sheffield Wednesday. 19 Republic of Ireland.
20 Barcelona.

Answers

35

Quiz 28 **David Beckham**

Answers – see page 34

1   David Beckham was born in which city?

2   In what number shirt does he play at Manchester United?

3   Against which team did he score from a free-kick in the 1998 World Cup: Colombia, Argentina or France?

4   Which pop group was David Beckham's wife a member of?

5   What was special about his goal against Wimbledon in 1996?

6   Against which country was Beckham sent off in the 1998 World Cup?

7   What is the name of David Beckham's son?

8   What excuse did David give for missing Manchester Utd training in 199?

9   What did David do in the 2000 World Club Championship against Neca?

10 Where did David finish in the *Sun*'s 1999 poll of hunkiest men?

11 In which competition was David playing when he made a v-sign to supporters?

12 In which year was Beckham voted Young Player of the Year?

13 Which 1950s hair product did David officially endorse in 1997?

14 Who said 'Beckham's passing isn't great, his heading is negligible and he doesn't score enough goals – apart from that, he's not too bad!'?

15 In March 1995 Beckham went on loan to which club: Preston, Manchester City or West Ham?

16 Who was Beckham's best man? Gary Neville, Phil Neville or Diego Simeone?

17 What item of 'women's' clothing was Beckham pictured wearing during the 1998 World Cup?

18 What tattoo does Beckham sport: a Red Devil or an Angel?

19 What changed about David's appearance during the 1999-2000 seaso?

20 Becks prefers which: Porsches, Ferraris or Volkswagen Beetles?

Answers

Newcastle United (see Quiz 26)
1 St James' Park. 2 The Magpies. 3 Alan Shearer. 4 Bobby Robson. 5 Ruud Gullit. 6 Manchester United. 7 Kevin Keegan.
8 Andy Cole. 9 Black and white stripes. 10 Kieron Dyer. 11 Les Ferdinand. 12 Carl Cort. 13 Duncan Ferguson. 14 Jackie Milburn.
15 Blaydon Races. 16 Peter Beardsley. 17 Sunderland.
18 Arsenal. 19 Robert Lee. 20 Sir John Hall.

Quiz 29 **Pop and Football**

Answers – see page 39

LEVEL 1

1   Scottish side Clydebank are sponsored by which soggy pop group?

2   Which pop star, confused about his weight, put his record label on Brighton and Hove Albion's shirts?

3   Led Zeppelin's Robert Plant follows which Wanderers?

4   He wears funny glasses but he takes his football seriously. Who?

5   Rod Stewart would cross stormy waters to see which Scottish team?

6   John Barnes did the 'Anfield Rap' for which club in 1988?

7   Madness singer Suggs wrote 'Blue Day' for which London club?

8   'We Have A Dream' was which country's World Cup anthem in 1982?

9   Why does pop violinist Nigel Kennedy wear claret and blue underpants?

10 'I'm Forever Blowing Bubbles' was the Cockney Rejects' paen to which team?

11 Pop group Oasis's Gallagher brothers follow which Premier League 2000 newcomers?

12 'World in Motion' was New Order's hit intended to inspire which team?

13 Robbie Williams likes his football at the Vale – who's he supporting?

14 'Nice One... '? Who was the focus of the Spurs fans song in 1973?

15 Mick Hucknall is simply red, but which red-shirted team?

16 Which Argentinian's knees had gone 'all trembly' in a Chas and Dave hit?

17 'Back Home' was a hit record for which England World Cup squad: 1970, 1974 or 1986?

18 Who were the Glenn and Chris who recorded 'Diamond Lights' in 1987?

19 What 'is the colour' in a 1972 hit football record?

20 Which Geordie cried for 'Fog on the Tyne' with Lindisfarne in 1990?

Answers

Arsenal (see Quiz 31)
1 Liverpool. 2 N5. 3 George Graham. 4 1997-98. 5 1970-71.
6 Kenny Sansom. 7 David O'Leary. 8 Ian Wright. 9 Middlesbrough.
10 Manchester United. 11 Alan Sunderland. 12 Seven times.
13 Parma. 14 Alan Smith. 15 Zaragoza. 16 Internazionale.
17 Nigel Winterburn. 18 1993. 19 Sheffield Wednesday.
20 1886.

Quiz 30 TV and Football

LEVEL 1

1   *Football Focus* is which channel's football magazine programme?

2   Which England player and Republic of Ireland manager has presented TV programmes on fishing?

3   What is the name of Sky TV's football-based soap opera?

4   What was unique about television coverage of the 1985-86 season from August to December?

5   How many million viewers watched ITV's coverage of the 1998 World Cup match between England and Argentina? 18m, 22m or 26m ?

6   An episode of which classic 70s comedy series showed our heroes desperately avoiding hearing the result of an England match?

7   Supposed Premier League foreigner Julio Geordio appeared on which show?

8   *Boys from the Blackstuff* featured footballers from which club?

9   Which TV fun quiz takes its name from Kenneth Wolstenholme's commentary in the 1966 World Cup?

10 Which ex-Tottenham player has presented TV sports and current affairs?

11 Which daughter of a Leeds United and Wales player presents a football show with Barry Venison?

12 Who entered *Celebrity Stars in their Eyes* in 1999 as Sacha Distel?

13 ITV football presenter Bob Wilson played for which club?

14 Which imaginary local team do the characters in *EastEnders* support?

15 Which team did comedy cockney bigot Alf Garnett support?

16 Which ex-Wimbledon striker presented *Gladiators*?

17 Frank Skinner and David Baddiel presented which football-related show?

18 Which ex-England manager co-created the BBC TV series *Hazell*?

19 Which former footballer presented *Friday Night's All Wright*?

20 TV drama *My Summer With Des* referred to which football presenter?

Quiz 31 **Arsenal**

LEVEL 1

1   Who did Arsenal beat in their opening home game of the 2000-01 season?

2   In which London postal district do Arsenal play?

3   Who was Arsenal manager from 1986 to 1995?

4   When did Arsenal last win the double?

5   When did Arsenal first win the double?

6   Who is Arsenal's most capped player?

7   Who has made most league appearances?

8   Who is Arsenal's all-time record goalscorer?

9   Who did Arsenal beat 6-1 away in April 1999?

10   Who did Arsenal beat with a last-minute goal in the 1979 FA Cup final?

11   Who scored the winning goal in that match?

12   How many times have Arsenal won the FA Cup?

13   Who did Arsenal beat in the 1994 European Cup Winners' Cup final?

14   Who scored the winner in that match?

15   Who beat Arsenal in the same match the following year?

16   From whom did Arsenal sign Dennis Bergkamp?

17   Which Arsenal full-back joined West Ham in summer 2000?

18   In which year did Arsenal win both the FA Cup and the Coca-Cola Cup?

19   They played the same team in both finals. Which team?

20   In which year were Arsenal formed?

1   Who scored twice for Newcastle in the 1999 FA Cup semi-final?

2   Who scored two penalties for Manchester Utd in the 1994 FA Cup final?

3   Who scored four goals for Holland in the Euro 2000 quarter-final against Yugoslavia?

4   Who scored 30 goals for Sunderland in season 1999-2000?

5   Who scored on his debut for Celtic after his £7m transfer from Chelsea in summer 2000?

6   Whose goals kept Everton in the Premier League in 1998-99?

7   Which Frenchman scored 26 goals for Arsenal in 1999-2000?

8   Who scored Chelsea's winner in the 1998 Cup Winners' Cup final?

9   Who scored Manchester Utd's winner in the 1999 Champions League final?

10 Who scored the winning goal in the 100th FA Cup final in 1981?

11 Who scored twice for Chelsea on his debut against in August 2000?

12 Whose goal put Italy one up against France in the Euro 2000 final?

13 Who scored twice for Barcelona against Manchester United in November 1998?

14 What is the record victory in an FA Cup final?

15 Who scored twice for Liverpool in the 1995 League Cup final against Bolton?

16 Who scored a hat-trick for Rangers in a 5-1 thrashing of Hearts in the 1996 Scottish FA Cup final?

17 Who won the European Cup in 1960 in Glasgow?

18 Who were their opponents in the final?

19 What was the score in that match?

20 Who scored four goals as Manchester United beat Everton in December 1999?

Quiz 33 **Who Did What? 3**

Answers – see page 43

LEVEL 1

1 Which team lost both the Scottish FA Cup and League Cup finals in 2000?

2 Who took over as manager of Celtic in summer 2000?

3 Who retired from International football after Euro 2000 having scored 30 goals for England?

4 Which club reached the FA Cup final in 1998 and 1999 and lost both?

5 Who returned to Holland after being manager of Chelsea and Newcastle United?

6 Who were relegated to Division One in 2000 after 14 years at the top?

7 Who were knocked out of Euro 2000 semi finals by a Golden Goal penalty?

8 Who scored a hat-trick in England's 1966 victorious World Cup Final?

9 Who kept goal for Manchester United and captained the Danish international team?

10 Who moved back to The Valley after seven years of sharing a ground with Crystal Palace?

11 Who shocked the world by beating Italy in the World Cup in 1994?

12 Who held the FA Cup aloft with one hand and his baby with the other?

13 Who played for Turkey in Euro 2000 despite being born in London?

14 Who joined Everton from Monaco in 1998?

15 Who had his floppy locks shaved off during Manchester United's 1999-2000 campaign?

16 Who won 5-0 in Turkey but still were eliminated from the 1999-2000 Champions League?

17 Who received a ban for spitting in the 1999-2000 season?

18 Who leapt into the crowd at Crystal Palace to kick an abusive supporter?

19 Which two countries played in the last international at Wembley stadium?

20 Who was knighted after his team completed a famous treble?

Answers

South America (see Quiz 35)
1 Diego Maradona. 2 Yellow with green trimmings. 3 Ardiles.
4 Light blue and white stripes. 5 Argentina. 6 Pele.
7 Manchester United. 8 His corkscrew hair-do. 9 Middlesbrough.
10 Barcelona. 11 Mexico. 12 Ronaldo. 13 Chile. 14 Arsenal.
15 Colombia. 16 Newcastle United. 17 Batistuta. 18 Socrates.
19 Winning it three times. 20 Chelsea.

LEVEL 1

1   Who were England's first opponents in the Euro 2000 finals?

2   What was the score in that match?

3   Who were the only team beaten by England in those finals?

4   Who scored England's winning goal in that match?

5   Who beat England in the semi-final of Euro 96?

6   Who were England's first opponents in the Euro 96 finals?

7   What was the score in that match?

8   Who scored England's second goal against Scotland at Wembley in Euro 96?

9   Who saved a penalty for England in that same match?

10   Who scored England's first goal in the Euro 2000 finals?

11   Who was England's manager during Euro 96?

12   Who did England play in the quarter-finals of Euro 96?

13   The quarter-finals of Euro 96 were played at Wembley, Villa Park, Anfield and which other ground?

14   England's Euro 96 group featured Scotland, Switzerland and which other country?

15   Who beat England in the final group match of Euro 2000?

16   Who gave away a penalty in that same match?

17   Which was the only team to beat England in Euro 92?

18   What was the score in that match?

19   Who scored the winning goal?

20   Which rule was introduced in the quarter-finals of Euro 96?

Quiz 35 South America

Answers – see page 41

LEVEL 1

1   Which Argentinian scored the 'hand of god' goal against England in the 1986 World Cup?

2   In what colour shirts do Brazil play?

3   The Argentinian who played for and managed Spurs is called Ossie...

4   In which colour shirts do Argentina play?

5   Claudio Lopez, Diego Simone and Juan Veron play for which country?

6   Perhaps the world's greatest ever player, Edson Arantes do Nascimento has a more commonly used four-letter name. What is it?

7   Which English team played in the first World Club Championship?

8   What feature distinguished Carlos Valderrama from his teammates?

9   South Americans Emerson, Junhino and Ricard have all played for which club in the North East?

10   Brazilian Rivaldo plays for which Spanish giants?

11   Which Central American country hosted the 1970 and 1986 World Cup?

12   Which Brazilian forward cost Inter Milan £18 m in 1997?

13   Lazio's Marcelo Salas hails from which South American country?

14   Brazilian Silvinho plays for which Premier League team?

15   Andres Escobar was murdered after scoring an own-goal when playing for which South American country in the 1994 World Cup?

16   South Americans Mirandinha, Asprilla and Solano have all played for which club in the North East?

17   Which Argentinian arch-marksman Gabriel earned Fiorentina £22 m from Roma?

18   Who was one of Brazil's great players: Plato, Socrates or Descartes?

19   Why did Brazil get to keep the Jules Rimet Trophy?

20   Poyet, Thome and Lambourde all play for which London club?

Quiz 36 **Anything But Football**

LEVEL 1

1 Which Leeds star is engaged to *Emmerdale* barmaid Sheree Murphy?

2 Which film starred Sylvester Stallone and featured a football team escaping from a World War II POW camp?

3 Which footballer had a role in the feature film *Elizabeth*?

4 Which French player works for the UN campaign to ban land mines?

5 What does Roy Race have in common with Dennis the Menace?

6 Which Prime Minister tried to introduce ID cards for football supporters?

7 Which footballer is married to a former Spice Girl?

8 Which former England captain appeared in television advertisements for an American hamburger chain?

9 Which footballer had roles in the feature films *Lock, Stock and Two Smoking Barrels* and *Snatch*?

10 Which great 60s Northern Ireland footballer vowed to give up alcohol after being admitted to hospital in 2000?

11 Billy plays in goal in a *Viz* comic strip. What kind of animal is he?

12 Middlesbrough player Christian Karembeu's wife Adriana is associated with which profession?

13 Which American singer began 1994 World Cup by missing a penalty?

14 *An Evening with...* which presenter was a hit West End theatre show?

15 Which 1980 Scottish film featured a boy's infatuation with the female star of his school football team?

16 What kind of food did Pearce, Waddle and Southgate advertise?

17 Which Nick Hornby book and film featured his relationship with Arsenal?

18 Which former Eternal pop star has been linked with Jamie Redknapp?

19 'You'll Never Walk Alone' was a 60s number one for which pop group?

20 Which renowned chef is a former Glasgow Rangers player?

Answers

England in Europe (see Quiz 34)
1 Portugal. 2 3-2 to Portugal. 3 Germany. 4 Alan Shearer.
5 Germany. 6 Switzerland. 7 1-1. 8 Paul Gascoigne. 9 David Seaman. 10 Paul Scholes. 11 Terry Venables. 12 Spain. 13 Old Trafford. 14 Holland. 15 Romania. 16 Phil Neville. 17 Sweden. 18 2-1 to Sweden. 19 Tomas Brolin. 20 'Golden Goals'.

44

Quiz 37 **Premier League 2**

Answers – see page 47

1 Who were the first winners of the Premier League?

2 What was the first televised match from the Premier League?

3 Who were the Premier League runners up that season?

4 Who won the Premier League in 1994-95?

5 Who were relegated from the Premier League in 1996-97 having had three points deducted for failing to fulfil a fixture?

6 Which team has only ever finished first or second in the Premiership?

7 Who led the Premier League after only one game of the 2000-01 season?

8 Who were relegated from the Premier League in 1995-96 and returned in 1999-2000?

9 Which is the biggest ground in the Premier League?

10 What is the highest points total for a Premier League season?

11 In which year was that points total achieved?

12 How many matches did champions Manchester United lose during the 1999-2000 season?

13 Which player was sent off in his first two matches of the 2000-01 season?

14 Who failed to win an away match in the Premier League for 16 months beween 1999 and 2000?

15 Which team scored the fewest league goals in a Premier League season?

16 Which team scored the most goals in a Premier League season?

17 Which is the only team to concede 100 goals in a Premier League season?

18 What is the smallest points total for a Premier League season?

19 Which team achieved this distinction?

20 Which Premier League team bought Mark Viduka from Celtic in summer 2000?

Answers

Managers (see Quiz 39)
1 Bobby Robson. **2** Terry Venables. **3** Sir Alf Ramsey. **4** Arsene Wenger. **5** Franz Beckenbauer. **6** Don Revie. **7** Aberdeen. **8** Tottenham Hotspur & Arsenal. **9** Leicester City. **10** Sir Matt Busby. **11** Gordon Strachan. **12** Glenn Hoddle. **13** Brian Clough. **14** Harry Redknapp. **15** Bryan Robson. **16** Dutch. **17** Republic of Ireland. **18** Wales. **19** Bill Shankly. **20** Trevor Francis.

Quiz 38 Great Players

Answers – see page 48

1   Who was England's hat-trick hero in the 1966 World Cup final?

2   Who is England's all-time top scorer?

3   Who scored 48 international goals before becoming a TV presenter?

4   Which former England hero Kevin became the manager?

5   Who played the first of his 84 matches for England in 1934?

6   Who played his 106th and last international against West Germany in 1970?

7   Which England player was known as 'Captain Marvel'?

8   Which England player was leading scorer in the Euro 96 tournament?

9   Which England hero of the 1950s was married to a Beverley Sister?

10 Who scored England's equaliser in the 1990 World Cup semi-final against West Germany?

11 Who is England's youngest-ever goalscorer?

12 Who was regarded as England's best player during Euro 2000?

13 Who was England's goalkeeping hero against Scotland in Euro 96?

14 What made him a hero in that game?

15 Who scored all three goals against Poland in the last group match of the 1986 World Cup finals?

16 Who scored for England against Belgium in the second-round match in Italia 90?

17 Which London player scored 44 goals in 57 appearances for England during the 1960s?

18 Which England hero played his last international against Italy at Wembley in November 1973?

19 Who retired from international football after defeat by Romania in Euro 2000?

20 Who scored England's second goal against Portugal in the opening game of Euro 2000?

Answers

The World Cup (see Quiz 40)
1 1930. **2** Uruguay. **3** Uruguay. **4** Italy. **5** Six. **6** West Germany.
7 England v Uruguay. **8** Japan and Korea. **9** Brazil, four times.
10 Los Angeles. **11** Pickles. **12** Brazil and Italy. **13** Mexico.
14 Holland. **15** Robbie Earle. **16** France. **17** France and Brazil.
18 Didier Deschamps. **19** Once. **20** The Jules Rimet Trophy.

Quiz 39 Managers

Answers – see page 45

LEVEL 1

1 Which manager's clubs have included Ipswich Town, England, Barcelona and Newcastle?

2 Who was the England manager on home soil during Euro 96?

3 Who was the manager of the World Cup winning side in 1966?

4 Who is Arsenal's French manager?

5 Which German became the first man to play in and coach a World Cup-winning team?

6 Who was Leeds' manager during their glory years of the 60s and 70s?

7 Which Scottish club did Alex Ferguson manage before Manchester Utd?

8 Which London Premier League teams had George Graham managed?

9 Celtic manager Martin O'Neill moved from which English team in 2000?

10 Which legendary Manchester United manager was celebrated for his young team of the late 50s?

11 Which manager sold Gary McAllister to Liverpool?

12 Who was dismissed as England manager in 1999 after making?

13 Which famous manager took Nottingham Forest to European Cup finals in the 1979 and 80?

14 Which happy Harry is West Ham's manager?

15 Which former England captain took charge at Middlesbrough?

16 What nationality is Rangers boss Dick Advocaat?

17 Which national team enjoyed their greatest times under Jack Charlton?

18 John Toshack, Bobby Gould, and Mark Hughes have all managed which national team?

19 'If Everton were playing at the bottom of my garden I'd draw the curtains'. Which Liverpool manager said that?

20 Which clever Trevor is Birmingham City's manager?

Answers

Premier League 2 (see Quiz 37)
1 Manchester United. 2 Nottingham Forest v Liverpool. 3 Aston Villa. 4 Blackburn Rovers. 5 Middlesbrough. 6 Manchester United. 7 Charlton. 8 Manchester City. 9 Old Trafford. 10 92. 11 1993-94. 12 Three. 13 Patrick Vieira. 14 Coventry City. 15 Leeds with 28 in 1996-97. 16 Manchester United with 97 in 1999-2000. 17 Swindon in 1993-94. 18 24. 19 Watford. 20 Leeds United.

1   When was the first World Cup held?

2   Where did it take place?

3   Who won the competition?

4   Who won the competition in both 1934 and 1938?

5   How many host countries have won the World Cup?

6   Where was the 1974 tournament held?

7   What was the first match of the 1966 tournament?

8   Where will the 2002 tournament be held?

9   Which country has won the World Cup the most times?

10   In which city was the 1994 final played?

11   What was the name of the dog that found the stolen World Cup trophy in 1966?

12   Which two teams contested the 1970 World Cup final?

13   Where was that tournament played?

14   Who did Argentina beat in the final to win the 1978 trophy?

15   Who scored Jamaica's first goal in World Cup finals in 1998?

16   Where was the 1998 tournament held?

17   Which two teams contested the final?

18   Which player lifted the trophy at the end of the game?

19   How many times have England won the World Cup?

20   What was the original World Cup trophy called?

Answers

England Heroes (see Quiz 38)
1 Geoff Hurst. 2 Bobby Charlton. 3 Gary Lineker. 4 Kevin Keegan.
5 Stanley Matthews. 6 Bobby Charlton. 7 Bryan Robson. 8 Alan
Shearer. 9 Billy Wright. 10 Gary Lineker. 11 Michael Owen.
12 David Beckham. 13 David Seaman. 14 He saved a penalty.
15 Gary Lineker. 16 David Platt. 17 Jimmy Greaves. 18 Bobby
Moore. 19 Alan Shearer. 20 Steve McManaman.

Quiz 41 The North West

Answers – see page 51

LEVEL 1

1   Stanley Matthews played in tangerine for which Lancashire resort side?

2   Dixie Dean is a hero at which Merseyside club?

3   Graeme Souness is in charge at which former Premier League Rovers?

4   Are Nationwide League Stockport a United, an Athletic or a County?

5   Shaun 'The Goat' Goater is part of which team's strikeforce?

6   Which North West claret and blue team play at Turf Moor?

7   Wesley Brown and Quinton Fortune play for which team?

8   Which Premier League team from the North West have a French manager?

9   In which position does Everton's Kevin Campbell play?

10 Are Tranmere a Town, a Rovers or a Wanderers?

11 Who was Manchester City's young English goalkeeper in 2000?

12 Which team is not in the Football League: Altrincham, Macclesfield Town or Wigan Athletic?

13 Which Manchester United striker is the Premier League's all-time leading goalscorer?

14 Which team were featured in a TV advert for milk in the 1980s?

15 England legend Tom Finney played for which North End 'Lillywhites' in Lancashire?

16 Nat Lofthouse played for these Wanderers, but never at their Reebok Stadium. Who are they?

17 True or false: Bury have won the FA Cup on two occasions?

18 Which Liverpool and Scotland hero managed Blackburn Rovers in their Championship-winning season?

19 Former Liverpool star John Aldridge is still on Merseyside – managing which club?

20 Which club in the region has the name Alexandra?

Answers

Nicknames (see Quiz 43)
1 United. 2 Boro. 3 The Owls. 4 The Hammers. 5 The Foxes.
6 The Toffees. 7 The Villains. 8 The Eagles. 9 Pompey. 10 The Hornets. 11 The Dons. 12 The Magpies. 13 The Cottagers.
14 The Saints. 15 Spurs. 16 The Sky Blues. 17 The Red Devils.
18 The Pool or The Reds. 19 The Blues or The Citizens. 20 The Rams.

1   Who conceded four goals in their first game on their return to the Premiership in 2000-01?

2   Who beat Barcelona 3-1 in Europe in 2000?

3   Which keeper thwarted England during a Wembley 1974 World Cup qualifier?

4   Who was he playing for?

5   Which Second Division team beat Manchester United to win the 1976 FA Cup final?

6   Who beat Peru 6-0 to qualify for the final of the 1978 World Cup?

7   Who did Liverpool beat in the final of the European Cup in 1981?

8   Who scored a sensational goal for England against Brazil in 1984?

9   Liverpool won the title in 1985-86. Who scored the winning goal in the final match of the season at Stamford Bridge?

10 In which match did Schumacher perform his infamous 'foul' on Battiston

11 In which World Cup match did it all go wrong for Chris Waddle and Stuart Pearce?

12 Which World Cup did the Republic of Ireland start with a victory over Italy?

13 Who sensationally beat Germany in the Euro 92 final?

14 Who equalised for France against Brazil in the 1986 World Cup?

15 Who scored the winning penalty in that same quarter-final?

16 Which player had a goal disallowed when England played Argentina in the 1998 World Cup?

17 Who scored a superb goal for Germany against Russia in Euro 96?

18 Which two London teams contested the 1967 FA Cup final?

19 Who missed the deciding penalty in England's World Cup 98 match against Argentina?

20 Who did Chelsea beat in the 1998 Worthington Cup semi-final?

Answers

Chelsea (see Quiz 44)
1 Stamford Bridge. 2 Aston Villa. 3 Ken Bates. 4 Bobby Tambling. 5 Dennis Wise. 6 David Webb. 7 Fifth. 8 Ray and Graham Wilkins. 9 Barcelona. 10 Manchester United. 11 The Blues. 12 'Carefree'. 13 Jimmy Floyd Hasselbaink. 14 Gianfranco Zola. 15 Gianluca Vialli. 16 Ron Harris. 17 Ruud Gullit. 18 Lord Attenborough. 19 Real Madrid. 20 Glenn Hoddle.

Leeds United?

Middlesbrough?

Sheffield Wednesday?

West Ham United?

Leicester City?

Everton?

Aston Villa?

Crystal Palace?

Portsmouth?

Watford?

Wimbledon?

Newcastle United?

Fulham?

Southampton?

Tottenham Hotspur?

Coventry City?

Manchester United?

Liverpool?

Manchester City?

Derby County?

The North West (see Quiz 41)
1 Blackpool. **2** Everton. **3** Blackburn Rovers. **4** County.
5 Manchester City. **6** Burnley. **7** Manchester United. **8** Liverpool.
9 Striker. **10** Rovers. **11** Nicky Weaver. **12** Altrincham. **13** Andy
Cole. **14** Accrington Stanley. **15** Preston North End. **16** Bolton
Wanderers. **17** True (1900 and 1903). **18** Kenny Dalglish.
19 Tranmere Rovers. **20** Crewe Alexandra.

1   What is the name of Chelsea's ground?

2   Who did Chelsea beat in the 2000 FA Cup Final?

3   Who has been the Chelsea chairman since 1982?

4   Who is Chelsea's current record goalscorer?

5   Which Chelsea player played for England in Euro 2000?

6   Who scored Chelsea's winner in the 1970 FA Cup Final Replay?

7   Where did Chelsea finish in the Premiership in the 1999-2000 sea

8   Which brothers starred for Chelsea during the 1970s?

9   Who knocked Chelsea out of the Champions League in 2000?

10 Who did Chelsea beat 5-0 in the Premiership on 3 October 1999?

11 What is Chelsea's nickname?

12 What is the Chelsea fans' anthem?

13 Who was Chelsea's record signing in 2000?

14 Who was the Footballer of the Year in 1997?

15 Who is Chelsea's Italian manager?

16 Which player has played in more games for Chelsea than any other

17 Which Dutch superstar joined Chelsea in 1995?

18 Who is Chelsea's life vice-president?

19 Who did Chelsea beat in the 1971 European Cup Winners' Cup Fir

20 Who became the Chelsea manager in 1993?

Quiz 45 Pot Luck

Answers – see page 55

1 How many teams are there in the Premiership?

2 What is the most common score in a professional football match?

3 Who will host Euro 2004?

4 How many substitutes can be named for a Champions League game?

5 Who plays at Priestfield Stadium?

6 Who is 'The Bald Eagle'?

7 Which Scottish team is nicknamed 'The Bankies'?

8 Who won the UEFA Cup in 1999?

9 Who won the Women's FA Cup in 2000?

10 Who won the Division 1 Championship in both 1957-58 and 1958-59?

11 In which year did Sir Matt Busby die?

12 In what year did *Match of the Day* start?

13 Who resigned as manager of Holland after Euro 2000?

14 Who is the manager of Aston Villa?

15 Which Ukrainian striker plays for AC Milan?

16 Who won the Spanish championship in 1999-2000?

17 Who is the author of *Football Against the Enemy*?

18 Which Dutchman Edgar plays for Juventus?

19 Which player lifted the Premier League trophy in May 2000?

20 Which keeper signed for Spurs in the summer of 2000?

Answers

England's World Cups 2 (see Quiz 47)
1 1950. 2 USA. 3 1-0. 4 Brazil. 5 Uruguay. 6 Uruguay.
7 Portugal. 8 2-1 to England. 9 1-0 to Brazil. 10 Three. 11
Paraguay. 12 Fourth. 13 Cameroon. 14 3-2 to England. 15
Tunisia 16 Paul Scholes. 17 Romania. 18 Dan Petrescu. 19 Alan
Shearer (pen). 20 St Etienne.

53

Quiz 46 Centre-Forwards

Answers – see page 56

LEVEL 1

1   What number does a centre-forward traditionally wear on his shirt?

2   Who played centre-forward for Manchester United in 1999-2000?

3   Who wore the No. 9 shirt for England in Euro 2000?

4   Which centre-forward scored 68 goals in 62 internationals for West Germany?

5   Which Liverpool centre-forward scored five goals in three FA Cup final-winning appearances?

6   Who was Holland's centre-forward when they won the 1988 European Championships?

7   Who played centre-forward for England in the 1966 World Cup final?

8   Which centre-forward did Chelsea sign in summer 2000?

9   Who is Wolves highest-scoring centre-forward ever?

10 Which centre-forward did Manchester City buy from West Ham in summer 2000?

11 Which Everton centre-forward holds the record for most goals in a season in the top division?

12 Which Bournemouth No. 9 holds the record for the most goals in any FA Cup match?

13 How many goals did he score in that match?

14 Which German centre-forward did Spurs sign in 1994?

15 Who captained Manchester United to European Cup success in 1968?

16 Which centre-forward was transferred from Newcastle to Everton in summer 2000?

17 Who was Glasgow Rangers' Dutch centre-forward in 2000?

18 Which ex-Arsenal centre-forward ended his career in 2000 at Burnley?

19 Who was Sunderland's centre-forward in 2000?

20 Who did West Ham sign from Arsenal for free in summer 2000?

Answers

Penalties (see Quiz 48)
1 Gary Lineker. 2 Stuart Pearce. 3 Dennis Bergkamp. 4 Alan Shearer. 5 Brazil. 6 Matt Le Tissier. 7 David Batty. 8 Wimbledon. 9 Tottenham Hotspur. 10 Kanu. 11 Five. 12 Gary McAllister. 13 Dwight Yorke. 14 Charlton. 15 12 yards. 16 David Seaman. 17 Liverpool. 18 Zidane. 19 Galatasary. 20 Gareth Southgate.

Quiz 47 England's World Cups 2

LEVEL 1

1 When did England first take part in the World Cup finals?
2 England suffered an embarrassing defeat in that tournament. Who beat them?
3 What was the score?
4 Where was that tournament held?
5 England lost in the quarter-finals of the 1954 tournament. Who beat them?
6 Who were England's first opponents in the 1966 finals?
7 Who did England beat in the semi-final?
8 What was the score?
9 England played Brazil in the group stages of the 1970 competition. What was the score?
10 How many wins did England have in the group stages of the 1982 tournament?
11 England played a second-round match in 1982 against which South American team?
12 Where did England finish in Italia 90?
13 Who did they beat in the quarter-finals of that tournament?
14 What was the score?
15 Who did England play in their opening game in the 1998 finals?
16 Who scored England's second goal in that game?
17 Who did England lose to in the group stages of the 1998 World Cup finals?
18 Who scored the winning goal in that game?
19 Who scored England's first goal in the eighth-final against Argentina?
20 In which city was that match played?

Quiz 48 Penalties

Answers – see page 54

1 Who would have equalled Bobby Charlton as England's greatest goalscorer if he hadn't missed a penalty against Brazil?

2 Which 'psycho' missed a penalty against Germany in the 1990 World Cup?

3 Which Arsenal player missed a penalty that could have knocked Manchester United out of the FA Cup in 1998?

4 Who scored a penalty for England against Portugal in Euro 2000?

5 Who beat Italy on a penalty shoot-out to win the 1994 World Cup?

6 Who is Southampton's penalty king?

7 Who missed the penalty to eliminate England from the 1998 World Cup?

8 Which team won the FA Cup after Dave Beasant saved a penalty?

9 Which team won the FA Cup in 1991 despite missing a penalty?

10 Which Arsenal player missed a penalty awarded to Nigeria in the shoot-out of the 2000 African Cup of Nations final?

11 How many penalties do teams take before the sudden death rule applies?

12 Who missed a penalty for Scotland against England in Euro 96?

13 Who usually takes Manchester United's penalties?

14 In 1998 the First Division play-off between Charlton and Sunderland was decided by a penalty shoot-out. Who won?

15 How far from the goal line is the penalty spot: 8, 10 or 12 yards?

16 Who saved a penalty for England in the Euro 96 quarter-final shoot-out against Spain at Wembley?

17 For which team did Bruce Grobbelar go wobbly-legged in a shoot-out for the 1984 European Cup?

18 Who scored the penalty for France to to reach the Euro 2000 final?

19 Who beat Arsenal in the penalty-shoot out for the 2000 UEFA Cup final?

20 Whose miss lost the shoot-out for England against Germany in Euro 96?

Answers

Centre-Forwards (see Quiz 46)
1 No. 9. 2 Andy Cole. 3 Alan Shearer. 4 Gerd Müller. 5 Ian Rush. 6 Marco Van Basten. 7 Geoff Hurst. 8 Jimmy Floyd Hasselbaink. 9 Steve Bull. 10 Paulo Wanchope. 11 Dixie Dean, 6 in 1927-28. 12 Ted MacDougall. 13 9. 14 Jürgen Klinsmann. 15 Bobby Charlton. 16 Duncan Ferguson. 17 Michael Mols. 18 Ian Wright. 19 Kevin Phillips. 20 Davor Suker.

Who beat Poland to allow England to qualify for the Euro 2000 play-offs: Luxembourg, Bosnia or Sweden?

Who declined to take part in the 1999-2000 FA Cup competition?

Who reputedly signed a £50,000-a-week contract with Manchester Utd in 1999?

Who became the first English club ever to field a team of foreigners?

Who gave up alcohol and supposedly took up poetry and playing piano?

Who was fined after an alleged cocaine-sniffing goal celebration?

Who imitated a famous cocktail guzzling incident after scoring in Euro 96?

Who temporarily replaced their manager after he was charged with alleged offences against children?

Who did Kevin Keegan leave out of his Euro 2000 squad: Kevin Phillips, Emile Heskey or Andy Cole?

Who grabbed Gazza by the unmentionables to earn notoriety?

Who agreed to replay their FA Cup tie against Sheffield United after winning with an 'unsporting' goal in 1999?

Who signed Dion Dublin from Coventry City in 1998?

Who had four local MPs demanding they should sack their manager?

Who broke his jaw in the 2000 Scottish FA Cup final?

Who sold Robbie Keane to Coventry City?

Who earned £1m from their testimonial at Old Trafford in 1999?

Who appeared in three League Cup finals between '97 and 2000?

Who was threatened with expulsion from Euro 2000 due to their fans?

Who broke a leg playing for West Ham while being touted as the best emerging English youngster?

Who named Dave Beasant as their player of the year for 1999-2000?

Quiz 50 Old Football

Answers – see page 60

1 Which Yorkshire club win the League three times in a row in the 192

2 Which great Stoke City, Blackpool and England winger had the 1953 FA Cup Final unofficially named after him?

3 Greaves, Mullery and Jennings were stars of which team in the 60s?

4 Which great Scottish striker played for both Manchester City and Manchester United in the 60s?

5 Which Nat was Bolton Wanderers and England's 50s goalscoring her

6 For which team did Bonetti, Cooke and Osgood play in the 60s?

7 World Cup heroes Peters, Hurst and Moore played for which London cl

8 In which decade was a live match commentary first broadcast on the ra

9 Which country shocked the world by beating England in 1950 (and it again in 1993)?

10 For which country did goal-scoring hero Billy Meredith play?

11 Which 17-year-old helped win the 1958 World Cup for Brazil?

12 Which Billy became the first man to win 100 caps for England, in 19

13 What was unique about Queen's Park reaching the English FA Cup F twice in the 1880s?

14 What do Accrington Stanley, Bradford Park Avenue and Southport ha in common?.

15 Which Premier League giants began life as Newton Heath?

16 Which club take their name from the armoury at Woolwich in Londo

17 Which club is still called the Irons after their origins at Thames Ironwo

18 Who in 1927 became the only club to take the FA Cup out of Englan

19 The FA Cup in 1923 is remembered for an appearance by which ani

20 What was unique about Sir Walter Winterbottom's appointment as manager of England in 1946?

Quiz 51 Goals Galore 3

Answers – see page 57

LEVEL 1

1 Which *Match of the Day* presenter scored 48 goals for England?
2 Which Manchester United player lobbed Wimbledon keeper Neil Sullivan from near the half-way line?
3 Which Argentinian scored the 'hand of god' goal against England in the 1986 World Cup?
4 Which Welshman scored a fabulous goal for Manchester United against Arsenal in the 1998-99 FA Cup?
5 Tony Cottee was which team's leading scorer in 1999-2000?
6 Which player scored after only 43 seconds in the 1997 FA Cup Final?
7 Which England captain is Newcastle's goal machine?
8 Which French goalscorer left Arsenal for Real Madrid in 1999?
9 Which marksman do Tottenham fans refer to as 'Sir Les'?
10 Which Norwegian is Manchester United's baby-faced assassin?
11 Which Robbie is a Liverpool goal ace?
12 Who is the Republic of Ireland and Sunderland's towering targetman?
13 Which Arsenal player was the top scorer in Euro 2000?
14 Which player is Brazil's leading goalscorer?
15 Who scored a hat-trick for England in the 1966 World Cup Final?
16 Which Englishman scored in the 2000 European Cup final?
17 Which player revealed a t-shirt proclaiming 'Just done it' when he became Arsenal's record goalscorer?
18 Which Manchester United player scored twice for England at Hampden in the Euro 2000 qualifying play-offs?
19 Michael Thomas's last-minute goal at Anfield won the League for which club in 1989?
20 David Trezeguet's last-minute goal won which trophy in 2000?

Who Did What? 4 (see Quiz 49)

Quiz 52 England Managers

LEVEL 1

1 Whose 'wingless wonders' won the World Cup in 1966?

2 Which club did Don Revie take to 60s and 70s glory?

3 Joe Mercer took which club to the League championship?

4 Which England manager played for Scunthorpe, Liverpool, Hamburg, Southampton and Newcastle?

5 Sir Alf Ramsey referred to which international opponents as 'Animals'?

6 Bobby Robson was made England manager after success with which team?

7 The *Sun* newspaper portrayed Graham Taylor as which vegetable?

8 Which manager was in charge of England when they hosted Euro 96?

9 Who was appointed after taking charge of Swindon and Chelsea?

10 England manager Bobby Robson was in charge of which team in 2000?

11 Which manager took England to the World Cup semi-finals in 1990?

12 Which England manager resigned to take up a post in the United Arab Emirates in 1977?

13 Graham Taylor has known most success with which club?

14 Terry Venables took which club to the European Cup final in 1986?

15 Alleged remarks about which section of the community resulted in Glenn Hoddle's dismissal as England manager in 1999?

16 Which England player did Bobby Robson claim was 'as daft as a brush'?

17 What became ex-England manager Graham Taylor's unwanted catch-phrase after his appearance on a television documentary?

18 Ron Greenwood was England's manager during which World Cup finals: 1974, 1978 or 1982?

19 Which former Sheffield Wednesday and Leeds United manager became caretaker England manager between Glenn Hoddle and Kevin Keegan?

20 Which one out of Robson, Taylor and Hoddle never played for England?

Quiz 53 Scotland

Answers – see page 63

1   In which stadium do Scotland usually play their home games?

2   Who was the manager of Scotland in 2000?

3   Who was their previous manager?

4   Who knocked Scotland out of Euro 2000?

5   When Scotland beat the Faeroes in Aberdeen in October 1998, what was the score?

6   Who scored Scotland's goals that day?

7   Who scored Scotland's goal against Brazil in the 1998 World Cup?

8   What was the score in the group match against Norway in the same competition?

9   Where was that match played?

10 Who did Scotland play in the last group match of that tournament?

11 What colour shirts do Scotland usually play in?

12 Who did Scotland beat in the group stage of Italia 90?

13 What was the score?

14 What was the score in Scotland's opening match of that tournament against Costa Rica?

15 Who scored Scotland's winner against Switzerland in Euro 96?

16 Who was in goal for Scotland that day?

17 Where was that match played?

18 Scotland were involved in the first ever international match. Who did they play?

19 When was that match played?

20 What was the score in that match?

Answers

Champions League (see Quiz 55)
1 UEFA Cup. 2 Galatasary. 3 Real Madrid. 4 Once. 5 Wembley.
6 Germany. 7 False. 8 Arsenal. 9 Italy (San Siro). 10 Two.
11 Ajax. 12 Barcelona. 13 Steve McManaman. 14 Norway. 15 AC
Milan. 16 Bayern Munich 17 Rangers. 18 Teddy Sheringham.
19 Spain. 20 Twice.

Quiz 54 The 90s

Answers – see page 64

1   In which season did the Premier League begin?

2   Who won the Division 1 title in 2000?

3   Who won the first Premiership title?

4   Who won the Premier League in 1994-95?

5   Who was the leading scorer that season?

6   Which team appeared in five FA Cup finals in the 1990s?

7   How many of those did they win?

8   How many World Cup tournaments were there during the 1990s?

9   When was the first Worthington Cup played?

10 What was the tournament called before that?

11 What was the same tournament called in 1991 and 1992?

12 Which team appeared in six Scottish Cup finals during the 1990s?

13 How many of those did they win?

14 Which two London clubs contested the Charity Shield in 1991?

15 How many Charity Shields did Manchester United win during the 1990s?

16 Which two teams contested the FA Cup Final in 1997 and the Coca-Cola Cup final in 1998?

17 How many English clubs contested the UEFA Cup final during the 1990s?

18 Who was the last English club to appear in the European Cup Winners Cup final?

19 In what year was that match?

20 When did Manchester United last win the European Cup?

Answers

Midfielders (see Quiz 56)
1 Georgi Kinkladze. 2 George Boateng. 3 Mario Stanic. 4 Carlton Palmer. 5 Republic of Ireland 6 Arsenal. 7 Paul Gascoigne.
8 Manchester United and Leeds. 9 Leicester City. 10 Tottenham.
11 Right. 12 Nigel Clough. 13 Roy Keane. 14 Patrick Vieira.
15 Nolberto Solano. 16 Southampton. 17 Argentina. 18 Frank Lampard 19 Vladimir Smicer. 20 Lothar Matthaus.

Quiz 55 Champions League

LEVEL 1

1 Teams knocked out of the first round can enter which cup?

2 Which team did Chelsea travel to Turkey to beat 5-0 in 1999?

3 Which team eliminated Manchester United from the 1999-2000 competition?

4 How many times have Manchester United won the Champions League?

5 Where did Arsenal play their home games in 1999-2000?

6 Bayer Leverkusen and Borussia Dortmund have been among which country's Champions League representatives?

7 True or False: Tottenham played in the 1998-99 Champions League?

8 A goal by Gabriel Batistuta for Fiorentina effectively knocked which English team out of the 1999-2000 Champions League?

9 In which country will the 2001 Champions League final be played?

10 How many English teams automatically enter the first stage?

11 Which Dutch team has won the Champions League on two occasions?

12 In which city did Manchester United win the Champions League?

13 Which England international scored in Real Madrid's 2000 Champions League final victory?

14 Rosenborg have been regular representatives of which country?

15 Which Milan team won the competition in 1995?

16 Who did Manchester United beat in the 1999 final: Valencia, Bayern Munich or Barcelona?

17 Albertz and Kanchelskis play for which British Champions League team?

18 Which Manchester United sub scored the equaliser in the 1999 final?

19 Raul and Morientes both scored in the 2000 final. For what national team do they play?

20 How many times have Real Madrid won the title since 1995?

Quiz 56 Midfielders

Answers – see page 62

LEVEL 1

1   Who is Derby County's magic Georgian Georgi?

2   Which Ghanaian George patrols Aston Villa's midfield?

3   Which Mario is Chelsea's Croatian midfielder?

4   Which leggy former England International did Coventry sign from Nottingham Forest?

5   For which country does Leeds United's Stephen McPhail play?

6   Everton's Stephen Hughes was signed from which London club?

7   Which Everton midfielder damaged knee ligaments in a Cup final and broke a leg in a Lazio training session?

8   Name one of the former clubs of Bradford City's Lee Sharpe?

9   Izzet, Lennon and Savage are which club's midfield assets?

10 Tim Sherwood won a Championship medal at Blackburn – who did he join after leaving?

11 Where does David Beckham usually play in midfield: left, right or central?

12 Which Nigel played in England midfield and was the son of a great manager?

13 Which Manchester United midfielder was sent off in the 2000 Charity Shield?

14 Who is Arsenal and France's volatile midfield lynchpin?

15 Which Nolberto is Newcastle's sweet-footed South American?

16 For which club does Hassan Kachloul play?

17 Middlesbrough's young midfielder Carlos Marinelli is from which South American country?

18 Which Frank is West Ham's England Under 21 captain?

19 Which Liverpool Vlad scored for the Czech Republic in Euro 2000?

20 Which Lothar was Germany's ageing midfield ace in Euro 2000?

Answers

The 90s (see Quiz 54)
1 1992-93. 2 Leeds United. 3 Manchester United. 4 Blackburn Rovers. 5 Alan Shearer. 6 Manchester United. 7 Four. 8 Three. 9 1999. 10 The Coca-Cola Cup. 11 The Rumbelows League Cup. 12 Rangers. 13 Four. 14 Spurs and Arsenal. 15 Four. 16 Chelsea and Middlesbrough. 17 None. 18 Chelsea 19 1998. 20 1999.

Quiz 57 Grounds 2

LEVEL 1

1 In which year was the last game played at the old Wembley stadium?
2 Which team calls Upton Park home?
3 St James' Park is the ground of which North East team?
4 Take the Maine Road to which Premier League team?
5 The San Siro, the Olympico Stadio and the Delle Alpi stadio are in which country?
6 Which team has a cottage down by the Thames?
7 The Foxes turn out at Filbert Street to see which Premier League team?
8 What is the name of Ipswich Town's ground?
9 Who are the pride of Pride Park?
10 Who play their football down in The Valley?
11 Is the Maracana Stadium in Brazil or Argentina?
12 Which Rovers come home to Ewood Park?
13 What is the name of the Wolverhampton Wanderers stadium?
14 Tynecastle is the home ground of which Edinburgh club?
15 Which London stadium used to have a popular Shed End?
16 Which Bristol team have played home matches at Twerton Park, Bath?
17 Queens Park Rangers share their Loftus Road ground with which buzzing rugby club?
18 Villa Park is the imaginative name of which Premier League team's ground?
19 Ayresome Park in Middlesbrough, Sunderland's Roker Park and the Baseball Ground in Derby have what in common?
20 Which Premier League club has a popular Stretford End?

Quiz 58 **London Teams**

Answers – see page 68

LEVEL 1

1   Which London team is known as 'The Addicks'?

2   Which team plays its home games at Upton Park?

3   Which two teams share Selhurst Park?

4   Who two clubs play in SW6?

5   Which was the last London team to win the Premier League?

6   Which London club has an Egyptian chairman?

7   Which two London teams are nicknamed 'The Bees'.

8   Which was the last London team to win the FA Cup?

9   Who plays in E10?

10   Whose stadium is in Bermondsey?

11   Who used to play at the White City?

12   Which Greater London team is managed by Graham Taylor?

13   Which London team plays in white shirts with navy blue shorts and socks?

14   Which was the last London team to win the League Cup?

15   Which London team was relegated from the Premier League in 1999-2000?

16   Which London team is known as 'The Hammers'?

17   Is Wembley stadium in London?

18   Which London club is managed by Gerry Francis?

19   Who plays in SE16?

20   Which London club has a French manager?

LEVEL 1

Which Dutchman plays in the centre at the back for Manchester United?

Who played centre-half for England in the 1966 World Cup final?

Which 6 foot 4 inch bearded stopper dominated the Chelsea defence during the 1970s?

Which German centre-half was known as 'The Kaiser'?

Which Arsenal centre-half was unfairly nicknamed 'Donkey'?

Which South African plays centre-half for Leeds United?

Who is Leicester City's goal-scoring centre-half?

What number does the centre-half traditionally wear?

Which French centre-half missed the 1998 World Cup final because of suspension?

Who took his place?

Which England centre-half left Ipswich to join Glasgow Rangers in 1987?

Which famous Wolves centre-half won 105 England caps?

Which ex-Manchester Utd centre-half now manages Huddersfield Town?

Which current Everton centre-half had a spell as caretaker manager for the club in the 1990s?

Which Arsenal centre-half scored the winner in the 1993 FA Cup final replay?

Which Blackburn player was Scotland's centre-half during Euro 96?

In Aston Villa's defence Gareth Southgate is paired with which other centre-half?

Which Finnish centre-half joined Liverpool in summer 1999?

Which centre-half captained Everton for most of the 1960s?

Which Dutchman plays No. 5 for Glasgow Rangers?

---

1 Grimsby Town supporters cheered up the football world with their inflatable what?

2 Which of the following clubs is a Football League Club: Scunthorpe United, Scarborough or Frickley Colliery?

3 Which Yorkshire Terriers play in the McAlpine Stadium?

4 Which Sheffield team play in red and white?

5 Which England penalty-shoot out 'villain' helped Sheffield Wednesday t Wembley in 1993?

6 Bradford City's Windass and Saunders share which first name?

7 What is the name of the Football League team: Hull City, Hull Kingstor Rovers or just Hull?

8 At which ground do Sheffield Wednesday play?

9 Martyn, Bakke and Bridges play at which Premier League club?

10 Do Rotherham play under the name of City, United or Academicals?

11 Which Sheffield team were relegated in 1999-2000?

12 What nickname is given to Barnsley manager Dave Bassett?

13 Why was Sheffield United's 1915 FA Cup Final victory known as 'The Khaki Cup'?

14 Which Town play in black and white just minutes from the North Sea?

15 The tragic fire at Valley Parade took place at which team's ground?

16 Hull City manager Brian Little previously managed which Premier League Foxes and Villains?

17 Huddersfield Town share their stadium with a team playing which spo

18 What is emblazoned on the chest of Leeds United shirts?

19 Which group of supporters began at Sheffield Wednesday matches?

20 Which Yorkshire Tykes had never played in the top flight until 1997-9i

Quiz 61 Shirt Colours

Answers – see page 71

1 Which 'Owls' play in blue and white striped shirts?

2 Which south coast Premiership team play in red and white stripes?

3 What colour are Wolves shirts?

4 West Ham and Aston Villa both play in the same colours. What are they?

5 Which 'Eagles' have red and blue vertical stripes?

6 Are QPR shirts striped or hooped?

7 Which Glasgow team play in green and white hoops?

8 Who are 'The Reds' on Merseyside?

9 Which 'Pilgrims' play in green and white shirts?

10 What colour shirts do Burnley play in?

11 Why are Chelsea called 'The Blues'?

12 What colour shirts do Bradford City play in?

13 Which 'Baggies' play in navy blue and white striped shirts?

14 Which is the blue half of Manchester?

15 What colour shirts do Norwich City play in?

16 What kind of blue do Coventry play in?

17 Which is the blue half of Bristol?

18 Which Tyneside team play in black and white stripes?

19 What colour shirts do 'Pompey' play in?

20 Who are 'The Lilywhites'?

Quiz 62 Managers

Answers – see page 72

LEVEL 1

1   Sheffield Wednesday manager Paul Jewell previously helped to keep which Yorkshire team in the Premier League?

2   Joe Royle manages which Premier League club in the North West?

3   Swansea manager John Hollins was a cup-winner for which London club?

4   Which portly former Denmark and Liverpool star is in charge of League new boys Kidderminster Harriers?

5   Colin Harvey, Joe Royle and Howard Kendall have managed which Blues?

6   Craig Brown has managed which national team since 1993?

7   John Gregory is in charge at which Midlands club?

8   Watford have which favourite manager back after his time at England, Wolves and Aston Villa?

9   Sunderland's hot-seat is occupied by which former Everton and Manchester City midfielder?

10   Where did Glenn Hoddle take over from Dave Jones as manager?

11   Dino Zoff resigned as manager of which national team after Euro 2000?

12   Bertie Mee managed which London side that did the double in 1971?

13   Brian Little, Martin O'Neill and Peter Taylor have all managed which Midlands team?

14   Mick McCarthy is manager of which national team?

15   Which team did Ruud Gullitt manage after Chelsea?

16   Name the Everton boss who won five championships at Rangers?

17   Bill Nicholson took which London club to glory in 1961?

18   Which London club is managed by French 80s hero Jean Tigana?

19   Tommy Docherty, Ron Atkinson and Matt Busby all managed which club?

20   He has managed Crystal Palace, QPR, Tottenham, Barcelona and Portsmouth. Who is he?

Answers

Pot Luck 2 (see Quiz 64)
1 Ole Gunnar Solskjaer. 2 Udinese. 3 Jean Tigana. 4 1923.
5 Carling. 6 Ibrox. 7 Nwankwu. 8 Gordon Strachan. 9 Carrow Road. 10 Leeds United. 11 Italy. 12 Utrecht 13 Valencia.
14 Sweden. 15 Lisbon. 16 Pierluigi Collina. 17 Mark Hughes.
18 Crewe Alexandra. 19 Brazil. 20 AC Milan and Internazionale.

LEVEL 1

1   Who was Tottenham Hotspur's manager in 2000?

2   What colour shirts and shorts do Tottenham play in at home?

3   Which country does striker Sergei Rebrov come from?

4   Who was the manager of Spurs' double-winning side?

5   What is Tottenham's stadium called?

6   Who received a career-threatening injury during Spurs 1991 Cup Final against Nottingham Forest?

7   Which Spurs forward joined Manchester United and won the treble in 1999?

8   Which Ramon is in Spurs' 2000-01 squad?

9   Which 60s Spurs' striker scored 44 goals for England?

10 Which Argentinian scored for Spurs in the 1981 FA Cup final replay?

11 Which Tottenham and England star went on to play for Barcelona and Nagoya Grampus 8?

12 Who was the club captain at the start of the 2000-01 season?

13 Which exiled Frenchman joined Tottenham from Newcastle and left them to play for Aston Villa?

14 Which Spurs' captain lifted the 1980 and 81 FA Cup?

15 Tottenham full-back Stephen Carr plays for which national team?

16 Who is Spurs and England's injury-prone midfielder?

17 Who is Tottenham's high-profile chairman?

18 What is the name of Spurs' Scottish international goalkeeper?

19 Which goalkeeper did Tottenham supporters call Erik the Viking?

20 Spurs striker Steffen Iverson has played for which country?

Quiz 64 Pot Luck 2

Answers – see page 70

1   Who is nicknamed 'the baby-faced assassin'?

2   Which team plays in Udine, Italy?

3   Who was the new manager of Fulham in 2000?

4   When was the first Wembley FA Cup final?

5   Who sponsors the Premier League?

6   What is the name of Glasgow Rangers ground?

7   What is the first name of Arsenal's Kanu?

8   Who is the manager of Coventry City?

9   Where do Norwich City play?

10 Which team sold Eric Cantona to Manchester United?

11 For which country does Paolo Maldini play?

12 From which club did Michael Mols join Glasgow Rangers?

13 Who plays at Mestalla?

14 From which country does Celtic's Henrik Larsson come?

15 In which city do Benfica play their football?

16 Which famous bald referee took charge of the 1999 Champions League final?

17 Who became Welsh national team manager in 1999?

18 Who plays at Gresty Road?

19 In which country was the FIFA World Club Championship held in 2000?

20 Which two teams share the San Siro stadium in Italy?

Quiz 65 **Premiership Stars 2**

Answers – see page 75   **LEVEL 1**

1   Which Dutch Dennis has enriched the Premiership with his goals for the Gunners?

2   Who is Manchester United's 'Goal King Cole'?

3   Which tiny Brazilian starred for Middlesbrough during the 1990s?

4   Which tall Norwegian striker leads the Chelsea line?

5   Which Wimbledon striker was transferred to Newcastle during summer 2000?

6   Which French favourite left Spurs for Villa in summer 2000?

7   Which young Malcolm is Derby County's striking sensation?

8   Which Liverpool midfielder's father manages West Ham?

9   Which Nicky crossed Stanley Park in summer 2000?

10   Which Dutch superstar was player/manager at Chelsea during the 1990s?

11   Which Glasgow Rangers striker joined Charlton during summer 2000?

12   Which striker left Chelsea for Celtic during summer 2000?

13   Who cost Spurs £5m during summer 2000?

14   Which Premiership star is married to an ex-Spice Girl?

15   Which German star provided dead-ball accuracy for Middlesbrough during 1999-2000?

16   Which American appeared regularly in the Everton team?

17   Which Moroccans star for Coventry City?

18   Which Moroccans star for Southampton?

19   Which Liverpool youngster scored against Argentina in the 1998 World Cup?

20   Whose volley was the Premier League's Goal of the Season in 2000?

Ireland (see Quiz 67)

Answers
1 David O'Leary. 2 Roy Keane. 3 Leeds United. 4 Robbie Keane. 5 Mark Kennedy. 6 Green. 7 Packie Bonner. 8 Italy. 9 Paul McGrath. 10 John Aldridge. 11 Stephen Carr. 12 Niall Quinn. 13 Frank Stapleton. 14 Jason McAteer. 15 Turkey. 16 Dennis Irwin. 17 Liverpool. 18 Jack Charlton. 19 Tony Cascarino. 20 Arsenal.

Quiz 66 Euro 2000
Answers – see page 76

LEVEL 1

1   What was the opening game of the tournament?

2   What was the score in that match?

3   Who did France play in their opening game?

4   Who finished higher in Group B, Italy or Turkey?

5   Who were co-hosts of the tournament with Belgium?

6   Who did Holland play in their first match?

7   Who scored the quickest goal in the tournament?

8   What was the score between Yugoslavia and Slovenia?

9   Where was England's match against Germany played?

10 France played Holland in the last match of the group stage. What was the score?

11 Holland played Yugoslavia in the quarter-finals. What was the final score?

12 Who scored twice for Portugal against Turkey in their quarter-final match?

13 France, Portugal and Holland were semi-finalists with which other team?

14 Which two teams won through to the final?

15 What was the score in the final?

16 How many goals were scored altogether during the Euro 2000 finals?

17 How many matches were played during the tournament?

18 Which two players top-scored during the tournament?

19 Who scored the fewest goals of any team in the tournament?

20 Which two teams scored the most goals?

Quiz 67 **Republic of Ireland**

Answers – see page 73

LEVEL 1

1   Which Premier League manager scored the Republic of Ireland's most important penalty ever in the 1990 World Cup?

2   Which Republic of Ireland player captains Manchester United?

3   The Republic of Ireland's Gary Kelly plays at which Premier League club?

4   Which Republic of Ireland striker moved from Coventry to Milan in 2000?

5   Which Republic of Ireland winger plays for Manchester City?

6   In what colour shirts do the Republic of Ireland play?

7   Which Packie was the Republic's goalkeeper throughout the 80s?

8   Which nation knocked the Republic of Ireland out of the 1990 World Cup?

9   Which former Manchester United and Aston Villa defender has won the most caps for the Republic of Ireland?

10   Which Tranmere Rovers manager and former Liverpool striker scored 19 goals for the Republic of Ireland?

11   Who is Tottenham's Republic of Ireland full-back?

12   Which Sunderland centre-forward is the equal leading goalscorer?

13   Which former Arsenal and Manchester Utd forward is the Republic's equal leading goalscorer?

14   Which Jason plays on the wing for Blackburn Rovers and the Republic?

15   Which country knocked the Republic out of the Euro 2000 play-offs?

16   Which Manchester Utd full-back has played over 50 times for the Republic of Ireland?

17   Republic of Ireland defender Steve Staunton plays for which club?

18   Who is the Republic of Ireland's most successful manager?

19   Which Irish forward plays his club football for Marseilles?

20   Liam Brady made his name as a player at which London club?

Quiz 68 Who Did What? 5

Answers – see page 74

LEVEL 1

1   Who signed for Manchester United from Newcastle in 1995 for a British record £7m?

2   Which club won the Scottish FA and League cups as well as the Cup-Winners' Cup in 1983?

3   Who had a ruling named after him after he went to the European Court of Justice over transfer fees for players out of contract?

4   Who were banned indefinitely from European competitions in 1985?

5   Which team played West Ham in the all-London FA Cup final in 1975?

6   Who did Michael Bridges score 21 goals for in 1999-2000?

7   Who did Nuno Gomes score four goals for in Euro 2000?

8   Who did Savo Milosavic score five goals for in Euro 2000?

9   Who won the FA Cup final in 1985 courtesy of a Paul Rideout goal?

10 Who won the League Championship four times in his first five seasons in England before retiring to follow an acting career?

11 Who played for Cameroon in the 1994 World Cup at the age of 42?

12 Who played alongside his brother Brian in the Danish national side?

13 Who was the assistant manager of Manchester United who left to manage Blackburn Rovers?

14 Which West Indies batsman played for Antigua & Barbuda in the 1980s?

15 Which famous player played for Santos and New York Cosmos?

16 Who became the first African country to win Olympic gold in 1996?

17 Who utilised a 'Christmas tree' formation when England manager?

18 Who became 'assistant referees' for the 1996-97 season?

19 Who sunk Arsenal with a goal from the halfway line in the 1995 Cup-Winners Cup final?

20 What did Pierre van Hooijdonk do to leave Nottingham Forest?

Answers

Euro 2000 (see Quiz 66)
1 Belgium v Sweden. 2 2-1 to Belgium. 3 Denmark. 4 Italy.
5 Holland. 6 Czech Republic. 7 Paul Scholes. 8 3-3.
9 Charleroi. 10 France 2 Holland 3. 11 Holland 6 Yugoslavia 1.
12 Gomes. 13 Italy. 14 France and Italy. 15 France 2 Italy 1.
16 85. 17 31. 18 Patrick Kluivert and Savo Milosevic.
19 Denmark. 20 France and Holland.

LEVEL 1

---

1   Of which Nationwide League team was Dave Bassett manager in 2000?

2   Who finished sixth in the table in both 1998-99 and 1999-2000?

3   What is the Nationwide?

4   Who does striker Clyde Wijnhard play for?

5   Who lost in the Second Division play-off final in 1999 but won promotion by the same route in 2000?

6   Who does Ade Akinbiyi play for?

7   Who was the new manager of West Bromwich Albion in 2000?

8   Who missed the play-offs by one place in 1999-2000?

9   Which Nationwide League team knocked two Premiership sides out of the FA Cup during the 1999-2000 season?

10 Who was the manager of Nottingham Forest in 2000?

11 Which Lee leads the Pompey attack?

12 Which Nationwide League team plays in Lincolnshire?

13 Who plays at Carrow Road?

14 Which former Manchester United youngster now plays at Huddersfield?

15 How many Division One teams begin with B?

16 Which Nationwide League team plays on the bank of the river Thames?

17 Which Nationwide League team is nicknamed 'The Tykes'?

18 Who is the manager at Birmingham City?

19 Who has the most expensive squad in the Nationwide League?

20 Who plays at the Reebok Stadium?

Quiz 70 **Leeds United**

Answers – see page 80

LEVEL 1

1   Which former Leeds manager took charge at Spurs?

2   Which fiery Frenchman left Elland Road in 1993 after winning the championship with Leeds?

3   From which Scottish club did Leeds sign Mark Viduka?

4   Which South African has captained Leeds United?

5   Which Leeds midfielder missed in the penalty shoot-out against Argentina in the 1998 World Cup?

6   From which country are Galatasary, Leeds' opponents in the UEFA Cup 2000 semi final?

7   Who is Leeds' England International goalkeeper?

8   Which Leeds Erik comes from Norway?

9   Who was Leeds United's manager in 2000?

10 Olivier Dacourt previously played for which North West team?

11 Which two Leeds players were charged after alleged violent behaviour the city centre?

12 Which legendary Leeds skipper captained Scotland in the 1974 World Cu

13 Which Darren did Leeds sign from Coventry City?

14 Which manager took Leeds to League, Cup and European glory in the 60s and 70s?

15 Who was Leeds' England and Republic of Ireland World Cup hero?

16 What colours have Leeds played in since the 1960s?

17 Who was the Leeds manager when they won the league in 1991-92?

18 In which position does Leeds' Michael Bridges play?

19 Which Leeds player was the 2000 Young Player of the Year?

20 Which Leeds star of the 60s and 70s reputedly had the hardest shot i football?

Answers

Cup Winners (see Quiz 72)
1 USA. 2 Egypt. 3 South Africa. 4 Lucas Radebe. 5 Ferencvaros.
6 London Select XI. 7 Marcel Desailly. 8 Marseille & AC Milan.
9 Belgrade. 10 True. 11 South Africa. 12 Laurent Blanc.
13 Inter-Toto. 14 Oliver Bierhoff (Euro 96). 15 False. 16 Jürgen
Klinsmann. 17 Two. 18 Manchester Utd. 19 Galatasary.
20 Copenhagen.

1   What colour shirts do Wales play in?

2   In what city is Wales' national stadium?

3   Which former Everton goalkeeper is Wales' most capped player?

4   Which English-born Manchester United winger chose to play for Wales?

5   Which former Liverpool star is Wales' leading goalscorer?

6   What did Wales do in 1958 that they haven't done since?

7   Which Welsh legend played for Leeds United and Juventus?

8   Which former Welsh team manager played alongside Kevin Keegan at Liverpool?

9   Which Jones the film star was sent off playing for Wales in 1995?

10 Which Leeds, Everton and Newcastle Gary has won over 50 caps for Wales?

11 Which 'Sparky' became Wales' player-manager?

12 Which Bradford City Dean has scored over 20 goals for Wales?

13 Where do Cardiff City play?

14 Which Welsh team famously knocked League Champions Arsenal out of the FA Cup in 1992?

15 Which creature appears on the Wales team's badge?

16 Where do Swansea City play?

17 Who are the only Welsh club to win the FA Cup?

18 In which decade was the League of Wales founded: 50s, 70s or 90s?

19 Robbie Savage plays for Wales and which Premier League club?

20 Which ginger-haired Arsenal, West Ham and Wimbledon striker first played for Wales in 1995?

Answers

Nationwide League (see Quiz 69)
1 Barnsley. 2 Bolton Wanderers. 3 A building society.
4 Huddersfield Town. 5 Gillingham. 6 Wolves. 7 Gary Megson.
8 Wolves. 9 Tranmere Rovers. 10 David Platt. 11 Lee Bradbury.
12 Grimsby Town. 13 Norwich City. 14 Ben Thornley. 15 Five.
16 Fulham. 17 Barnsley. 18 Trevor Francis. 19 Blackburn Rovers.
20 Bolton Wanderers.

79

Quiz 72 Cup Winners

Answers – see page 78

1   Which country won the women's World Cup in 1996?

2   Who won the African Cup of Nations in 1998?

3   Who lost in the final?

4   Which Leeds player captained the losing side?

5   Which Hungarian side won the Fairs Cup in 1965?

6   Which English club contested the first Fairs Cup in 1958: London Unfair XI, London Select XI or Wimbledon?

7   Which French player won the European Cup in 1993 and 94?

8   Which teams did he play for?

9   Which Red Star won the European Cup in 1991?

10 The game was settled on penalties: True or false?

11 Which country are Kaiser Chiefs from?

12 Which French player was banned from the 1998 World Cup final?

13 Which cup did West Ham win in 1999?

14 Who scored the first golden goal to win a major tournament?

15 A Scottish club has never won the Cup Winners Cup: True or false?

16 Who captained the Germany side that won Euro 96?

17 How many times has Trevor Brooking received an FA Cup winners medal: Ten, two or none?

18 Which team set a record by winning a domestic double and the European Cup in the same season?

19 Which Turkish side is the only one to win a major European competition?

20 Where did they play the game that won them the cup?

Quiz 73 Paul Gascoigne

Answers – see page 83

LEVEL 1

1 What is Paul Gascoigne's nickname?

2 With which club did he make his league debut?

3 Who was pictured holding Gascoigne by his privates?

4 For whom was Gascoigne playing in the infamous 1991 FA Cup final?

5 What was the original reason for Gascoigne crying in the semi-final against Germany in the 1990 World Cup?

6 For which Italian club did Gascoigne play?

7 Which ginger-haired ex-Radio One DJ is Gascoigne's long-time friend?

8 Which item of comedy clothing did Gascoigne wear on his return from the World Cup in 1990?

9 What is the name of Gascoigne's rotund friend and sometime minder?

10 Which Scottish club did Gascoigne play for?

11 In Scotland, what was the consequence of Gascoigne 'booking' the referee when returning a dropped yellow card?

12 Which Gascoigne 'musical' goal celebration was judged to be inappropriately sectarian?

13 Against which team did Gascoigne score from a free-kick in a Wembley FA Cup semi-final?

14 What did Gascoigne do in a training session for his Italian club that would make him miss many games?

15 Bryan Robson brought Gascoigne from Scotland to play for which club?

16 In what year did Gascoigne make his England debut?

17 For which Premier League club did Gascoigne sign in 2000?

18 In 1996 Gascoigne was voted Footballer of the Year in which country?

19 Against which country did Gascoigne score at Wembley in Euro 96?

20 Which foggy river did Gascoigne celebrate in his pop hit?

European Football (see Quiz 75)
1 Roma and Lazio. 2 Raul of Real Madrid. 3 Sporting Lisbon.
4 The Stadium of Light. 5 Copa del Rey. 6 Hamburg. 7 PSV.
8 Eindhoven. 9 Paris Saint Germain. 10 Valencia. 11 Naples.
12 Amsterdam. 13 Rotterdam. 14 Real Madrid. 15 Monaco.
16 Serie A. 17 Real Madrid. 18 Marseille. 19 Juventus. 20 The San Siro.

Answers

Quiz 74 Everton

Answers – see page 84

LEVEL 1

1 Where do Everton play?

2 Who was the manager of Everton as the 2000–01 season began?

3 When was the last time Everton won the FA Cup?

4 Which player holds the league appearance record for the club?

5 Which player is the club's record goalscorer?

6 Who did Everton beat to win the 1966 FA Cup final?

7 When were Everton last league champions?

8 Who was Everton's leading scorer in 1999-2000?

9 Who is the current owner of Everton?

10 Who scored twice in his first match after rejoining the club in summer 2000?

11 Who did Everton beat in the 1985 European Cup Winners' Cup final?

12 Who played for Everton in the 1970 title-winning season and managed them to the same trophy in 1984-85?

13 Which striker left Everton for Barcelona in 1986?

14 Which Everton player won a World Cup winner's medal in 1966?

15 Who scored Everton's winner in the 1995 FA Cup final?

16 Who managed Everton for 305 days in 1994?

17 Who took over from him?

18 Who did Everton play in the 1987 Charity Shield?

19 Who was 'The Golden Vision'?

20 Which centre-forward scored 135 goals for Everton in the 1970s?

Quiz 75 **European Football**

LEVEL 1

1 Which two clubs share the Olympic Stadium in Rome?
2 Who was reputedly the world's highest-paid player in 2000?
3 Who won the Portuguese championship in 1999-2000?
4 What is the name of Benfica's ground?
5 What is the Spanish Cup called?
6 Who did Tony Yeboah play for in 2000?
7 Who were the Dutch champions in 2000?
8 In which city do they play their football?
9 Which French club bought Nicolas Anelka during summer 2000?
10 Which Spanish club does Gaizka Mendieta play for?
11 Where is the San Paolo Stadium?
12 In which city do Ajax play their football?
13 In which city do Feyenoord play their football?
14 Who won the European Cup in 2000?
15 Which French club did Glenn Hoddle play for?
16 What is the Italian equivalent of the Premier League?
17 Who play at the Bernabeu?
18 Which French club won the European Cup in 1993 but were subsequently stripped of the title?
19 Which Italian club did Ian Rush play for?
20 In which stadium would you watch the Milan Derby?

Quiz 76 England Captains

Answers – see page 82

LEVEL 1

1   Who is the only England captain to hold up the World Cup trophy?

2   Which Wolves centre-half skippered England in 70 of his 105 appearances?

3   Who was the first black player to captain England?

4   Who led England during Euro 2000?

5   Who captained England to six successive victories between 1960 and 1962?

6   Which Arsenal player led England during the 'Battle of Highbury' against Italy in 1934?

7   Who did Terry Venables name as his England captain for Euro 96?

8   Who captained England in the 1986 World Cup campaign in Mexico?

9   Who took over as captain for the infamous match against Argentina in the same tournament?

10   Which goalkeeper led England during several wartime internationals?

11   Which England captain is now the team manager?

12   Which 'Crazy Horse' captained England during the 1970s?

13   Who led England before Bobby Moore took over in 1963?

14   Who scored twice when he led England against Israel in February 1986?

15   Which Chelsea brother went on to captain England during the 1980s?

16   Which Ipswich full-back led England during the early 80s?

17   Which QPR midfielder led England eight times in the 1970s?

18   Who took over from his injured team-mate Moore to captain England during 1973-74?

19   How many times did Bobby Charlton skipper England?

20   Which Wolves player captained England in their 10-0 win over the US in 1964?

Answers

Everton (see Quiz 74)
1 Goodison Park. 2 Walter Smith. 3 1995. 4 Neville Southall.
5 Dixie Dean. 6 Sheffield Wednesday. 7 1986-87. 8 Kevin
Campbell. 9 Bill Kenwright. 10 Duncan Ferguson. 11 Rapid
Vienna. 12 Howard Kendall. 13 Gary Lineker. 14 Ray Wilson.
15 Paul Rideout. 16 Mike Walker. 17 Joe Royle. 18 Coventry City
19 Alex Young. 20 Bob Latchford.

Quiz 77 **Have Boots, Will Travel**

Answers – see page 87   **LEVEL 1**

1   Which Man Utd midfielder has played for Forest and Cobh Rangers?

2   Which Arsenal striker has played for Ajax and Inter Milan?

3   Which Everton player has played for Newcastle, Tottenham, Lazio, Rangers and Middlesbrough?

4   Which England international played at Leeds, went to Blackburn and Newcastle, then returned to Leeds?

5   Which England international returned to Chelsea from Blackburn Rovers?

6   Which Tottenham forward began at QPR, then signed for Newcastle?

7   Which manager played at Tottenham, Monaco and Chelsea?

8   Which Manchester City forward played for Derby and West Ham?

9   Which Southampton and England player came from Guernsey and stayed?

10 Which Chelsea midfielder came all the way from Wimbledon?

11 Which Villa forward played for Cambridge, Manchester Utd and Coventry?

12 Which Arsenal forward came from Nigeria to play for Ajax and Inter Milan?

13 Which Scotland and Coventry defender won championships at Blackburn and Rangers?

14 Which Newcastle and England forward hit the net at Southampton and Blackburn Rovers?

15 Which Derby player came from Georgia to play for Man City, then Ajax?

16 Which veteran West Ham defender played at Highbury?

17 Which Premier League manager played for Aberdeen, Manchester United, Leeds United and Coventry?

18 Which striker's travels have taken him from Norwich to Chelsea to Celtic?

19 Which Premier League manager played for West Bromwich Albion and Manchester United and captained England?

20 Which keeper began at Watford before moving to Liverpool, then Villa?

Answers

All Around the World (see Quiz 79)
1 USA. 2 South Korea and Japan. 3 Nigeria. 4 Brazil (4),
Argentina (2). 5 South Africa. 6 Gary Lineker. 7 Harry Kewell.
8 Cameroon. 9 1-0. 10 Nolberto Solano. 11 Australia.
12 Jamaica. 13 George Weah. 14 Titi Camara. 15 Colombia.
16 Iran 2-1. 17 China. 18 Cameroon. 19 Iran. 20 Argentina.

85

Quiz 78 Alan Shearer

Answers – see page 88

1   In which city was Alan Shearer born?

2   Which Saints were Shearer's first club?

3   How old was Shearer when he scored his first Football League hat-trick 17, 18 or 19?

4   Which club paid a record £3.3m to buy him in 1992?

5   Which Celtic player formed the SAS partnership with Shearer that help win the Championship in 1995?

6   How many goals did he score in the 4-1 victory over Holland in Euro 96

7   In which year was Shearer voted the PFA and the Writers Footballer of the Year: 1994, 1995 or 1996?

8   Which Newcastle manager signed him in 1996 for £15m?

9   In which European championship was Alan Shearer the top scorer?

10 Has Shearer ever missed a penalty in England's penalty shoot-outs?

11 In Euro 96 who was the only team Shearer didn't score against: Scotland, Spain or Switzerland?

12 In which year did Shearer make his debut for England: 1992, 93 or 94

13 Which English club tried to sign to Shearer in 1996?

14 Who did Shearer score against on his England debut: Scotland, France or Germany?

15 How did Shearer score against Germany in Euro 96 and Euro 2000?

16 Which of the five penalties has Shearer always taken for England in penalty shoot-outs?

17 Which tournament did Shearer miss because of a knee injury?

18 Against which country did Shearer score a penalty in Euro 2000?

19 Against which country did Shearer score England's winner in Euro 200

20 In which year did Shearer retire from international football?

Quiz 79 All Around the World

Answers – see page 85

LEVEL 1

1   Joe Max-Moore and Kasey Keller are from which country?

2   Which two Far East countries are to host the 2002 World Cup finals?

3   Kanu and Celestine Babayaro are from which country?

4   Who has won more World Cups: Argentina or Brazil?

5   Leeds' Lucas Radebe and Bolton's Mark Fish play for which country?

6   Which England international left Spurs to join Grampus Eight in Japan?

7   Which Australian won England's 2000 Young Player of the Year award?

8   Which African country were the first to reach the World Cup quarter finals, losing to England in 1990?

9   What was the score of Argentina's game against Japan in the 1998 World Cup?

10   Which Newcastle United player hails from Peru?

11   Goalkeepers Mark Bosnich and Mark Schwarzer play for which nation?

12   Wimbledon's Robbie Earle scored which country's first and only goal in the World Cup finals?

13   Which former World Footballer of the Year hails from Liberia and has played for AC Milan, Chelsea and Manchester City?

14   Who is Liverpool's Guinean forward?

15   Rene Higuita shocked Wembley with his 'scorpion kick' save in 1995. For which South American country was he playing?

16   Who won the match between the USA and Iran in the 1998 World Cup?

17   Crystal Palace's Fan Zhiyi came from which country?

18   Liverpool's Rigobert Song, Arsenal's Lauren and Middlesbrough's Joseph-Desire Job are from which African Country?

19   Which Middle Eastern country is Charlton's Karim Bagheri from?

20   River Plate and Boca Juniors are teams from which country?

Have Boots, Will Travel (see Quiz 77)
1 Roy Keane. 2 Dennis Bergkamp. 3 Paul Gascoigne. 4 David Batty. 5 Graeme Le Saux. 6 Les Ferdinand 7 Glenn Hoddle. 8 Paulo Wanchope. 9 Matt Le Tissier 10 Dennis Wise. 11 Dion Dublin. 12 Kanu. 13 Colin Hendry. 14 Alan Shearer. 15 Georgi Kinkladze. 16 Nigel Winterburn. 17 Gordon Strachan. 18 Chris Sutton. 19 Bryan Robson. 20 David James.

Answers

Quiz 80 Tony Adams

Answers – see page 86

LEVEL 1

1   In which county was Adams born?

2   Besides Arsenal, which other clubs has Adams played for?

3   In which position does Adams play?

4   Against which team did Adams score the winning goal in the 1993 FA Cup semi-final?

5   In which year was Adams voted Young Player of the Year: 1986, 1987 or 1988?

6   What happened to Stephen Morrow's arm when celebrating winning the League Cup with Tony Adams in 1993?

7   In which year did Adams make his debut for England?

8   True or false: Adams has never scored for England?

9   In which tournament did Adams captain England?

10 Which trophy did Adams lift in 1994?

11 For what offence did Adams receive a custodial sentence?

12 Which Dutch striker so embarrassed Adams in the 1988 European Championship that it took him two years to regain his England place?

13 What is the name of Tony Adams' autobiography?

14 Which manager made Adams Arsenal's youngest ever captain?

15 With which model was Adams linked in 1999?

16 Which animal did opposing supporters imitate to jibe the young Adams.

17 From which player did Adams take over the England captaincy in 2000?

18 For his display against which country in 1993 did Adams earn the tag 'The Lion of Izmir'?

19 Why did 7,000 fans turn out to see an Arsenal reserves game in 1991?

20 Which of Shakespeare's plays did Adams take to read for inspiration in Euro 2000?

Quiz 81 Commentators

Answers – see page 91

LEVEL 1

1   Who famously said, 'Some people are on the pitch. They think it's all over... it is now!'

2   Which commentator is famous for his sheepskin coat?

3   Who left BBC for ITV in 1999?

4   Who presented ITV's *World of Sport*?

5   Who provided commentary for *Match of the Seventies*?

6   Which ex-player leads Sky Sports' football coverage?

7   Whose was the voice behind *The Big Match*?

8   Who presented *Match of the Day* after Des Lynham's departure?

9   Who ususally presents ITV's highlights programme?

10 Who is the anchorman for *Football Focus*?

11 Who is Channel 4's resident football expert?

12 Who is ITV's current main commentator?

13 Who is his usual expert summariser?

14 Who mentioned Aaron Winter's collection of Dutch caps during Euro 2000?

15 Whose *Football Night* dominates Radio 5's football coverage?

16 Who presents *Football Italia*?

17 Which famous Dutch ex-player joined the BBC team for Euro 2000?

18 Who is England's most famous female football pundit?

19 Who is her sidekick?

20 Which former Scottish international defender regularly appears on *Match of the Day*?

1   Which club did Danny Blanchflower captain to the double in 1961?

2   Which club suffered the tragedy of the 1958 Munich air crash?

3   Who or what was Accrington Stanley?

4   Which country humiliated England 6-3 at Wembley in 1953?

5   Jock Stein managed the first British team to win the European Cup. Who?

6   Which Tom played for Preston North End and England after World War II and was arguably the best winger England ever had?

7   Bremner, Giles and Gray played for which team in the 60s?

8   Which Portuguese team did Manchester United beat to win the European Cup in 1968?

9   Which was the first World Cup England took part in?

10 Which 1950s and 60s Manchester United manager was famous for his 'babes'?

11 In which year was *Match of the Day* first broadcast?

12 Which team were elected to the top division in 1919 and have never left it?

13 In which decade were the first floodlit league games played?

14 Which team used to play at Anfield before leaving in 1892?

15 Pickles the dog discovered which stolen trophy in England in 1966?

16 In 1965-66 what were English League clubs first allowed to do to injured players?

17 Bill Shankly began to mould which team in the 1960s?

18 Which Spanish club won the European Cup five times in succession from 1956?

19 For which country did the great Eusebio play?

20 Which British nation beat world champions England in 1967?

Pot Luck 3 (see Quiz 84)
Answers
1 Atletico Madrid. 2 Sunderland. 3 West Ham. 4 France.
5 Fulham. 6 Arsenal. 7 Chelsea. 8 Worthington (League) Cup.
9 Hearts. 10 Chile. 11 Vauxhall Conference. 12 Six. 13
Germany. 14 Wigan. 15 Installed artificial surfaces. 16 Bruce
Grobelaar. 17 Alan Shearer. 18 Sulzeer. 19 Manchester United.
20 Derby County.

Quiz 83 Eurostars

Answers – see page 89

LEVEL 1

1 Who is Barcelona's biggest Brazilian star?

2 Which Real Madrid player scored for Portugal against England in Euro 2000?

3 Which French club sold Robert Pires to Arsenal in summer 2000?

4 Who does Argentinian midfielder Juan Sebastian Veron play his club football for?

5 Which Spanish club does goalkeeping sensation Iker Casillas play for?

6 Which European club does Brazilian striker Mario Jardel play for?

7 Which Feyenoord defender joined Glasgow Rangers in summer 2000?

8 Who did Dutch 'genius' Johan Cruyff play for in his home country?

9 Which club does Patrick Kluivert play for?

10 Japanese star Nakata plays for which Italian club?

11 Who was the European and World Footballer of the Year in 1999?

12 Where does he play his club football?

13 Which Dutch superstar joined Chelsea in 1995?

14 Who holds the most international caps for Germany?

15 Which Portuguese legend of the 1960s was nicknamed 'The Black Panther'?

16 Which Dutch striker joined Arsenal from Inter in 1995?

17 Which Frenchman joined Manchester United from Leeds in 1992?

18 Who scored France's equaliser in the Euro 2000 final against Italy?

19 Which German club signed Norwegian Erik Mykland in summer 2000?

20 Which Portuguese blond bombshell joined Everton in 2000?

Commentators (see Quiz 81)

Answers
1 Kenneth Wolstenholme. 2 John Motson. 3 Desmond Lynham.
4 Dickie Davies. 5 Dennis Waterman. 6 Andy Gray. 7 Brian Moore.
8 Gary Lineker. 9 Bob Wilson. 10 Ray Stubbs. 11 Paul Elliott.
12 Clive Tyldesley. 13 Ron Atkinson. 14 Barry Davies. 15 Trevor
Brooking. 16 James Richardson. 17 Johan Cruyff.
18 Gabby Yorath. 19 Barry Venison. 20 Alan Hansen.

1   Which team won the Spanish double in 1996?

2   Scottish international Don Hutchison joined which team from Everton?

3   Joe Cole and Michael Carrick are which team's young hopefuls?

4   Zinedine Zidane plays for which country?

5   Harrods owner Mohamed Al Fayed is chairman at which London club?

6   Goals from Overmars and Anelka won the 1998 FA Cup final for who?

7   For whom did Roberto Di Matteo score against Middlesbrough to win the FA Cup Final?

8   Tottenham Hotspur beat Leicester City in what Final in 1999?

9   Which Edinburgh team won the 1998 Scottish Cup Final?

10 For which South American national team does Lazio's Marcelo Salas play?

11 Which league's champions can be promoted to League Division Three?

12 Since season 2000-01 for how many seconds is a goalkeeper allowed to keep hold of the ball?

13 In 2000, England, South Africa and Germany all bid to host the World Cup – who was successful?

14 Which team share the JJB stadium with the town's Rugby League side?

15 Luton Town, Oldham Athletic, QPR and Preston all did what to their pitches in the 80s?

16 Which former Liverpool and Zimbabwe goalkeeper was cleared of match-fixing in the high court?

17 Whose goal against Germany gave England their only victory in Euro 2000?

18 What is the Sol in Sol Campbell short for?

19 Which English side competed in the inaugural FIFA World Club Championship in Brazil in January 2000?

20 Which Premier League team play in white shirts and black shorts?

Quiz 85 The North West 2

LEVEL 1

1 'Football isn't a matter of life and death. It's more important than that,' said which Liverpool legend?

2 Tony Book, Joe Mercer and Malcolm Allison were managers of which club?

3 Which Wanderers reached the 2000 FA Cup semi-final?

4 Which of the Lancashire clubs has spent the most seasons in the top flight?

5 Which team is based in Birkenhead?

6 Which North West Athletic play at the JJB stadium?

7 Who are Preston North End's nearest neighbours and fiercest rivals?

8 Pop group Dario G are named after Crewe Alexandra's long-serving manager. What is his surname?

9 Which club shares the name of its ground with a cricket ground?

10 Which North West reds have won more League titles than any other club?

11 Which are the only County playing League football in the North West?

12 Manchester City striker Paulo Wanchope hails from which country?

13 Gallagher, Gillespie and McAteer are in which team's 2000-01 squad?

14 Which Turf Moor Clarets had to win their last game of the season in 1987 to stay in the Football League?

15 Wigan manager Bruce Rioch was previously in charge at which London Premier League club?

16 Bergsson, Fish and Holdsworth play for which of the region's Wanderers?

17 French defender Laurent Blanc kissed which part of Manchester United's Fabien Barthez's anatomy before each international match?

18 Blackpool's Steve McMahon played for which clubs in the North West?

19 Which team is older, Liverpool or Everton?

20 Which potteries team, managed by Gudjon Thordarson, has a distinctly Icelandic feel to their squad?

Answers

Midlands Clubs 2 (see Quiz 87)
1 Leicester City and Stoke City. 2 Walsall. 3 Walsall v Port Vale.
4 Birmingham City. 5 Coventry City. 6 Billy Wright. 7 West Brom.
8 Aston Villa. 9 Coventry City. 10 Walsall. 11 Terry Butcher.
12 Stoke City. 13 Aston Villa. 14 Wolves. 15 Internazionale.
16 Stoke City's. 17 Peter Taylor. 18 Kidderminster Harriers.
19 Leicester City. 20 Coventry City.

Quiz 86 London Teams 2

1   Who used to play at Cold Blow Lane?

2   Jimmy Greaves played for three London teams: Spurs, Chelsea and who else?

3   Who plays at Underhill?

4   Which ground featured the Shelf?

5   Who play in SW6?

6   Which London club did Kevin Keegan manage in 1998-99?

7   Who was manager of Arsenal before Arsène Wenger?

8   Which two London rivals contested a 1991 FA Cup semi-final at Wembley?

9   Which London club won the European Cup Winners Cup in 1965?

10 Who plays at Loftus Road?

11 Which London team is the most 'athletic'?

12 Which London team finished highest in the 1999-2000 Premier League?

13 Who is the chairman of Watford?

14 Which former West Ham player managed Millwall in 1997-98?

15 Which London team play in white shirts with a red V?

16 Whose last three managers have been an Englishman, a Dutchman and an Italian?

17 Which London club plays in Middlesex?

18 Which London club began life as Dial Square FC?

19 Whose headquarters are known as 748 High Road?

20 Who plays in E13?

---

1 Which Midlands clubs did legendary goalkeeper Gordon Banks play for?

2 Who plays at the Bescot Stadium?

3 If you saw the Saddlers playing the Valiants, who would you be watching?

4 Karren Brady is managing director of which Midlands club?

5 Who plays at Highfield Road?

6 Which Wolves player played 70 consecutive matches for England?

7 Leeds United midfielder Johnny Giles had two spells as manager of which Midlands club?

8 For which club does Lee Hendrie play?

9 For which club does Steve Ogrizovic hold the appearances record?

10 Who used to play at Fellows Park?

11 Which ex-Ipswich and Glasgow Rangers defender managed Coventry between 1990 and 1992?

12 Who used to play at the Victoria Ground?

13 From which club did Manchester United buy Dwight Yorke in 1998?

14 Robbie Keane moved from which club to Coventry in 1999?

15 Where did he go after that?

16 Whose stadium will you find in Stanley Matthews Way?

17 Who became manager at Filbert Street in 2000?

18 Which Midlands team were promoted to the Third Division in 1999-2000?

19 For which club did Stan Collymore sign for from Aston Villa?

20 Manager John Sillett led which club to FA Cup glory in 1987?

Answers

The North West 2 (see Quiz 85)
1 Bill Shankly. 2 Manchester City. 3 Bolton. 4 Everton.
5 Tranmere Rovers. 6 Wigan. 7 Blackpool. 8 Gradi. 9 Old Trafford. 10 Liverpool. 11 Stockport. 12 Costa Rica.
13 Blackburn Rovers. 14 Burnley. 15 Arsenal. 16 Bolton. 17 His (bald) head. 18 Liverpool and Everton. 19 Everton. 20 Stoke City.

Quiz 88 Premier Stars 3

Answers – see page 94

LEVEL 1

1   What did Rio Ferdinand, Frank Lampard and Kieron Dyer do on their holidays in Ayia Napa?

2   Dave Watson and Richard Gough are which team's ageing club and team captains?

3   Who got in trouble for punching the air after a Patrik Berger goal for Liverpool?

4   Are Ryan Giggs, Davor Suker and Patrik Berger all right- or left-footed?

5   West Ham's Davor Suker plays for which European nation?

6   Lauren Bisan-Etame Mayer left Real Mallorca for which Premier League team in 2000?

7   The defender Alpay plays at which Midlands Premier League club?

8   Jonatan Johansson is which London red-shirted team's striker?

9   Eidur Gudjohnsen replaced Chris Sutton at which London club?

10 Which Jody is a rare Englishman at Stamford Bridge?

11 Croatian Alen Boksic has taken up arms at which Riverside club?

12 Which club does Belgian striker Cedric Roussel play for?

13 Which club fields an Estonian goalkeeper in Mart Poom?

14 Stephen and Mark Hughes are unrelated but are together at which club?

15 Which Holland player was captain of Ipswich Town in 2000?

16 Derby County's Craig Burley has an uncle in charge of which top team?

17 What injury has befallen Stuart Pearce (twice), Ian Pearce, Shaka Hislop and Joe Cole at West Ham?

18 Which Ade moved from Wolves to Leicester City?

19 Which Alf-Inge is Norway and Manchester City's midfielder?

20 Which Jordi was a son of a great Dutchman and played a bit-part at Manchester United?

Answers

London Teams 2 (see Quiz 86)
1 Millwall. 2 West Ham. 3 Barnet. 4 White Hart Lane. 5 Chelsea and Fulham. 6 Fulham. 7 Bruce Rioch. 8 Spurs and Arsenal. 9 West Ham. 10 QPR. 11 Charlton Athletic. 12 Arsenal. 13 Sir Elton John. 14 Billy Bonds. 15 Leyton Orient. 16 Chelsea. 17 Brentford. 18 Arsenal. 19 Spurs. 20 West Ham.

LEVEL 1

Which part of your anatomy did a banner claim Norman Hunter would bite?

Which England star, now a pundit, played for West Ham in the 70s?

Which QPR manager scored twice in a 5-1 victory over Scotland in 1975?

Which Premiership-winning team were relegated in 1974?

Which London team featured Venables, Marsh and Bowles?

Who were the only British team in the 1974 and 1978 World Cup finals?

In which postion did Mike Channon play for Southampton and England?

Vogts, Beckenbauer and Hoeness played for which World Cup-winning nation in 1974?

Which controversial Derby County and Nottingham Forest manager spent 44 days in charge of Leeds United in 1974?

Bob Wilson, George Graham and Charlie George played for which team in the 70s?

What current European club competition replaced the Inter-Cities Fairs Cup in 1972?

Which London club entered the Football League in 1977, made the top flight by 1988 and were relegated in 2000?

Cruyff, Neeskens and Rensenbrink played for which country in the 70s?

In which position did Peter Bonetti play for Chelsea and England?

What fate befell Keegan and Bremner in the 1974 Charity Shield?

Which Doc took Manchester Utd to the 1977 Cup Final?

Which 70s England captain would eventually end up as their manager?

Which team did Ray Clemence help win European Cups in the 70s?

Which Scottish 'reds' did Alex Ferguson manage in the late 70s?

For which club did Kenny Dalglish score over 100 goals before joining Liverpool?

Who Are They? (see Quiz 91)
1 Everton. 2 Leicester City. 3 Coventry City. 4 France. 5 Watford.
6 Southampton. 7 Chelsea. 8 Aston Villa. 9 Italy. 10 Leeds
United. 11 Manchester City. 12 Tottenham Hotspur. 13
Manchester United. 14 Brighton and Hove Albion. 15 Wimbledon.
16 Arsenal. 17 Liverpool. 18 Newcastle United. 19 QPR.
20 West Ham.

Quiz 90 The 80s 2

Answers – see page 100

1 Which 80s cup-winning side featured Beasant, Wise and Fashanu?

2 How many times did Spurs win the league championship in the 80s?

3 Which cup did Liverpool win four times in succession in the early 80s

4 Which Dons were the last non-Glasgow team to win the Scottish Prem Division (in 1985)

5 How many points did a football league team get for a win in 1980-81

6 What great goalscorer missed Liverpool's penalty in the 1988 FA Cup fin

7 Which manager took Watford to second place in the League in 1982-8

8 In 1981 which London club became the first to have an artifical pitch

9 Which former England manager went to manage Barcelona in the 80s

10 Who was the darling of Newcastle and Tottenham before joining Marseille in 1989?

11 Which 20-year-old Manchester United and Northern Ireland striker scored their winning goal in the 1985 FA Cup final?

12 The occasion of the Hillsborough tragedy of 1986 was an FA Cup sem final between Nottingham forest and who?

13 Which Ally is Rangers greatest goalscorer and *A Question of Sport* capta

14 The 80s football TV show Saint and Greavsie was presented by which former players?

15 Who did Tottenham sign from Newcastle for £2m in 1988?

16 Which unfairly nicknamed 'Quasimodo' won a championship with Liverpool before helping rejuvenate Keegan's Newcastle?

17 Which 80s championship winning team included Southall, Reid and Gra

18 Which international 80s team included Tigana, Platini and Giresse?

19 Which Champagne Charlie did Arsenal sign from Celtic in the 80s?

20 Which England cricketing hero played for Scunthorpe United in the 8

LEVEL 1

Can Walter Smith take the School of Science back to the top?

These Foxes are Worthington Cup kings and Premier League stayers.

These Sky Blues have an explosive manager and a Moroccan touch.

This team won a successive World Cup and European Championship.

Taylor, Blissett and Barnes helped these Hornets to good times in the 80s.

Channon, Keegan and Le Tissier have been their stars.

Blue is the colour for these continental Kings Road strollers.

They might have Merson, Southgate and Joachim but they are still the Villains.

These *Azzurri* reached the Euro 2000 final.

Revie, Wilkinson... Can O'Leary win the championship for them as well?

Maine Road has seen many glory days from this team. But not for years.

Bill Nicholson, Keith Burkinshaw and Terry Venables are among this club's successful managers.

The biggest club in the world?

Since this south coast outfit reached the FA Cup final in 1984 they have been down, down, down?

This small club Crazy Gang made the top flight, stayed there and won the FA Cup to boot.

Arsene's French polished outfit.

'You'll Never Walk Alone' sang this team's Kop as they won everything in sight in the 80s.

Kevin Keegan's Magpies who blew a massive lead in the 1995-96 championship.

These Superhoops play at Loftus Road.

Ron Greenwood turned this London club into a 'Football Academy'.

The 70s 2 (see Quiz 89)
1 'Yer Legs'. **2** Trevor Brooking. **3** Gerry Francis. **4** Manchester United. **5** Queens Park Rangers. **6** Scotland. **7** Forward. **8** West Germany. **9** Brian Clough. **10** Arsenal. **11** EUFA Cup.
12 Wimbledon. **13** Holland. **14** Goalkeeper. **15** They were both sent off. **16** Tommy Docherty. **17** Kevin Keegan. **18** Liverpool.
19 Aberdeen. **20** Celtic.

1   Who left Arsenal with Marc Overmars for Barcelona in 2000?

2   Who won the Worthington Cup in 2000 with a goal by Matt Elliott?

3   Who were relegated from the Premier League when manager Alan Ball mistakenly told them to play the game out for a draw?

4   Who won the Division One play-off in 1998: Sunderland or Charlton?

5   Which club was ordered to replay a 1999 Worthington Cup game?

6   Who just avoided relegation in 2000, then entered the Inter-Toto Cup?

7   Who were involved in a near disaster at Stanstead airport after a match at West Ham in 1998?

8   Who won the PFA Merit Award in 2000 after a career playing for Tottenham and England despite suffering from diabetes?

9   Who won promotion at Gillingham before moving to Leicester?

10 Who won promotion to Division One under Ossie Ardiles in 1990 only to be found guilty of 'financial irregularities' and immediately demoted?

11 Who won the League Cup and FA Cup double in 1993?

12 Who has celebrated his goals for Bradford City by somersaulting?

13 Who broke a leg in a EUFA Cup match playing for Celtic against Lyon?

14 In 1996 who was Blackburn Rovers' leading scorer?

15 Who called the referee 'a muppet' at Highbury in 1996?

16 Which Ghanaian won two consecuive *Match of the Day* goal of the month in 1995 with explosive shots for Leeds United?

17 In 1991 who scored from a free-kick for Spurs in the first FA Cup semi final at Wembley?

18 Who won the Manager of the Year award on five occasions in the 1990

19 Which former England captain died in 1993?

20 Who retired in 1993 after 17 years in charge of Nottingham Forest?

Answers

The 80s 2 (see Quiz 90)

1 Wimbledon. **2** None. **3** The League (Milk) Cup.
4 Aberdeen. **5** Two. **6** John Aldridge **7** Graham Taylor. **8** QPR.
9 Terry Venables. **10** Chris Waddle. **11** Norman Whiteside.
12 Liverpool. **13** Ally McCoist. **14** Ian StJohn and Jimmy Greaves
15 Paul Gascoigne. **16** Peter Beardsley. **17** Everton. **18** France.
19 Charlie Nicholas. **20** Ian Botham.

Quiz 93 **Pot Luck 4**

Answers – see page 103

LEVEL 1

1 Patrick Kluivert plays for which country?

2 Which Harriers were Football League new boys in 2000?

3 Which two London clubs share Selhurst Park?

4 Which ex-Arsenal player's autobiography is called *Mr Wright*?

5 Which Sky pundit former player wagered his hair against Bradford City avoiding relegation in 2000 – and lost?

6 Which club had the original Kop end?

7 Euro 2000 star Luis Figo plays for which country?

8 How many League games do Premiership teams play in a season?

9 Who won a World Cup as a player with England and went to two as the Republic of Ireland's manager?

10 Three times European Footballer of the Year Michel Platini played for which country?

11 Businessman Sam Hammam was associated with which club?

12 Which Manchester United brothers played for England in Euro 2000?

13 Which country lost the Euro 2000 final in extra time?

14 Upson and Manninger are among which London club's young stars?

15 Which Manchester United midfielder scored a hat-trick for England against Poland in 1999?

16 Ken Bates is the Chairman of which Premier League club?

17 Which of these clubs has Alan Shearer not played for: Newcastle United, Blackburn Rovers or Leeds United?

18 In 2000 Chelsea spent £15m on who: Hasselbaink, Stanic or Panucci?

19 Who scored the goal in the 'They think it's all over' commentary?

20 Which Middlesbrough and England player never puts his shirt on until he is on the pitch?

Answers

United (see Quiz 95)
1 Newcastle United. 2 False. 3 Davor Suker. 4 Lucas Radebe.
5 Everton. 6 Leeds. 7 Torquay. 8 West Ham. 9 Hartlepool.
10 Dundee. 11 Manchester. 12 Sheffield. 13 Carlisle. 14 Dwight Yorke. 15 Rotherham. 16 Cambridge United. 17 Nigel Martyn.
18 Upton Park. 19 1994. 20 True.

101

Quiz 94 City

Answers – see page 104

1   Which City plays at Vetch Field?

2   Joe Royle is manager at which City?

3   Which City plays in the Potteries?

4   St James Park is home to which City?

5   Who was the last City to win the FA Cup?

6   Which City is managed by Bruce Rioch?

7   Which City play at Bootham Crescent?

8   How many Citys were there in the Premier League in 2000-01?

9   When City play Rovers in a local derby in Division Two in 2000-01, where is the match being played?

10 Which City play in amber and black striped shirts?

11 Which City is found on Moss Side?

12 Which City escaped relegation from the Premier League in 1999-2000

13 Which City is nicknamed 'The Bluebirds'?

14 Which City won the European Cup Winners' Cup in 1970?

15 Which City won the Worthington Cup in 2000?

16 Which City became United in 1919?

17 Which City would play a local derby against Villa?

18 Which City did Martin O'Neill leave to join Celtic in summer 2000?

19 Which City is nicknamed 'The Bantams'?

20 If your team were playing away against the Minstermen, where would the match be played?

Quiz 95 **United**

Answers – see page 101

1   Which United reached the FA Cup final in 1998 and 1999?

2   True or false: West Ham United are nicknamed the Cockneys?

3   Which United player plays for Croatia and used to play for Arsenal?

4   Which United captain is also captain of South Africa?

5   Newcastle United bought Duncan Ferguson from and sold him back to which club?

6   Which United play at Elland Road?

7   Torquay or Exeter – which one is United?

8   Which United play in claret and blue?

9   Which United have never played at Wembley: Peterborough or Hartlepool?

10 Which Scottish United reached the 1987 EUFA Cup final: Dundee or Ayr?

11 Which United won the 'treble' in 1999?

12 Which United are Wednesday's local rivals?

13 Which United are Britain's most northerly league club?

14 Which United player plays for Trinidad and Tobago?

15 Rotherham or Darlington – which one is United?

16 Which team plays in the football league – Cambridge City or Cambridge United?

17 Which United goalkeeper played for England in Euro 2000?

18 Where do West Ham United play?

19 Which World Cup took place in the United States – 1990, 1994 or 1998?

20 True or false: Ian Botham played football for Scunthorpe United?

Quiz 96 Complete the Name

Answers – see page 102

LEVEL 1

1   Plymouth...

2   Preston...

3   Wolverhampton...

4   Tranmere...

5   Aston...

6   Leyton...

7   Brighton...

8   Charlton...

9   Huddersfield...

10   Notts...

11   Bolton...

12   Crystal...

13   West Bromwich...

14   Partick...

15   Blackburn...

16   Nottingham...

17   Raith...

18   Crewe...

19   Derby...

20   Port...

Answers

City (see Quiz 94)
1 Swansea City. 2 Manchester City. 3 Stoke City. 4 Exeter City.
5 Coventry City in 1987. 6 Norwich City. 7 York City. 8 Three.
9 Bristol. 10 Hull City. 11 Manchester City. 12 Bradford City.
13 Cardiff City. 14 Manchester City. 15 Leicester City. 16 Leeds.
17 Birmingham City. 18 Leicester City. 19 Bradford City.
20 York.

LEVEL 1

1 Steven Gerrard and Jamie Carragher are young guns at which club?

2 Which of these teams does not play at home in a red shirt: Arsenal, Newcastle United or Liverpool?

3 Mohammed Al Fayed is associated with which London team?

4 Which club's ground has the Stretford End stand behind one goal?

5 Graeme Souness, Kenny Dalglish and Brian Kidd have all managed which club?

6 Croydon met Doncaster Belles in which Cup final in May 2000?

7 Fulham's John Collins played for which national team?

8 Who is found near the benches at football matches?

9 How many games did Kevin Phillips play for England in Euro 2000: One, two or none?

10 How many goals did Thierry Henry score in Euro 2000: Three, two or one?

11 Which Frenchman appeared in a shampoo advert?

12 Which country do Sampdoria come from?

13 Which Premier League manager's autobiography is called *Managing My Life*?

14 True or False: George Best never played in the World Cup Finals?

15 What shirt number did Bobby Moore usually play in for club and country?

16 Alan Curbishley was manager at which London club in 2000?

17 Which Aston Villa and England midfielder admitted to drink, gambling and drug problems while at Arsenal?

18 Which Tottenham Hotspur German player initiated the 'diving' goal celebration?

19 Which Football League team have the name Argyle?

20 Which England striker has a soccer school on television?

Answers

Name That Team (see Quiz 98)
1 Rangers. 2 Manchester City. 3 Sunderland. 4 Tottenham Hotspur. 5 West Ham. 6 Newcastle 7 Southampton. 8 Everton. 9 Liverpool. 10 Ipswich. 11 Aston Villa. 12 Bradford City. 13 Coventry City. 14 Leicester City. 15 Middlesbrough. 16 Sheffield Wednesday. 17 Celtic. 18 Arsenal. 19 Chelsea. 20 Manchester United.

Quiz 98 **Name that Team**

Answers – see page 105

1   Mols, Van Bronckhorst, Wallace.

2   Weaver, Goater, Kennedy.

3   Gray, Quinn, Phillips.

4   Sullivan, Campbell, Sherwood.

5   Potts, Cole, Kanoute.

6   Dabizas, Solano, Shearer.

7   Dodd, Kachloul, Pahars.

8   Pistone, Gascoigne, Jeffers.

9   Song, Gerrard, Fowler.

10 Wright, Scales, Stewart.

11 Barry, Dublin, Nilis.

12 Petrescu, Windass, Carbone.

13 Hedman, Hadji, Whelan.

14 Flowers, Izzet, Eadie.

15 Ziege, Karembeu, Ricard.

16 Srnicek, Rudi, De Bilde.

17 Berkovic, Larsson, Sutton.

18 Keown, Parlour, Bergkamp.

19 De Goey, Le Saux, Flo.

20 Stam, Butt, Yorke.

Answers

Pot Luck 6 (see Quiz 99)
1 Highbury. **2** Gascoigne's arm. **3** Wimbledon. **4** Andy Cole.
5 Stanley Matthews. **6** Failed fitness test. **7** 1966 World Cup
winners. **8** Nine. **9** Ten **10** Brazil. **11** Dino Zoff.
12 Newcastle. **13** Both also managed Arsenal. **14** Broken leg.
15 England's. **16** Gianfranco Zola. **17** Tottenham. **18** Bristol
Rovers. **19** Don Hutchison. **20** Hampden Park.

Quiz 99 Pot Luck 6

Answers – see page 106

1 Which ground has the Clock End behind one goal?

2 What broke when Paul Gascoigne elbowed George Boateng?

3 Sam Hammam sold his remaining shares in which club in 2000?

4 Who scored his 100th goal for Manchester United at Wimbledon in February 2000?

5 100,000 people attended the funeral of which footballer in 2000?

6 Why didn't Ruud van Nistelrooy sign for Manchester United in June 2000?: He failed a fitness test; they wouldn't give him and his wife a Mercedes; he didn't like English food.

7 Hunt, Stiles, Wilson and Cohen were part of what famous team?

8 Which shirt number does Alan Shearer play in?

9 What shirt number did Pele, Cruyff and Maradona all play in?

10 Which country do Pele's club Santos come from?

11 Which former Italian goalkeeper resigned as manager after Euro 2000?

12 Who have a popular Gallowgate End at their stadium?

13 What do Spurs managers George Graham and Terry Neill have in common?

14 What injury has befallen Stuart Pearce (twice), Shaka Hislop and Joe Cole – all at West Ham?

15 Howard Wilkinson is whose technical director?

16 Which Chelsea forward signed from Italian club Parma in 1996?

17 What was Steve Perryman's only club?

18 Which club have played at Eastville, Bath City's Twerton Park and the Memorial Ground since 1986?

19 Which Sunderland Don is a self-confessed Newcastle United fan?

20 Which ground was reopened in time for the Scottish FA Cup final in 1999?

Answers

Pot Luck 5 (see Quiz 97)
1 Liverpool. 2 Newcastle United. 3 Fulham. 4 Manchester United. 5 Blackburn Rovers. 6 The Women's FA Cup Final. 7 Scotland. 8 The fourth official. 9 None. 10 Three. 11 David Ginola. 12 Italy. 13 Alex Ferguson. 14 True. 15 Six. 16 Charlton Athletic. 17 Paul Merson. 18 Jürgen Klinsmann. 19 Plymouth. 20 Michael Owen.

The Medium Questions

This next selection of questions is getting a little more like it. For an open entry quiz then you should have a high percentage of medium level questions – don't try to break people's spirits with the hard ones, just make sure that people play to their ability.

Like all questions, this level of question can be classed as either easy or impossible depending on whether you know the answer and although common knowledge is used as the basis for these questions, there is a sting in the tail of quite a few. Also, if you have a serious drinking squad playing, then they can more or less say goodbye to the winners' medals, but that isn't to say they will feel any worse about it.

Specialists are the people to watch out for, as those with a good knowledge of a particular subject will doubtless do well in these rounds, so make sure that you use a variety of questions to flummox them.

Quiz 1 **Who Did What?**

Answers – see page 111

LEVEL 2

1 Who did Kevin Keegan pick as England captain following Alan Shearer's retirement from international football?

2 Who rejoined Southampton from Blackburn in 1999 having been away for only a year?

3 Which team opted out of the 2000 FA Cup?

4 Who did England international Kieron Dyer play for before his move to Newcastle?

5 In what year did Sir Alf Ramsey die?

6 Which team beat Glasgow Rangers at Ibrox in August 2000?

7 Which English team plays at the Stadium of Light?

8 Who scored the winner in the 2000 FA Cup final?

9 Which referee controversially sent three players off in an Arsenal v Liverpool match in August 2000?

10 Who currently manages Wales and plays for Everton?

11 Who won his 50th Scotland Cap in the opening game of World Cup '98?

12 Who became manager of Glasgow Celtic in 2000?

13 Who scored for England in Euro 2000 while playing his club football in Spain?

14 Which former Arsenal player has his own TV chat show?

15 Which leggy Costa Rican led the Manchester City attack in 2000?

16 Who scored twice for Vasco Da Gama in a FIFA Club World Championship match against Manchester United in January 2000?

17 Who was manager of Southampton at the start of the 2000 season?

18 Who won the League Cup in 1996?

19 Who was sent off during the 2000 Charity Shield?

20 Who scored for Leeds in the second leg of the Champions League qualifying round against Munich 1860 in August 2000?

Answers

Who Plays At...? (see Quiz 3)
1 St Johnstone. 2 Motherwell. 3 Rangers. 4 Hearts.
5 Dunfermline. 6 Dundee. 7 Dundee United. 8 Aberdeen.
9 Hibernian. 10 Raith Rovers. 11 Stenhousemuir. 12 St Mirren.
13 Kilmarnock. 14 Ayr United. 15 Celtic. 16 Queen's Park (and Scotland). 17 Falkirk. 18 Dumbarton. 19 Morton. 20 Stranraer.

Quiz 2 Goals Galore

Answers – see page 112

1   Who scored on his debut for Celtic after moving from Chelsea in summer 2000?

2   Who scored four goals for Man Utd against Newcastle in August 1999?

3   Who scored twice for Germany in the Euro 96 final?

4   Who scored a hat-trick for Chelsea in the FA Cup third round against Hull in January 2000?

5   Who was the last player to score more than one goal in an FA Cup final?

6   Who scored a hat-trick for Everton in a league game against West Ham in February 2000?

7   What is the record score in a World Cup qualifying match?

8   Who scored for Bayern Munich in the 1999 European Cup final?

9   Who scored Manchester United's equaliser in that same match?

10 Who scored a hat-trick for Portugal against Germany in Euro 2000?

11 Who was the last player to score more than once in a League Cup final?

12 Who scored a stunning hat-trick for Arsenal in a league game against Leicester in Feburary 1999?

13 Who scored two own goals in a match between Liverpool and Manchester United in September 1999?

14 Who lost 7-2 to Spurs in a league game in 1999-2000?

15 Who scored a hat-trick on his home debut for Man City in August 2000?

16 Which American scored 8 goals in 18 games for Everton in 1999-2000?

17 Who scored a hat-trick for Charlton in a league game against Southampton in 1999-2000?

18 Which ex-Middlesbrough striker was known as 'The White Feather'?

19 Who lost 5-0 to Everton in the league on Boxing Day 1999?

20 Which Icelandic striker left Bolton for Chelsea in summer 2000?

Quiz 3 **Who Plays At...?**

Answers – see page 109

LEVEL 2

1   McDiarmid Park?

2   Fir Park?

3   Ibrox?

4   Tynecastle?

5   East End Park?

6   Dens Park?

7   Tannadice?

8   Pittodrie?

9   Easter Road?

10   Stark's Park?

11   Ochilview Park?

12   Love Street?

13   Rugby Park?

14   Somerset Park?

15   Parkhead?

16   Hampden Park?

17   Brockville Park?

18   Boghead Park?

19   Cappielow Park?

20   Stair Park?

Quiz 4 The Premier League

Answers – see page 110

1. Which club received their record fee for Danny Mills?
2. Which member of Everton's 2000 squad is the only Premiership player to have managed the club he plays for?
3. Who is Aston Villa's 'deadly' chairman?
4. Nolan and Atherton joined which team in the 2000 close season?
5. Who was player-manager Vialli's right-hand man at Chelsea?
6. Who was the first Premiership player to collect 14 yellow cards in 1999-2000: Lee Bowyer, Patrick Vieira or Paolo Di Canio?
7. Which relegated side were the only club Manchester United did not beat in their 1999-2000 Premiership-winning season?
8. How many games did Manchester United lose in 1999-2000?
9. Rory Delap was which Premier League club's top scorer in 1999-2000?
10. Brewers Greene King sponsor which Premier League club?
11. King of the Kippax is a fanzine of which Premier League club??
12. Which Premier League referee punched the air after a Patrik Berger goal for Liverpool: Graham Poll, Uriah Rennie or Mike Reed?
13. Gerry Taggart was the Player of the Year for which team in 1999-2000?
14. Tottenham's Etherington and Davies were signed from which club?
15. Who did Chelsea cash in their insurance policy on in 2000?
16. True or False, up to and including the 1999-2000 season Everton have never finished in the top half of the Premier League?
17. Which team other than Coventry City have two Moroccans in their squad?
18. Newcastle United's Goma and Didi are from which country?
19. Who is Gerard Houllier's right-hand man at Liverpool?
20. Who is the oldest out of Tony Adams, Lee Dixon and Martin Keown?

Which team missed their chance the 1999-2000 Italian championship on the last day of the season?

Which Second Division Italian team did Luigi Riva join and take to the top in the 60s ?

Which Italian team featured Van Basten, Gullit and Rijkaard?

What is the name commonly given to the Italian championship?

Which Italian team featured Rummenigge, Matthaus and Klinsmann?

Inzaghi, Milhajlovic and Veron are stars of which club?

What is the name of the stadium shared by the Rome teams?

In which city is the Sampdoria club based?

What is the Italian word for football?

Gabriel Batistuta moved from Fiorentina to which club in May 2000?

Which Italian team play in an all white kit?

Which former England captain had a short and unsuccessful stint as manager of Sampdoria?

Why is an Italian club awarded a gold star above their badge?

What is the Italian word given to the defensive tactical system perfected in the 60s?

How much did Inter Milan pay Coventry City for Robbie Keane: £7m, £10m or £13m?

Which Chilean helped Lazio to their first European triumph in 1999?

Shevchenko, Bierhoff and Maldini play at which Italian club?

Which team share the Delle Alpi stadium with Juventus?

Giovanni Trapattoni managed which Italian club to six Serie A trophies in ten years?

For which Italian team does Brazilian star Ronaldo play?

Manchester United (see Quiz 7)

1 Ole Gunnar Solskjaer. **2** Ryan Giggs after 15 seconds v Southampton in 1995. **3** Chelsea. **4** George Best. **5** Andy Cole. **6** 7-0 to United. **7** Aston Villa. **8** Maine Road. **9** Brian Kidd. **10** George Best. **11** Newcastle United. **12** Twice, 1993-94 and 1995-96. **13** Eric Cantona. **14** Tommy Docherty. **15** Wes Brown. **16** Duncan Edwards. **17** Karel Poborsky. **18** Bryan Robson. **19** FC Porto. **20** Norman Whiteside.

Quiz 6 Goalkeepers

Answers – see page 116

1   Who is Derby County's Estonian goalkeeper?

2   What is Laurent Blanc's superstition involving Fabian Barthez?

3   What nationality is Middlesbrough's keeper Mark Schwarzer?

4   Which Everton goalkeeper famously refused to leave his posts at half time as a protest?

5   Which keeper has the record number of Spanish internationl caps?

6   Which keeper replaced the sick Gordon Banks for England against Germany in Mexico 1970?

7   Name a former club of West Ham's Shaka Hislop.

8   Which French goalkeeper did Liverpool sign on a free transfer from Leicester City in 2000?

9   Who is Arsenal's Austrian understudy to David Seaman?

10 Which goalkeeper scored for Manchester United in a UEFA Cup tie 1995-96?

11 Casillas is which major European outfit's young goalkeeping sensation?

12 Which keeper scored an own goal on his England debut in June 2000 against Malta?

13 Which keeper holds the record number of caps for Northern Ireland?

14 Which veteran keeper broke his jaw in a Scottish FA Cup final?

15 Which keeper has won championship medals with Leeds and Arsenal?

16 Why were keepers Segers and Grobbelaar in the news in 1994?

17 What 42-year-old keeper played for Coventry in 1999-2000?

18 For what country did Toldo keep goal during Euro 2000?

19 Free-kick and penalty-taking expert as well as goalkeeper, Chilavert plays for which country?

20 Which goalkeeper did Manchester United sign from Venezia in Aug 1999?

Answers

Memorable Matches (see Quiz 8)
1 Arsenal. 2 Ray Houghton. 3 Bulgaria. 4 Cameroon.
5 Inverness Caledonian Thistle. 6 Manchester United. 7 Holland (three in the shoot-out). 8 Romania. 9 Don Hutchison.
10 Chelsea. 11 7-0. 12 Manchester United. 13 Liverpool.
14 Leeds United. 15 3-3. 16 4-3. 17 Manchester City.
18 David Pleat. 19 Manchester United and Arsenal. 20 6-2.

LEVEL 2

Who went on as a sub and scored four goals in a league game against Nottingham Forest in February 1999?

Who scored United's quickest ever goal?

Who did United play in Bobby Charlton's last league game for the club?

Who is 'The Belfast Boy'?

Who scored United's winner in the Champions League semi-final against Juventus in 1999?

What was the score when United met Barnsley in the league in October 1997?

Who did United play in the last league match of the 1999-2000 season?

Where did United play their home games in World War II?

Who left United in September 1998 to manage Blackburn Rovers?

Who scored six goals for United in an 8-2 FA Cup victory over Northampton Town in 1970?

Who did United beat in the 1999 FA Cup final?

How many times did United win the double in the 1990s?

Who scored the winner in the 1996 FA Cup final v Liverpool?

Who was United's manager between 1972 and 1977?

Who made his international debut for England in April 1999 less than a year after making his first-team debut for United?

Which United legend once had the nickname 'Boom Boom'?

Which Czech joined United in 1996 but left two years later?

Who is the longest-serving captain in United's history?

Which club did Peter Schmeichel join after United?

Which United player became the youngest ever to appear in a World Cup in 1982?

1   Who won the league championship at Anfield in 1989?

2   Who scored the Republic of Ireland's goal in their memorable 1-0 win over Italy in the 1994 World Cup?

3   Who memorably knocked Germany out of the 1994 World Cup?

4   Who beat Argentina in their 1990 World Cup group match?

5   Whose victory led to the headline "'Supercallycelticareatrocious!'?

6   Who beat Nottingham Forest 8-1 in the Premiership in 1998-99?

7   Which country missed five penalties in a close match in Euro 2000?

8   Who did the Republic of Ireland beat on penalties to reach the World Cup quarter finals in 1990?

9   Who scored Scotland's goal in their 1999 1-0 victory over England?

10   Who beat Manchester United 5-0 in the 1999-2000 season?

11   What was the result of Leeds' 1972 humiliation of Southampton?

12   Whose inflicted Arsenal's worse defeat for 70 yearsin 1990?

13   Who destroyed Nottingham Forest 5-0 in 1988?

14   Who did Colchester memorably knock out of the FA Cup in 1971?

15   What was the result of the second leg of Manchester United's 1999 Champions League semi-final against Barcelona at the Nou Camp?

16   What score was repeated in 1996 and 1997 in the games at Anfield between Liverpool and Newcastle United?

17   Who came back from being 1-0 down against Blackburn Rovers to win 4-1 and gain promotion to the Premier League in 2000?

18   Which Luton Town manager famously jigged across the pitch at Maine Road after his side had avoided relegation in 1983?

19   Who had points deducted for an on-pitch brawl in the 1990-91 season?

20   By what score did Rangers get thumped at Celtic Park in the first Old Firm match of the 2000-01 season?

Answers

Goalkeepers (see Quiz 6)
1 Mark Poom. 2 Kisses his bald pate. 3 Australian. 4 Neville Southall. 5 Andoni Zubizarreta. 6 Peter Bonetti. 7 Reading or Newcastle. 8 Peggy Arphexad. 9 Alex Manninger. 10 Peter Schmeichel. 11 Real Madrid. 12 Richard Wright. 13 Pat Jennings. 14 Jim Leighton. 15 John Lukic. 16 Charged with match-fixing. 17 Steve Ogrizovic. 18 Italy. 19 Paraguay. 20 Massimo Taibi.

Quiz 9 The Nationwide League
LEVEL 2

Answers – see page 119

1   Which team lost the Division One play-off semi-finals in three consecutive years before finally winning the Wembley decider?

2   Former Chelsea player and manager John Hollins took which side to Division Two in 1999-2000?

3   Marcus Bent is which side's ace marksman?

4   Which side is managed by Jan Molby and plays at Aggborough?

5   O'Neill, Gregory and Sanchez have managed which club?

6   Who is Peterborough United's high-profile manager-owner?

7   Balti Boy Lee Hughes has been which Division 1 team's leading scorer?

8   Which club were relegated from Division Three in 1999 after gaining League status in 1987?

9   Ketsbaia, Bazeley and Emblen feature in which team's line-ups?

10   Which club did Sam Allardyce leave in October 1999?

11   Ricky Hill is in charge of his old team, now in Division 2. Which team?

12   Which Nationwide League team has ex-Wimbledon benefactor Sam Hamann invested in?

13   Which team are temporarily at home at the Withdean Stadium?

14   Dunn, Duff and Jansen are three of which team's stars?

15   Who is Brentford's owner-chairman-manager?

16   Who has won the Division One championship the most times since League re-organisation in 1993?

17   Which Nationwide team reached the FA Cup semi-finals in 2000?

18   Marco Gabbiadini and Jamie Forrester form the strike force at which bunch of cobblers?

19   Which Nationwide League player won his 60th Nothern Ireland cap in October 1995?

20   For which club does Indian international Baichung Bhutia play?

Quiz 10 Pot Luck

LEVEL 2

1   If you watched The Canaries v The Swans, which teams would you see?

2   Who does keeper Dave Beasant play for?

3   Louis Van Gaal manages which national team?

4   Former Arsenal striker Luis Boa Morte now plays for which other London club?

5   Who plays at Home Park?

6   Which country does Sunderland sensation Stanislav Varga come from?

7   Who is the captain of Charlton Athletic?

8   Who replaced Paul Jewell as manager of Bradford City in summer 2000?

9   Who were Manchester United's new sponsors in 2000?

10 Who is reputedly always lucky 'when the year ends in the figure one'?

11 For whom does Danish keeper Thomas Sorensen play his club football?

12 Which two teams contest the 'Old Firm' derby?

13 Which player was the subject of a 'tug-of war' between Middlesbrough and Liverpool in summer 2000?

14 Who plays at Bramall Lane?

15 For which club does Latvian Marian Pahars play?

16 What nationality is Leeds United's Harry Kewell?

17 Who is Middlesbrough's 'Ginger Warrior'?

18 Who is the German national coach?

19 Which Italian club have a strike force of Christian Vieri and Ronaldo?

20 For which club did Welsh international striker John Hartson start the 2000-01 season?

Answers

The Nationwide League (see Quiz 12)
1 George Best. 2 Arsenal. 3 Paper Lace. 4 Showaddywaddy.
5 Hibernian. 6 Rod Stewart. 7 Kevin Keegan. 8 David Byrne.
9 'Anfield Rap'. 10 The Lightning Seeds. 11 'Nessun Dorma'.
12 Nottingham Forest. 13 Gazza. 14 The Three Tenors.
15 Tottenham. 16 St Etienne. 17 Chelsea. 18 Stuart Pearce.
19 1982. 20 'Three Lions'.

Quiz 11 **Foreigners in Britain**

LEVEL 2

Answers – see page 117

---

1   Which club did French international Christian Karembeu join in summer 2000?

2   Which club does Jean Tigana manage?

3   What nationality is he?

4   Who started the 2000 campaign as the Premier League's only Italian manager?

5   Derby striker Branco Strupar is what nationality?

6   Markus Babbel joined Liverpool in summer 2000 from which German club?

7   Ex-Wimbledon manager Egil Olsen was from which country?

8   For which First Division team does French defender Ludovik Pollet play?

9   Southampton's Moroccan Tahar El Khalej joined them from which club?

10   Manchester City's George Weah comes from which African country?

11   Two Premiership clubs have French managers. One is Arsenal, which is the other?

12   Leeds' Eiric Bakke plays for which country?

13   Arsenal signed Laureano Mayer from Real Mallorca during summer 2000. For whom does he play his international football?

14   Which Portuguese star did Everton sign before Euro 2000?

15   What nationality is Watford's Nordin Wooter?

16   Eyal Berkovic joined Celtic from which London club?

17   Italian Alessandro Pistone left Newcastle in summer 2000 for which club?

18   Petter Rudi plays for which Yorkshire side?

19   Romanian Dan Petrescu left Chelsea for which Yorkshire club in summer 2000?

20   Alen Boksic joined Middlesbrough from which Italian team?

The Nationwide League (see Quiz 9)

1 Ipswich Town. **2** Swansea City. **3** Sheffield United.
4 Kidderminster Harriers. **5** Wycombe Wanderers. **6** Barry Fry.
7 WBA. **8** Scarborough. **9** Wolves. **10** Notts County. **12** Cardiff
City. **13** Brighton and Hove Albion. **14** Blackburn Rovers. **15** Ron
Noades. **16** Sunderland, twice. **17** Bolton Wanderers.
18 Northampton. **19** Nigel Worthington. **20** Bury.

Quiz 12 Music and Football

Answers – see page 118

1   Pop group The Wedding Present named an album after which footballer?

2   Tottenham's defeat of which team inspired Chas and Dave's 'banned' single 'The Victory Song'?

3   Which 70s band recorded 'Billy Don't Be a Hero' and helped Nottingham Forest with 'We've Got the Whole World in our Hands'?

4   The guitarist of which glam 70s rock 'n' roll revivalists is the father of Leicester City's Stefan Oakes?

5   Fish, Jim Diamond and The Proclaimers all support which team?

6   Which international recording star helped Scotland out in 1978 with 'Ole Ola (Mulher Brasiliera)'?

7   Which player was 'Head over Heels in Love' according to his 1979 hit?

8   Which member of the band Talking Heads is a Dumbarton supporter?

9   Which number one hit included a rap by John Barnes?

10   Which group accompanied Skinner & Baddiel on their 'Three Lions' record?

11   Which opera anthem was the 1990 official World Cup song?

12   Who enters the pitch accompanied by 'Robin Hood and His Merry Men'?

13   Whose rap song 'Geordie Boys' gently hit the charts in 1990?

14   Jose Carreras, Placido Domingo and Luciano Pavarotti performed together before all the 90s World Cups under which name?

15   Three-chord hit-makers Status Quo are supporters of which team?

16   'He's on the Phone' was a hit for which band named after a successful 70s French team?

17   Blur's Damon Albarn follows which London club?

18   Which England full-back introduced the Sex Pistols on stage in 1998?

19   'This Time (We'll Get It Right)' was the World Cup song in which year?

20   Which song were Germany asked to sing at their triumphant Euro 96 homecoming?

Answers

Pot Luck (see Quiz 10)
1 Norwich and Swansea. 2 Nottingham Forest. 3 Holland.
4 Fulham. 5 Plymouth Argyle. 6 Czech Republic. 7 Mark Kinsella.
8 Chris Hutchings. 9 Vodafone. 10 Spurs. 11 Sunderland.
12 Celtic and Rangers. 13 Christian Ziege. 14 Sheffield United.
15 Southampton. 16 Australian. 17 Andy Campbell. 18 Rudi
Völler. 19 Internazionale. 20 Wimbledon.

Quiz 13 Beards and Moustaches

LEVEL 2

1   Which Liverpool defender and *Match of the Day* expert has maintained a well-groomed moustache?

2   Who was Brazil's bearded captain in the 82 and 86 World Cup finals?

3   Which England goalkeeper has a much-admired moustache?

4   Which Liverpool goalscorer had a 'Yosser'-type moustache?

5   Which 60s icon played with a full beard and moustache ensemble?

6   Which player and broadcaster hides his extensive chin with a beard?

7   Who was Ipswich's, Liverpool's and Scotland's moustachioed midfielder?

8   Which side did Paul Mortimer captain in the 80s with full facial hair?

9   Which Portuguese and Everton defender entertained Euro 2000 with his dyed beard?

10   Which Liverpool, Rangers and Sampdoria player's moustache emphasised his hardman image?

11   Which sometime wispish bearded forward played at Spurs and Barcelona?

12   Which Birmingham City, Everton and England 70s marksman carried a full beard?

13   Which 80s bearded England striker scored in Aston Villa's European Cup triumph?

14   Which Northern Irish Wolves striker sported a ranchero-type moustache?

15   Which Premiership manager sported a fashionable goatee?

16   For which then non-league giantkillers did hirsute Dickie Guy keep goal?

17   Who was Chelsea's beard-and-moustache combination 70s centre-back?

18   Which chairman's facial hair emphasises his caricature as a farmer?

19   Who played and managed West Ham with a neat beard and moustache?

20   Which scruffily-bearded player scored a memorable FA Cup final goal?

Quiz 14 Shirt Numbers

LEVEL 2

1   Whose is the most famous of all number 10 shirts?

2   Which great Frenchman wore the number 10 shirt when his country won the 1984 European Championships?

3   Who always wore his Manchester United number 7 shirt with the collar up?

4   Which number 6 headed the winner for Chelsea v Leeds in the 1970 FA Cup final replay?

5   Who famously wore the number 6 shirt for West Ham and captained England to World Cup glory in 1966?

6   Which number 9 scored 68 goals in 62 matches for Germany?

7   Who wore number 5 for Spurs and scored to win the 100th FA Cup?

8   Which number 9 scored the winner for Villa in the 1992 European Cup final?

9   Which number 16 led Manchester United to the treble in 1998-99?

10   According to Leeds United fans, who is 'England's number 1'?

11   Who is Liverpool's number 10?

12   Which number 7 holds the Premier League record for the furthest successful strike at goal?

13   Who took the Chelsea number 9 shirt from Chris Sutton in summer 2000?

14   Who was England's number 1 when they won the World Cup?

15   Who famous number 6 for Liverpool now appears regularly on BBC's *Match of the Day*?

16   Which diminutive Italian plays in the number 25 shirt for Chelsea?

17   Which England number 9 opened the scoring in the Euro 96 semi-final against Germany?

18   Which number 9 holds the goalscoring record for Glasgow Rangers?

19   Which former number 1 managed his country to the final of Euro 2000?

20   Which Italian number 19 scored 6 goals as Italy won the 82 World Cup?

Answers

Euro 96 (see Quiz 16)
1 0-0. 2 1-1. 3 Jürgen Klinsmann. 4 Hristo Stoichkov. 5 4-1.
6 Ally McCoist. 7 Germany. 8 Czech Republic. 9 Karel Poborsky's
10 Stuart Pearce. 11 Spain. 12 Alan Shearer. 13 France.
14 Sammer. 15 1-1. 16 Teddy Sheringham. 17 Jamie Redknapp.
18 Gareth Southgate. 19 Turkey. 20 David Platt.

Quiz 15 **Leeds United**

LEVEL 2

1 Who was Leeds United's manager when they won the League in 1992?

2 Which England international returned to the club from Newcastle in 1998?

3 Which two current Leeds United players are related?

4 Who did Leeds United sell to Juventus in 1957?

5 Which Leeds United winger became their manager in 1982?

6 Who defeated Leeds United in the 1975 European Cup final?

7 Which team defeated Leeds United in the 2000 UEFA Cup semi-final?

8 Which wide-midfielder did Leeds sign from Blackburn Rovers in 1999?

9 Which 70s Leeds United manager lasted just 44 days before being sacked?

10 Who did Leeds sell to Atletico Madrid for £12m in 1999?

11 Which 'sniffer' was Leeds' profilic 1970s goalscorer?

12 Which Leeds striker's stunning shots won the BBC Goal of the Month award in August and September 1995?

13 Which manager permanently changed Leeds United's kit to all-white?

14 In which season did Harry Kewell make his debut for Leeds United?

15 Who did Leeds beat to win the 1972 FA Cup?

16 Leeds' leading goalscorer played his first game for them in 1962 and his last in 1985. Who is he?

17 Which Leeds and Scotland centre-forward left Leeds United for Manchester United in 1978?

18 Which forward joined Manchester United from Leeds in 1992 after scoring 14 goals in 25 games?

19 Who was Leeds' Republic of Ireland 60s and 70s midfield genius?

20 Which Leeds striker was called up to the full England squad in August 2000?

Answers

Beards and Moustaches (see Quiz 13)
1 Mark Lawrenson. 2 Socrates. 3 David Seaman. 4 Ian Rush.
5 George Best. 6 Jimmy Hill. 7 John Wark. 8 Aston Villa. 9 Abel
Xavier. 10 Graeme Souness. 11 Steve Archibald. 12 Bob
Latchford. 13 Peter Withe. 14 Derek Dougan. 15 Gianlucca Vialli.
16 Wimbledon. 17 Mickey Droy. 18 Ken Bates. 19 Billy Bonds.
20 Ricky Villa.

123

LEVEL 2

1   What was the result of Scotland's opening match, against Holland?

2   What was the result of England's opening match, against Switzerland?

3   Who scored one of the goals of the tournament for Germany against Russia?

4   Who scored in each of Bulgaria's matches in the tournament?

5   By what score did England beat Holland in the group stage?

6   Who scored Scotland's only goal in the tournament?

7   A 0-0 draw with which country in their last group game put Italy out of the tournament?

8   Who drew 3-3 with Russia at Anfield to qualify for the knock-out stage?

9   Whose chip won the Czech Republic's quarter-final with Portugal?

10 Who scored in the penalty shoot-out against Spain, having missed his previous England penalty?

11 Whose late goal at Elland Road put them into the quarter-finals?

12 Who scored England's goal after only three minutes of the semi-final?

13 Who did the Czech Republic beat on penalties in their semi-final?

14 Which German was suspended for the semi-final: Reuter, Möller or Sammer?

15 What was the score in the final after 90 minutes?

16 Who was England's only other scorer in the tournament besides Shearer and Gascoigne?

17 Which England half-time substitute was himself substituted in the Scotland match?

18 Whose penalty miss cost England a place in the final?

19 Which country failed to score in the tournament?

20 The semi-final against Germany proved to be who's last ever match for England?

Quiz 17 Liverpool

Answers – see page 127

1   How many times have Liverpool won the FA Cup?

2   Who was manager before Gérard Houllier?

3   Who is the most capped Liverpool player?

4   Which former Liverpool great is currently the assistant manager at Anfield?

5   Which fabulous Finn joined the Reds in summer 1999?

6   Whose free-kick gave Liverpool the lead in the league game against Manchester United in March 2000?

7   Whose goals won Liverpool the FA Cup in 1992?

8   When did Liverpool last win the League Cup?

9   For whom does Vladimir Smicer play his international football?

10 What nationality is Stephane Henchoz?

11 Where is Liverpool's Academy based?

12 Who did Liverpool beat to win the FA Cup in 1989?

13 Who was the Liverpool manager that day?

14 Who was Liverpool's captain in 1999-2000?

15 Who holds the Liverpool appearances record?

16 Which former Liverpool legend is the most successful manager ever in British football?

17 Which Liverpool player scored the first goal ever shown on *Match of the Day*?

18 Which former Liverpool player played a big part in putting Manchester United out of the 1999-2000 Champions League?

19 From which club did Liverpool sign Sander Westerveld?

20 Who is the latest player to play for both Liverpool and Everton?

Answers

Scotland International (see Quiz 19)
1 Kenny Dalglish. 2 Billy Bremner. 3 Ally MacLeod. 4 Brazil.
5 Archie Gemmill. 6 England. 7 Costa Rica. 8 Jim Baxter.
9 Gary McAllister. 10 Paul McStay. 11 Andy Goram. 12 0-0.
13 Morocco. 14 John Collins. 15 Jim Leighton. 16 Willie Ormond.
17 Denis Law. 18 Alex McLeish. 19 Zaire. 20 5-1.

1   Oldham Athletic?

2   Swansea City?

3   Millwall?

4   Huddersfield Town?

5   Port Vale?

6   Sheffield United?

7   Exeter City?

8   Colchester United?

9   Bury?

10   Mansfield Town?

11   Stoke City?

12   Wycombe Wanderers?

13   Grimsby Town?

14   Brentford?

15   Northampton Town?

16   Rochdale?

17   Gillingham?

18   Luton Town?

19   Peterborough United?

20   Hartlepool United?

Answers

Pot Luck 2 (see Quiz 20)
1 Wimbledon. **2** Hristo Stoichkov. **3** They re-entered as 'Lucky Losers'. **4** Leicester City. **5** Attilo Lombardo **6** Kanu. **7** Robbie Fowler. **8** Steve Bould. **9** Howard Wilkinson. **10** Swansea. **11** John Hartson. **12** Brighton and Hove Albion. **13** AC Milan. **14** Vasco de Gama. **15** Faith healer. **16** Lauren. **17** Barry Ferguson. **18** Alan Curbishley. **19** Bobby Robson. **20** The English F. A.

Quiz 19 Scotland Internationals
LEVEL 2

Answers – see page 125

1   Who is Scotland's most capped player?

2   Which Scotland captain was banned 'for life' along with four other players after a night club incident in Copenhagen?

3   Which manager led Scotland to the World Cup in Argentina in 1978?

4   Who did Scotland play in the opening game of the '98 World Cup?

5   Whose brilliant dribble and goal against Holland gave Scotland a chance of qualification for the knockout stage of the '78 World Cup?

6   Which country conceded a goal to Holland that denied Scotland qualification to the knockout stage of Euro 96?

7   Which Central American country beat Scotland in the 1990 World Cup?

8   Which player will forever be remembered for sitting on the ball during Scotland's 1967 victory over World Champions England?

9   Which Scottish midfielder retired from international football in 1998?

10   Which Celtic midfielder won 76 caps for Scotland from 1984 to 1997?

11   Which Scotland goalkeeper has also represented his country at cricket?

12   What was the result when Scotland met Brazil in the 1974 World Cup?

13   Who beat Scotland 3-0 in St Etienne in the 1998 World Cup?

14   Which former Celtic and Everton midfielder retired from international football on joining Fulham in 2000?

15   Which goalkeeper played 91 times for Scotland from 1983 to 1999?

16   Which manager took Scotland to the 1974 World Cup?

17   Who debuted for Scotland aged 18 and became equal leading goalscorer?

18   Who hasn't managed Scotland: Sir Matt Busby, Sir Alex Ferguson or Alex McLeish?

19   Which African team did Scotland beat 2-0 in the 1974 World Cup?

20   What was the score when Scotland's 'Wembley Wizards' famously beat England in 1928?

Answers

Liverpool (see Quiz 17)
1 Five times. 2 Roy Evans. 3 Ian Rush. 4 Phil Thompson.
5 Sami Hyypia. 6 Patrik Berger. 7 Michael Thomas and Ian Rush.
8 1995. 9 Czech Republic. 10 Swiss. 11 Kirkby. 12 Everton.
13 Kenny Dalglish. 14 Jamie Redknapp. 15 Ian Callaghan.
16 Bob Paisley. 17 Roger Hunt. 18 Steve McManaman.
19 Vitesse Arnhem in Holland. 20 Nick Barmby.

Quiz 20 Pot Luck 2

Answers – see page 126

LEVEL 2

1 Dave Bassett, Joe Kinnear and Egil Olsen have all managed which club?

2 Which Bulgarian hero went to play in the Japanese J-League?

3 In which way were Darlington lucky in the 2000 FA Cup competition?

4 Which team's players and officials were charged over their ticket distribution in the 1999 Worthington Cup Final?

5 Which bald Italian briefly managed Crystal Palace?

6 In 1999, who apologised to the opposition for his first goal for Arsenal?

7 Who was fined for making an unsavoury gesture at Graeme Le Saux?

8 In 1999, who left Highbury for Sunderland after 11 years at Arsenal?

9 Who took charge of the England squad between Hoddle and Keegan?

10 Cyril the Swan is which team's mascot?

11 Who kicked Eyal Berkovic in the head in a West Ham training session?

12 Which near bankrupt team wears the logo "Skint" on their shirts?

13 Silvio Berlusconi is the owner of which Italian club?

14 Which Brazilian team beat Manchester United 3-1 in the 2000 World Club Championship?

15 What role did Eileen Drewery play in England's 1998 World Cup campaign?

16 Which 2000 Premier League newcomer's surname is Bisan-Etame Mayer?

17 Which Rangers player was the Scottish Footballer of the Year in 2000?

18 At the start of the 2000-2001 season who was easily the Premier League's longest serving manager?

19 Which English manager 'discovered' Ronaldo?

20 Who moved from their home at Lancaster Gate in 2000?

What was the last year Newcastle won the FA Cup?

Who was manager of Sunderland in 1993?

Who is Middlesbrough's most capped player?

Who did Bryan Robson take over from as manager of Middlesbrough?

How much did Atletico Madrid pay for Juninho in July 1997?

What was the name of Middlesbrough's former ground?

If you were watching a match at Victoria Park, in which town would you be?

Sunderland's record league victory was 9-1 in 1908. Who were the opposition?

Who holds the appearances record at Sunderland?

What honour did Middlesbrough win in 1976?

Where did Sunderland finish in the Premier League in 1999-2000?

At which club did Kevin Phillips used to play?

Who scored Sunderland's winner in the 1973 FA Cup final?

Which Vauxhall Conference team did Newcastle defeat on the way to the FA Cup final in 1998?

Who did Newcastle play in 1999 FA Cup semi-final?

Which Newcastle player went without a squad number during Ruud Gullit's reign?

What is the name of Middlesbrough's training facility?

Who plays at the Feethams Ground?

In which Division do they play?

Noel Whelan joined Middlesbrough from which club in summer 2000?

Quiz 22 **Samba Soccer**

LEVEL 2

Answers – see page 132

1   In which country are the club Flamengo based?
2   Brazilian Mirandinha played for which English team in 1987-88?
3   Argentinian Alberto Tarantini joined which English club in 1978?
4   What is the difference between the Copa America and the Copa Libertadores?
5   In which country are the club Peñarol based?
6   Who is West Ham's Chilean defender?
7   With which Brazilian club is Pele associated?
8   In which country are the club Boca Juniors based?
9   With which club did Mexican Hugo Sanchez win the European Gold Boot?
10 In which country do Cruz Azul, America and Necaxa play?
11 Which player's clubs include Boca Juniors (twice), Barcelona, Napo Sevilla and Newell's Old Boys?
12 Who is the only Uruguayan playing in the Premier League?
13 Who won the inaugural World Club Championship in Brazil in 2000
14 Who did Real Betis sign from Sao Paulo for £21m in 1997?
15 Which Brazilian was the first player to win the World Footballer of Year award in successive seasons?
16 Gabriel Batistuta, Mario Kempes and Marcelo Salas all played for v famous Buenos Aires team?
17 Which Colombian celebrated his goals at Newcastle with a somersa
18 Who is Sunderland's Honduran?
19 Which Colombian was South American Player of the Year in 1987 1994?
20 Which Argentinian played for Real Madrid and Spain and was twice European Footballer of the Year?

Answers

The 70s (see Quiz 24)
1 Leeds United. 2 None. 3 Spurs and Wolves. 4 Bobby Moore
5 Ipswich Town. 6 Leighton James. 7 Celtic. 8 Asa Hartford.
9 Viv Anderson. 10 Sammy Nelson. 11 Hereford.
12 Ricky George. 13 Chelsea. 14 Trevor Francis. 15 Kenny
Dalglish. 16 Don Revie. 17 Billy Bremner and Kevin Keegan.
18 Argentina. 19 Derby County. 20 Brian Clough.

1   Which team won the Spanish league in 1999-2000?

2   Which club admits only players of Basque ethnic origin?

3   Which Spanish team lost in the 2000 Champions League final?

4   Which Spanish club bought Petit and Overmars from Arsenal?

5   In which city is the Bernabéu stadium?

6   Which former Liverpool player is a football presenter on Spanish TV?

7   Who are the smaller Spanish League team in Barcelona?

8   Jimmy Floyd Hasselbaink was the Spanish league's top scorer in 1999-2000 despite playing for which struggling team?

9   For which team did Nayim win the Cup Winners Cup in 1995 with a goal from the halfway line?

10 In which city are Real Betis based?

11 Which Welshman has managed Real Madrid (twice), Real Sociedad and Deportiva La Coruña?

12 Which English team did Athletic Bilbao model their strip on?

13 Who was sacked as Barcelona's coach in 2000 and soon took up a position as coach of Holland?

14 How many Spanish teams were in the 2000 Champions League semi-finals?

15 Which Argentinian is captain of Real Madrid?

16 In what colours do Valencia play?

17 Which Spanish team did Bobby Robson coach?

18 Which manager guided Barcelona to four successive Liga championships as well as European Cup and Cup Winners Cup glory?

19 Which 'malcontent' scored for Real Madrid in both legs of the 2000 Champions League semi-final?

20 Which club beat Leeds United 4-0 in the Champions League in 2000?

The North East (see Quiz 21)
1 1955. **2** Terry Butcher. **3** Wilf Mannion. **4** Lennie Lawrence.
5 £12m. **6** Ayresome Park. **7** Hartlepool. **8** Newcastle United.
9 Jim Montgomery. **10** The Anglo-Scottish Cup. **11** Seventh.
12 Watford. **13** Ian Porterfield. **14** Stevenage. **15** Spurs.
16 Rob Lee. **17** Rockliffe. **18** Darlington. **19** Third Division.
20 Coventry City.

Quiz 24 The 70s

LEVEL 2

Answers – see page 130

1   Third Division Colchester beat a mighty First Division team in one of the greatest giant kills in English football in 1971. Who did they beat?

2   How many 70s Scottish FA Cup finals featured neither Celtic or Rangers?

3   The 1972 UEFA Cup final was the first ever contested by two English teams. Who were they?

4   Which English legend played his 1,000th league game in May 1977 before retiring from football?

5   Which East Anglian team won the FA Cup in 1978?

6   Which winger scored Wales' winning goal against England in 1977?

7   Who won their ninth consecutive league title in Scotland in 1974?

8   Whose proposed transfer from West Brom to Leeds was cancelled when it was revealed the player had a 'hole in the heart'?

9   Who became the first black player to represent England, in 1978?

10 Which Arsenal player was suspended for dropping his shorts in April 1979?

11 Which Southern League team beat Newcastle in the 1972 FA Cup third round?

12 Who scored the winning goal?

13 Who did Stoke beat in the 1972 League Cup final?

14 Who became Britain's first million pound footballer in 1979?

15 Who did Liverpool sign from Celtic in August 1977?

16 Who resigned as England manager in July 1977?

17 Which two players were sent off during the 1974 Charity Shield?

18 Where was the 1978 World Cup played?

19 Who won their second First Division in four years in 1974-75?

20 Who was in charge at Elland Road for 43 days in 1974?

Answers

Samba Soccer (see Quiz 22)
1 Brazil. 2 Newcastle United. 3 Birmingham City. 4 *America* is for nations, *Libertadores* for clubs. 5 Uruguay. 6 Javier Margas. 7 Santos. 8 Argentina. 9 Real Madrid. 10 Mexico. 11 Diego Maradona. 12 Gustavo Poyet. 13 Corinthians. 14 Denilson. 15 Ronaldo. 16 River Plate. 17 Faustino Asprilla. 18 Milton Nunez. 19 Carlos Valderrama. 20 Alfredo Di Stefano.

Quiz 25 **The League Cup**

Answers – see page 135

LEVEL 2

1   When was the first League Cup competition?

2   Who were the first winners?

3   When did the League Cup become the Coca-Cola Cup?

4   When did the League Cup final move to Wembley?

5   Which clubs have won the competition the most times?

6   Which Scottish player scored both Arsenal goals in the 1987 final against Liverpool?

7   For whihc team did Andy Gray score a League Cup winnning goal?

8   Who lost in both the 1997 and 1998 finals?

9   Who won the competition in both 1989 and 1990?

10   Which Italian player scored in the 1997 final?

11   Who contests the League Cup?

12   What is the League Cup currently called?

13   Liverpool and Everton played each other in the 1984 final. Who won?

14   Sheffield Wednesday won the tournament in 1991. Who did they beat in the final?

15   Who won the tournament in 2000?

16   Which was the last London team to win the League Cup?

17   Who won the League Cup four times in a row in the early 1980s?

18   What was the tournament called in 1991 and 1992?

19   Which Scottish TV pundit scored for Liverpool in the 1981 League Cup final replay?

20   Who beat QPR 3-0 to win the 1986 final?

Managers (see Quiz 27)
Answers
1 Peter Taylor. **2** Gillingham. **3** John Gregory. **4** Danny Wilson.
5 Colin Lee. **6** Sam Allardyce. **7** Steve Bruce. **8** Christian Gross.
9 Graham Taylor. **10** Arsenal. **11** Howard Kendall. **12** Steve
Coppell. **13** West Ham with eight. **14** Brian Clough. **15** Franz
Beckenbauer. **16** Two. **17** Peter Reid. **18** Ron Atkinson.
19 Alan Ball. **20** George Graham.

133

Quiz 26 French Football

Answers – see page 136

LEVEL 2

1   Who were the French League champions in 1999-2000?

2   Which Channel ferry port part-timers made the 2000 French cup final?

3   Who became the only French club to win the European Cup in 1993, but were later stripped of the title?

4   What is the name of the major club in Paris?

5   In what colour shirts do St Etienne play?

6   Which French international returned to play in France after spells at Arsenal and Real Madrid?

7   Which former Monaco coach is now boss of a Premier League team?

8   Who left Lens to join Leeds United in 2000?

9   French heroes Henry and Trezeguet played together at which club?

10 Which Republic of Ireland striker left Marseilles to become a Nancy boy?

11 Which French stadium was opened for the 1998 World Cup?

12 Which England star joined Monaco in 1987?

13 Who captained France to victory in the finals of the World Cup and European Championship?

14 At the home of which club did England lose to Argentina in 1998?

15 Who was voted French Player of the Year in 1994, but was never picked again for the French national team?

16 Who left Marseilles to join Arsenal in 2000?

17 Who played for Auxerre, Marseilles, Bordeaux, Montpellier and Nimes before leaving for England?

18 Which Premier League manager was formerly manager of the French national team?

19 Who scored France's equalising goal in the Euro 2000 final?

20 Chris Waddle and Trevor Steven both played for which French club?

Answers

Rangers (see Quiz 28)
1 Mo Johnston. 2 Borussia Dortmund. 3 Ally McCoist. 4 Marco Negri. 5 The Treble. 6 Colin Hendry. 7 Barry Ferguson.
8 Fiorentina. 9 Nine. 10 David Murray. 11 True. 12 Dick Avocaat. 13 USA. 14 Arthur Numan. 15 1971. 16 Durie.
17 Jorg Alberz. 18 Lorenzo Amoruso. 19 Leeds United.
20 Chris Woods.

Quiz 27 **Managers**

Answers – see page 133

LEVEL 2

1 Who became manager of Leicester City in summer 2000?

2 Where was he previously?

3 Who led Aston Villa out for the 2000 FA Cup final?

4 Who was sacked by Sheffield Wednesday and took over at Bristol City during 2000?

5 Which ex-Spurs and Chelsea striker is now in charge at Molineux?

6 Who managed Bolton as they reached the 2000 FA Cup semi-final?

7 Which former Manchester United defender now pulls the strings at Huddersfield?

8 Who was surprisingly offered the job of head coach at Spurs in 1997?

9 Who gave up the managership at Watford in 1987 and took the job again ten years later?

10 Who did David O'Leary, manager at Leeds, play club football for?

11 Which ex-player managed Everton three times during the 1980s and 1990s?

12 Who has been manager at Crystal Palace four times?

13 Which Premier League team has had fewest managers in its history?

14 Which manager has had the longest post-war career?

15 Who captained West German to World Cup victory in 1974 and then managed them to victory in the same competition in 1990?

16 After how many matches of the 1998 season did Ruud Gullit replace Kenny Dalglish as manager at Newcastle?

17 Who managed Sunderland when they returned to the Premiership in 1999?

18 Who managed Manchester United between 1981 and 1986?

19 Which World Cup winner was manager at Maine Road in 1985-86?

20 Who did David O'Leary succeed as manager of Leeds United?

Quiz 28 Rangers

Answers – see page 134

1.   Which Rangers striker joined Leeds United in 1980

2.   Which German side knocked Rangers out of the 2000 EUFA Cup?

3.   Who is Rangers' all-time leading goalscorer?

4.   Which Italian striker makes a habit of falling out with Rangers' management?

5.   What did Rangers achieve in 1998-99 for only the second time in 20 years?

6.   Which Scotland captain returned from Rangers to England in 2000?

7.   Which Rangers midfielder scored his first goal for Scotland against the Republic of Ireland in May 2000?

8.   From which Italian club did Rangers sign Andrei Kanchelskis?

9.   How many championships did Rangers win consecutively from 1989?

10. Who is Rangers' steel magnate chairman?

11. True or False: Rangers have won more championships than any other club in the world?

12. Who is Rangers' Dutch manager?

13. Rangers' Claudio Reyna is an international with which country?

14. Which Rangers' defender played twice for Holland in Euro 2000?

15. When was the Ibrox disaster, in which 66 people were killed?

16. Who scored for Rangers in three FA Cup finals in the 70s?

17. Which German 'Ger' is nicknamed 'The Hammer' because of his spectacular goals?

18. Which Italian was made Rangers' club captain in the 1998-99 season?

19. Which English team did Rangers beat in the European Cup in 1992?

20. Which Rangers goalkeeper went a record 1196 minutes without conceding a goal in 1986-87?

Answers

French Football   (see Quiz 26)
1 Derek Parlane. 2 Calais. 3 Marseilles. 4 Paris St Germain (PSG). 5 Green. 6 Anelka. 7 Arsene Wenger. 8 Olivier Dacourt. 9 AS Monaco. 10 Tony Cascarino. 11 Stade de France. 12 Glenn Hoddle 13 Didier Deschamps. 14 St. Etienne. 15 David Ginola. 16 Derek Johnstone. 17 Eric Cantona. 18 Gerard Houillier. 19 Sylvain Wiltord. 20 Marseilles.

Quiz 29 **Who Plays At...? 2**

Answers – see page 139

LEVEL 2

1   Deepdale?

2   The County Ground?

3   Pride Park?

4   Brunton Park?

5   The City Ground?

6   The County Ground?

7   Fratton Park?

8   Blundell Park?

9   The Valley?

10   Brisbane Road?

11   Dean Court?

12   Plainmoor?

13   The Den?

14   Roots Hall?

15   Spotland?

16   Boundary Park?

17   Gay Meadow?

18   Layer Road?

19   Hillsborough?

20   Kenilworth Road?

Answers

Old Football (see Quiz 31)
1 Manchester City or Liverpool. **2** Celtic. **3** Newcastle United. **4** Bobby Charlton. **5** Italy. **6** Stan Cullis. **7** John White. **8** Alfredo Di Stefanao. **9** Eusebio. **10** Tottenham Hotspur. **11** West Ham United. **12** Jimmy Hill. **13** Pat Jennings. **14** Wales and Northern Ireland. **15** Ipswich Town. **16** Manchester City. **17** Sir Stanley Rous. **18** Russia. **19** First £1000 transfer. **20** The 50s.

Quiz 30 Africa

Answers – see page 140

1 Which Cameroon international became a favourite during the 1990 World Cup?

2 Which Nigerian striker played on Merseyside between 1994 and 1996?

3 Who is the only African player in the Manchester Utd first team squad?

4 Where does he come from?

5 Which Liberian striker joined Manchester City in summer 2000 after a year at Chelsea?

6 For which African country did Bruce Grobbelaar play?

7 Chelsea's Celestine Babayaro plays his international football for which country?

8 Liverpool's Titi Camara was born in which African country?

9 Moroccan Tahar El Khalej joined Southampton from which Portuguese team?

10 Who won the 1998 African Nations Cup?

11 How often is the African Nations Cup held?

12 Which was the last African team to play England?

13 For which country did Ibrahim Sunday play?

14 Which African country was in the running to stage the 2006 World Cup?

15 Which country topped England's group in the 1986 World Cup?

16 Who did England beat in the quarter-finals of the 1990 tournament?

17 Which Nigerian striker joined Arsenal in January 1999 from Internazionale?

18 Who contested the final of the 2000 African Nations Cup?

19 Who won the tournament?

20 In which African country was French star Just Fontaine born?

Answers

Pot Luck 3 (see Quiz 32)
1 Charlton Athletic. 2 Holsten. 3 Four. 4 Five: Crewe Alexandra, Oxford United, Wrexham, Halifax Town and Exeter City. 5 Leyton Orient. 6 Stuart Pearce. 7 Mikael Silvestre. 8 NTL. 9 David Ginola. 10 John Beresford. 11 Newcastle United. 12 Edgar Davids. 13 Crystal Palace. 14 £2m. 15 Bryan Hamilton. 16 Dave Challinor. 17 Ray Clemence. 18 Ron Atkinson. 19 Halifax Town. 20 Chelsea.

Quiz 31 Old Football

Answers – see page 137

1   Name one of the teams Sir Matt Busby played for in the 1930s?

2   Which 1967 European Cup winners were dubbed the 'Lisbon Lions'?

3   Which team won the FA Cup three times during the 1950s?

4   Which England player was European Footballer of the Year in 1966?

5   'The Battle of Highbury' in 1934 was a friendly between England and which other country?

6   Which manager masterminded Wolves' treble in the 1950s?

7   Which Tottenham and Scotland player was killed when struck by lightning in 1964?

8   Which Argentinian was the architect of Real Madrid's 50s European Cup domination?

9   Who was top scorer in the 1966 World Cup?

10 Which team won the FA Cup three times during the 1960s?

11 Which team did Ron Greenwood manage to Cup success in the 1960s?

12 Which former *Match of the Day* presenter is credited with getting the maximum wage abolished in 1961?

13 Which goalkeeper scored in the 1967 Charity Shield between Tottenham and Manchester United?

14 Which two teams from the British Isles reached the quarter-finals of the 1958 World Cup?

15 Sir Alf Ramsey managed which 60s championship-winning side?

16 The Revie Plan took which side to the 1955 and 1956 FA Cup finals?

17 Which famous English referee became president of FIFA in 1961?

18 Who did West Germany defeat in the 1966 World Cup semi-final?

19 Which record was set when Alf Common was transferred from Sunderland to Middlesbrough in 1910?

20 In what decade did the white ball come into official use?

Quiz 32 Pot Luck 3

Answers – see page 138

1   Which Premiership outfit has Hunt, Robinson and Pringle in its squad?

2   Which beer company sponsors Spurs?

3   How many Uniteds are there in the 2000-01 Premier League?

4   How many Football League teams have the letter x in their name?

5   Who plays at the Matchroom Stadium?

6   Which West Ham veteran broke a leg twice during the 1999-2000 season?

7   Which Frenchman partnered Jaap Stam in the Manchester United defence during 1999-2000?

8   Which communications company holds a 9 per cent stake in Everton?

9   Which French football star advertises L'Oreal 'because he's worth it'?

10 Which former Newcastle defender now plies his trade at The Dell?

11 With which English club did Philippe Albert make his name?

12 Which Dutchman plays football in glasses?

13 Which London club does Clinton Morrison play for?

14 How much did Fulham pay for Louis Saha in summer 2000?

15 Who was the manager of Norwich City at the beginning of the 2000-01 season?

16 Which Tranmere player has the longest throw-in in British football?

17 Tottenham's Stephen Clemence is the son of which famous English goalkeeper?

18 Who managed Sheffield Wednesday between 1989 and 1991 and again between 1997 and 1998?

19 Who plays at The Shay?

20 Which Premier League side fielded a team in the 1998-99 season in which every player was born outside the mainland of England?

Answers

Africa (see Quiz 30)
1 Roger Milla. 2 Daniel Amokachi. 3 Quinton Fortune. 4 South Africa. 5 George Weah. 6 Zimbabwe. 7 Nigeria. 8 Guinea. 9 Benfica. 10 Egypt. 11 Every two years. 12 Tunisia, in the 1998 World Cup. 13 Ghana. 14 South Africa. 15 Morocco. 16 Cameroon. 17 Nwankwo Kanu. 18 Nigeria and Cameroon. 19 Cameroon. 20 Morocco.

Quiz 33 The FA Cup

Answers – see page 143

LEVEL 2

1 How many FA Cup finals were played at the old Wembley?

2 Which Man City keeper broke his neck in the 1956 FA Cup final?

3 The FA Cup has once been won by a team not based in England. Which team was it?

4 What is the name of the Cup Final hymn?

5 Who was the first player sent off in an FA Cup final?

6 Whose spectacular diving header brought the scores level in the 1987 final between Coventry and Tottenham?

7 Who was manager at Wimbledon when they won the cup in 1988?

8 Who scored twice for Crystal Palace to force a replay against Manchester United in the 1990 final?

9 Whose short appearance in the 1991 final was his last for Spurs?

10 In which year was the FA Cup first sponsored by Littlewoods?

11 Which London team was banned from the competition during the 1994-95 season, but later reinstated?

12 In which year was 'The Matthews Final'?

13 Only two clubs won the FA Cup two years running during the 20th century: Spurs and which other club?

14 Who scored the quickest ever Cup final goal?

15 Who scored the opening goal for Manchester United in the 1999 final?

16 Which final was known as 'The Dustbin Final'?

17 Which legendary keeper was in goal for Leicester when they played Spurs in the 1961 final?

18 Who scored both West Ham's goals in the 1975 final against Fulham?

19 In which year was the FA Cup final first televised in full?

20 Which was the first year in which the losers went up to collect their medals before the winners?

Quiz 34 European Cup

LEVEL 2

1   Which club have won the European Cup the most times?

2   Which English club have won the European Cup the most times?

3   Which English club won the trophy in 1979 and 1980?

4   Which Eastern European side beat Barcelona in the 86 final?

5   Which English manager took Barcelona to the final in 86?

6   Which Spanish team reached the 1983 European Cup final?

7   Who beat Sampdoria to win the 92 final played at Wembley stadium?

8   Where was Real Madrid's 7-3 Cup final victory in 1960 played?

9   Waddle, Papin and Pele played in which team's final defeat in 1991?

10 Who beat Leeds United to win the European Cup in 1975?

11 In which year were English teams except Liverpool allowed to re-enter the tournament after the Heysel ban?

12 How many Portuguese clubs have won the European Cup?

13 How many Dutch clubs have won the European Cup?

14 Which ex-player managed Barcelona in their European Cup triumph?

15 Which two Dutchmen both scored two goals in AC Milan's 1989 Cup final victory?

16 Which Englishman played against Nottingham Forest in the 1980 European Cup final?

17 Which Frenchman scored the winning goal in the tragic 85 final?

18 Prosinecki, Pancev and Savicevic were in which 1991 winning side?

19 Which British club reached the European Cup semi-finals three times between 1970 and 1974?

20 Which England defender scored in two of Liverpool's European Cup victories?

Quiz 35 Old Players

Answers – see page 141

LEVEL 2

1   Who left West Ham in an exchange deal involving Jimmy Greaves during the 1969-70 season?

2   For which team did Gordon Banks play when he won the World Cup?

3   'Gigi' Riva starred for which country in the 1960s and 70s?

4   Which club did the great Ferenc Puskas join in 1956?

5   Which Wilf was a post-war Middlesbrough and England's forward?

6   For which London teams did Rodney Marsh play in the 1960s?

7   Who was Bobby and Jack Charlton's Newcastle United and England goalscoring uncle?

8   In which year was George Best voted European Footballer of the Year?

9   Which double-barrelled named forward played for Nottingham Forest and Manchester United in the1960s?

10   Which Craven Cottage hero was England's first £100-a-week player?

11   Which Raich was Sunderland, Derby County and England's famous inside forward?

12   Paddy Crerand was a midfielder for which English club in the 1960s?

13   Which three West Ham players were England World Cup winners?

14   Nordhal, Gren and Liedholm were which club's Swedish trio?

15   Just Fontaine won the 1958 Golden Boot playing for which team?

16   Which three Bobbys won the Footballer of the Year award in consecutive years in the 60s?

17   Who was the Brazilian star winger of the 1958 and 1962 World Cups?

18   Alan Gilzean joined which English club in the 1960s?

19   Which Newcastle and England Len was dubbed 'the clown prince of football' in the 50s?

20   Which Frank was Manchester City and England's post-war goalkeeper?

Answers

The FA Cup (see Quiz 33)
1 72, plus five replays. 2 Bert Trautmann. 3 Cardiff City.
4 'Abide With Me'. 5 Kevin Moran of Manchester United. 6 Keith Houchen. 7 Bobby Gould. 8 Ian Wright. 9 Paul Gascoigne.
10 1995. 11 Spurs. 12 1953. 13 Newcastle in 1951 and 1952.
14 Roberto Di Matteo after 43 seconds in 1997. 15 Teddy Sheringham. 16 The 1960 final between Wolves and Blackburn.
17 Gordon Banks. 18 Alan Taylor. 19 1938. 20 1992.

Quiz 36 **British Players Abroad**
LEVEL 2

Answers – see page 142

1 Who was the first major British player to play abroad?

2 Who noted that Italy 'was like a foreign country' on his arrival to play for Juventus in 1987?

3 Which English striker won the UEFA Cup in 1989 playing for Barcelona?

4 Which ex-Liverpool playmaker featured for Real Madrid in 1999-2000?

5 Who was nicknamed 'El Tel' during his time as Barcelona manager?

6 Which English player was Euro Footballer of the Year in 1978 and 79?

7 Who was allegedly transferred 'by mistake' from Watford to AC Milan for £1m in 1983?

8 Which English manager had success at Barcelona, PSV Eindhoven and Porto?

9 Which French club did Chris Waddle move to from Spurs in 1989?

10 David Platt became the most expensive player in British history when he left Aston Villa for Bari in 1991. How much did he cost?

11 Who moved from Spurs to Lazio in 1992?

12 Who left Man City for Torino in 1961 but returned to United a year later?

13 Which Welsh player played for Barcelona, Bayern Munich and Manchester United between 1986 and 1988?

14 Which current Fulham midfielder also played for AS Monaco?

15 Which current Everton striker had a spell in Turkey with Trabzonspor?

16 Which winger was killed in a car crash while with for Real Madrid?

17 Which Irish genius had success in Italy during the 1980s?

18 Who left Sampdoria in 1985 to take over at Glasgow Rangers?

19 Which ex-Chelsea player had three years with AC Milan between 1984 and 1987?

20 Which striker left Chelsea for Milan in 1961 only to return to Spurs a year later?

Quiz 37 Gingers

Answers – see page 147

LEVEL 2

1 Who is Arsenal and England's red-haired wide midfielder?

2 Who was Leeds and Scotland's fiery ginger genius?

3 Which redheaded Coventry City and Wolves favourite gained fame with his part in the 'donkey-kick' free-kick in the 70s?

4 Which Manchester United carrot-top has scored a hat-trick for England?

5 Which strawberry blond defender has given great service to Liverpool and the Republic of Ireland?

6 Which ginger striker has played for Yugoslavia and Croatia?

7 Who is Leicester City's peroxided red-headed dynamo?

8 Who was Liverpool's flame-haired 'supersub' in the 70s?

9 Which Scottish ginger-topped centre-half crossed North London from Spurs to Arsenal in 1977?

10 Which fiery character left Leeds United for Bradford City in 2000?

11 Who was Celtic and Scotland's ginger-haired impish winger in the 70s?

12 Which Welshman nearly took his red locks to Tottenham but eventually stayed with Wimbledon in 2000?

13 Which of England's 1966 World Cup heroes sported ginger locks?

14 Which Premier League manager has kept his red hair and enthusiasm?

15 Which Premier League captain and Northern Irish international is easily identifiable from his ginger hair?

16 Which brightly-topped Scottish midfielder played at Everton, Rangers and Bradford City?

17 Villa's red-haired Tommy Johnson joined which Scottish club in 2000?

18 Ginger bonce Perry Groves played for which London team in the 90s?

19 For which country was wild redhead Alexei Lalas a star?

20 Which redhead became the first player from the former East Germany to be voted European Footballer of the Year, in 1996?

Answers

Wales (see Quiz 39)
1 Leighton James. **2** Bryan Flynn. **3** Brazil. **4** Mike England was Wales' manager. **5** Cliff Jones and Terry Medwin. **6** Ian Rush. **7** Ryan Giggs. **8** Robbie Savage. **9** Noel Blake. **10** Fulham. **11** Craig Bellamy. **12** John Charles. **13** Gary Sprake. **14** Joe Jordan. **15** Mark Pembridge. **16** Bobby Gould. **17** John Toshack. **18** Germany. **19** Dean Saunders. **20** No (9).

Quiz 38 **Arsenal**

LEVEL 2

Answers – see page 148

1   When did Arsenal last win the FA Cup?

2   Which legendary full-back left Arsenal for West Ham in summer 2000?

3   Which keeper played 472 league games for Spurs and then 237 for Arsenal?

4   Who did Arsenal beat to clinch the league title in 1971?

5   Who did Arsenal beat to win the FA Cup that season and so win the double?

6   Who was manager of Arsenal when they were beaten by Walsall in a Milk Cup-tie in 1983?

7   Who top-scored for Arsenal when they won the league title in 1991?

8   How many games did Arsenal lose that season?

9   Who did Arsenal beat in both the League Cup and FA Cup finals in 1993?

10 Martin Keown joined Arsenal from which other club?

11 In what year was Arsenal founded?

12 Which Danish midfielder's transfer was at the centre of allegations of financial wrong-doings that ended with George Graham's sacking in 1995

13 How many times have Arsenal appeared in the League Cup final?

14 How many times have they won it?

15 Which Arsenal player was voted Footballer of the Year in 1971?

16 Keeper John Lukic has played for Arsenal and which other club throughout his career?

17 How many times have Arsenal won the league title?

18 When was the last time?

19 What is the official name of the Arsenal ground?

20 For which country does full back Silviniho play his international football?

Answers

Pot Luck 4 (see Quiz 40)
1 Bramble. **2** John Aldridge. **3** Most World Cup games (21). **4** Pete Reid. **5** Justice Taylor Report. **6** Bobby Charlton. **7** Emerson Thome. **8** The Rokermen changed grounds. **9** Norwich. **10** Feyenoord (1970) **11** Australia. **12** Busby Babes. **13** Marseilles. **14** Crystal Palace. **15** Coventry. **16** Jimmy Greaves. **17** Carlos Alberto. **18** Coventry, Leicester, Liverpool, Oxford. **19** Ukraine. **20** Dundee.

LEVEL 2

1   Which Welsh short-sighted 70s winger made his name at Burnley?

2   Which diminutive Burnley and Leeds midfielder won 66 caps between 1975 and 1984?

3   Who eliminated Wales from the quarter finals of the 1958 World Cup?

4   In which way did England lead Wales in the late 70s and early 80s?

5   Which Welsh wingers were part of the Tottenham double-winning side?

6   Which Welshman was part of Liverpool's double-winning team?

7   Which Welshman has twice helped Manchester United to the double?

8   Which Welsh midfielder was originally dropped from the game against Italy for being disrespectful to Paolo Maldini's shirt?

9   Which Blackburn Rovers goal ace is eligible to play for Wales because of his parents' commonwealth status?

10   Wales defenders Melville and Coleman play for which League team?

11   Which Wales star joined Coventry City from Norwich City in 2000?

12   Which Welsh player was voted Juventus's best ever foreign player?

13   Who was the Welsh keeper in Don Revie's popular Leeds United team?

14   A 'hand of God' goal by which former Leeds and Manchester United striker put Scotland rather than Wales into the 1978 World Cup?

15   Which Everton midfielder has won over 35 caps for Wales?

16   Which former Wimbledon boss took over as manager of Wales in 1995?

17   Which successful club manager played 40 times for Wales and managed them for 47 days?

18   Wales shocked the football world by earning a 1-1 draw in which country in the European Championship qualifying rounds in 1995?

19   Who scored Wales' goal in the 1-0 victory over Brazil in Cardiff in 1991?

20   Did Vinny Jones win more than 10 caps for Wales?

Quiz 40 Pot Luck 4

Answers – see page 146

LEVEL 2

1   Which Titus is Ipswich's promising young defender?

2   Who was the first person to miss a penalty in a Wembley FA Cup final?

3   What record does Maradona share with Matthaus?

4   Whose managerial performance was the subject of the BBC's *Premier Passions*?

5   What was the name of the report that gave rise to the all-seater stadiums?

6   Which England player's portrait hangs in the National Portrait Gallery?

7   Who is Sunderland's Brazilian defender?

8   Why did Sunderland have to change their nickname?

9   Craig Bellamy and Darren Eadie left which club for Premiership pastures?

10 Who was the first Dutch club to win the European cup?

11 Middlesbrough's Paul Okon hails from which country?

12 What was the nickname given to the team that featured Duncan Edwards, Roger Byrne and Eddie Colman?

13 Which French team was relegated from the first division in 1993 after being found guilty of match-fixing?

14 Which Terry Venables side was given the tag 'team of the 80s'?

15 Which team ended a 16-month run without an away win with a victory at Southampton in August 2000?

16 Which Englishman scored on his debut for AC Milan in 1961?

17 Who was the last skipper to collect the Jules Rimet trophy?

18 Which four League club cities are mentioned on the Monopoly board?

19 Shakhtar Donetsk were which country's surprise qualifiers in the 2000-01 Champions League?

20 Ivano Bonetti is manager of which Scottish Premier League club?

Answers

Arsenal (see Quiz 38)
1 1998. **2** Nigel Winterburn. **3** Pat Jennings. **4** Spurs.
5 Liverpool. **6** Terry Neill. **7** Alan Smith. **8** One. **9** Sheffield Wednesday. **10** Everton. **11** 1886. **12** John Jensen. **13** Five times. **14** Twice. **15** Frank McLintock. **16** Leeds United.
17 Eleven times. **18** 1997-98. **19** The Arsenal Stadium.
20 Brazil.

Quiz 41 Bobby Charlton

Answers – see page 151

LEVEL 2

1   How many appearances did Charlton make for United?

2   In which year did Charlton make his England debut?

3   How many goals did he score in the 1968 European Cup final against Benfica?

4   How many goals did he score for England during his career?

5   In what year was Bobby Charlton born?

6   How many times did Manchester United win the league title with Charlton in the side ?

7   Bobby Charlton won his 100th England cap in 1970. Who were the opposition that day?

8   In which year was Charlton voted both the Football Writers and European Footballer of the Year?

9   Which was Bobby Charlton's first World Cup?

10 How many times was Bobby Charlton booked in his career?

11 How many goals did Charlton score in his career at United?

12 How many goals did he score in the 1966 World Cup Finals?

13 In which year did Charlton retire from playing?

14 What did he do next?

15 With which other two clubs was he associated before returning to United as a director?

16 How many England caps did Charlton win?

17 When did Charlton become Sir Bobby?

18 Bobby Charlton won only one FA Cup winner's medal with United; who were their opponents at Wembley that day?

19 In which year was it?

20 How many times did Charlton captain his country?

Chelsea (see Quiz 43)

Answers

1 John Dempsey. **2** Athens, Greece. **3** Peter Houseman.
4 Maidstone, Kent. **5** John Spencer. **6** 150. **7** CSKA Moscow.
8 Tony Hateley. **9** Liverpool. **10** Bobby Tambling. **11** Dan
Petrescu. **12** David Speedie. **13** Everton. **14** Hibs. **15** 5
(Winterbottom, Mercer, Greenwood, Venables and Hoddle). **16** The
Chelsea FC Chronicle. **17** Stoke City. **18** 'Blue is the Colour'.
19 Nine months. **20** Tottenham Hotspur.

Quiz 42 Scotttish Domestic

LEVEL 2

Answers – see page 152

1   Scotland internationals Ally McCoist and Ian Durrant now play at which club?

2   What colour shirts do Dundee wear?

3   David Narey and Maurice Malpas were heroes of which club?

4   Which team play at McDiarmid Park?

5   In which year did Celtic break Rangers run as Scottish champions?

6   Apart from Aberdeen who is the only non-Glasgow team to be crowned Scottish champions?

7   Who did Rangers beat 7-0 in the semi-final of the 2000 FA Cup?

8   Which Fife team beat Celtic in a penalty shootout in the 1995 League Cup to win a place in Europe?

9   Which Accies beat Rangers at Ibrox in 1995?

10   Jim Jeffries is manager of which Premier League team?

11   Hansen, Rough and Johnston are famous old boys of which club?

12   Which club signed Eyal Berkovic from West Ham in 1999?

13   In which colour shirts do Heart of Midlothian play?

14   Which club play at Firhill Park?

15   Lovell, Paatelainen and Lehmann appear in which team's line-up?

16   Miller, Cooper and McGhee were which team's Cup-Winners Cup winners?

17   Which Scottish team were formerly known as Ferranti Thistle?

18   Which club arose out of the amalgamation of Inverness teams in 1994?

19   How many of the starting Scotland eleven that beat England in the Euro 2000 play-offs in 1999 were playing in the Scottish League?

20   Which 'County' played in the Highland League until joining the Scottish League in 1995?

Answers

Local Derbies (see Quiz 44)
1 Glasgow. 2 Arsenal. 3 Milan and Internazionale. 4 Juventus and Torino. 5 1984. 6 Eight: London, Manchester, Liverpool, Nottingham, Sheffield, Birmingham, Bristol and Newcastle/Sunderland. 7 1996. 8 Spurs won 3-1. 9 Rome. 10 Newcastle and Sunderland. 11 Fulham. 12 1984. 13 Hibs and Hearts. 14 Goodison Park. 15 Nick Barmby. 16 Stanley Park. 17 Sandy Brown. 18 United won 2-0. 19 Celtic won 6-2. 20 Notts County v Forest in 1892.

1 Who scored Chelsea's equaliser against Real Madrid in the European Cup Winners' Cup final replay in 1971?

2 Where was that match played?

3 Which former Chelsea winger died tragically in a car crash in 1977?

4 Where was Andy Townsend born?

5 Who signed for Chelsea from Glasgow Rangers in August 1992?

6 In all, how many goals did Peter Osgood score for Chelsea?

7 From which team was Dmitri Kharine signed in 1982?

8 Who was Chelsea's first £100,000 signing?

9 Against which team did Paul Elliott receive his career-ending injury in 1992?

10 Who scored five goals for Chelsea in a 6-2 league win at Villa Park in 1966?

11 Who is Chelsea's most capped player?

12 Who was Kerry Dixon's usual striking partner?

13 Who did Pat Nevin join on leaving Chelsea in 1988?

14 From which team did Gordon Durie join Chelsea in 1986?

15 How many England managers have played for Chelsea?

16 What was the Chelsea matchday programme originally called?

17 Who beat Chelsea in the League Cup Final in 1972?

18 What was the name of Chelsea's hit single released that same year?

19 For how long was Danny Blanchflower manager of Chelsea?

20 Against which club did George Weah score his first goal for Chelsea?

Quiz 44 Local Derbies

Answers – see page 150

LEVEL 2

1   In which city does the 'Old Firm' derby take place?

2   Who are Tottenham's local derbies played against?

3   Which two teams contest the Milan derby?

4   If you were in Turin, which two teams would you watch in the local derby?

5   In which year was the League Cup final a local derby?

6   In how many English cities can you find a derby?

7   In which year was the last Manchester derby of the 20th century?

8   Who won the local derby FA Cup semi-final between Spurs and Arsenal in 1991?

9   In which city do Lazio play their derby games?

10 Who contests England's North-East derby?

11 Which team is regarded as Chelsea's local rival?

12 When was the last time these two teams met in the the league?

13 Which two teams play in the Edinburgh derby?

14 The Merseyside derby is played at Anfield and which other ground?

15 Which England player moved from one Merseyside rival to the other in summer 2000?

16 What is the name of the park that sits between the Liverpool and Everton grounds?

17 Which Evertonian's name became synonymous with an 'own goal' when he scored one in a derby in 1969?

18 Manchester United played City in Denis Irwin's testimonial before the start of the 2000-01 season. Who won the match?

19 Who won the first Glasgow derby of the 2000-01 season?

20 Which was the first ever official English local league derby?

Quiz 45 Hairstyles

Answers – see page 155

Answers – see page 155

LEVEL 2

1 Which Colombian had a head full of curly locks?

2 Which legendary Brighton centre-back played in a headband?

3 Which former Manchester United Czech forward sported an alice band?

4 Which club sold dreadlock caps in celebration of their manager's hair?

5 Which French World Cup winner wears his hair in a ponytail?

6 Which Newcastle and Tottenham player was best known for the footballer's mullet hairstyle?

7 Which entire 1998 World Cup team (except one) dyed their hair peroxide blonde after qualifying for the second stage of the tournament?

8 Which player's hair style led him to be teased with the chant: "He's got a pineapple on his head."

9 What colour does Taribo West dye his hair when playing for Nigeria?

10 Which country left Redondo out of their squad because he wouldn't get his hair cut?

11 What did Bobby Charlton and Ralph Coates both do with their hair?

12 Which long-haired striker sunk Liverpool in the 1971 Cup final?

13 Which goalkeeper started the 2000-2001 season sporting a ponytail?

14 Which manager is known as 'bald eagle'?

15 What colour did Robbie Fowler, Neil Lennon and Gazza all dye their hair?

16 Which West Ham defender possibly didn't make the England squad because of his skinhead crop?

17 Who appeared on a shampoo advert with expertly coiffeured hair?

18 What was Kevin Keegan's 70s contribution to football hair fashion?

19 Which entire Premier League squad began the 1995-96 season with a number one crop?

20 Who is Manchester United's dome-headed keeper?

Answers

Bad Boys (see Quiz 47)
1 Peter Storey. 2 Cathay Pacific. 3 Charlie Nicholas. 4 Roy Keane. 5 Jody Morris. 6 Bowyer and Woodgate. 7 Tony Adams. 8 Rangers. 9 Arsenal. 10 Dennis Wise. 11 Paul Merson. 12 Stanley Bowles. 13 Kenny Sansom. 14 Duncan Ferguson. 15 Chris Armstrong. 16 Graham Rix. 17 Mark Bosnich. 18 Jimmy Johnstone. 19 Diego Maradona. 20 Teddy Sheringham.

Quiz 46 Celebrity Fans

Answers – see page 156

LEVEL 2

1   Cricket umpire Dicky Bird and Michael Parkinson support which home town team?

2   Commentator John Motson can't get to see his favourites too often?

3   Johnny Briggs (Mike Baldwin) closes the factory to see which Lancashire team?

4   Eddie Large and Bernard Manning will be glad to see their side back with the big boys?

5   Does Jeremy Paxman ask tough questions of his northern heroes?

6   Sean Bean's allegiances are tatooed on his arm?

7   Julian Lloyd Webber hears some sweet music in the East?

8   Frank Skinner's boys haven't given him much to laugh about?

9   Michael Palin would travel the world to see which team?

10 Chancellor of the Exchequer Gordon Brown has a taxing time at which Scottish team?

11 Luciano Pavarotti supports a giant of European football?

12 Formula One's Johnny Herbert races to which Premiership team?

13 Which Spanish team do Placido Domingo and Julio Iglesias sing their hearts out for?

14 Finlay Quayle and Irvine Welsh share a love of which big city side?

15 Uri Geller's team could certainly do with some miracles?

16 Which team does comedian Jim Davidson hope will 'nick, nick' a goal?

17 Funny man Vic Reeves favours an unfashionable north-eastern outfit?

18 Does TV's Nick Hancock think it's all over for his team?

19 Tory MP Kenneth Clarke has a lot of time for the reds?

20 After a Big Breakfast Johnny Vaughan will be off to see who?

Answers

Eastern Europe (see Quiz 48)
1 Red Star Belgrade. 2 Marseilles. 3 1953. 4 Alen Boksic.
5 Quarter-finals. 6 6-1 to Holland. 7 Romanian. 8 Partisan.
9 Split. 10 Ukrainian. 11 Red Star Belgrade. 12 CSKA Sofia.
13 1994. 14 Bulgaria. 15 Zbigniew Boniek. 16 Dynamo Kiev in
1986. 17 Savo Milosevic. 18 Four: Yugoslavia, Romania, Czech
Republic and Slovenia. 19 Yugoslavia, letting in 13 goals in four
games. 20 Lev Yashin.

Quiz 47 Bad Boys

Answers – see page 153

LEVEL 2

1　Which Arsenal defender was found guilty of importing pornography?

2　Which Airline's plane were England accused of damaging in 1996?

3　Which Arsenal star stole a chip then allegedly hit a woman in Ibiza?

4　Which Man Utd captain allegedly assaulted two women in a night club?

5　Which Chelsea player allegedly assaulted someone in a supermarket?

6　Which players allegedly assaulted an Asian student in Leeds city centre?

7　Which international served a prison sentence for drink driving in 1990?

8　Who were England stars Butcher, Roberts and Woods playing for when charged with 'conduct likely to provoke a breach of the peace' in 1987?

9　For which team was David Hillier playing when allegedly involved in a bag-stealing operation at an airport?

10　Who had an altercation with a taxi driver outside Scribes club?

11　Which former Arsenal and England forward confessed to a gambling and cocaine addiction?

12　Which 70s QPR star reputedly blew £500,000 on gambling?

13　Which 80s Arsenal and England full-back was reputedly given a transfer in order to clear his gambling debts?

14　Which international has earned the nickname 'Duncan Disorderly'?

15　Which Tottenham forward was found guilty of smoking cannabis?

16　Which assistant manager was imprisoned for underage sex in 1999?

17　Which Man. Utd goalkeeper was arrested on his stag night?

18　Which legendary Scottish winger and boozer was found drunk and stranded in the Irish Sea in a rowing boat?

19　In 1994, who was given a 15-month worldwide ban after being charged with cocaine abuse?

20　Which Manchester United striker was forced to publicly apologise for going to a night club shortly before the 98 World Cup?

Answers

Hairstyles (see Quiz 45)
1 Carlos Valderrama. 2 Steve Foster. 3 Karel Poborsky. 4 Chelsea.
5 Emmanuel Petit. 6 Chris Waddle. 7 Romania. 8 Jason Lee.
9 Green. 10 Argentina. 11 Flick a long strand across their bald patch. 12 Charlie George. 13 David Seaman. 14 Jim Smith.
15 Peroxide blond. 16 Julian Dicks. 17 David Ginola. 18 The curly perm. 19 Wimbledon. 20 Fabien Barthez.

Quiz 48 Eastern Europe

Answers – see page 154

1   Who won the European Cup in 1991?

2   Which French team did they beat in the final?

3   In which year did the Mighty Magyars famously crush England 6-3 at Wembley?

4   Which Croatian joined Middlesbrough in summer 2000?

5   In which round were Yugoslavia beaten in Euro 2000?

6   Who did they lose to?

7   What nationality is the great Gheorghe Hagi?

8   There are two major teams in Belgrade: Red Star and which other?

9   Hajduk are based in which Yugoslavian city?

10 What nationality is Andrei Kanchelskis?

11 Which club is known at home as Crvena Zvezda?

12 With which Eastern European club did Hristo Stoichkov make his name?

13 In which year did he win the European Footballer of the Year award?

14 For whom did he play his international football?

15 Which great Polish player had success in Italy with Juventus and Roma in the 1980s?

16 Which was the last Eastern European team to win the European Cup Winners Cup?

17 Which Eastern European player was equal top scorer in Euro 2000?

18 How many Eastern European teams qualified for Euro 2000?

19 Of those teams, who had the worst defensive record?

20 Who was the first Soviet player to be European Footballer of the Year?

Celebrity Fans (see Quiz 46)
1 Barnsley. 2 Barnet. 3 Burnley. 4 Manchester City. 5 Leeds.
6 Sheffield United. 7 Orient. 8 West Bromwich Albion.
9 Sheffield Wednesday. 10 Raith Rovers. 11 Juventus. 12 West Ham. 13 Real Madrid. 14 Hibernian. 15 Reading. 16 Charlton Athletic. 17 Darlington 18 Stoke City. 19 Nottingham Forest.
20 Chelsea.

Quiz 49 **The UEFA Cup**

Answers – see page 159

1   What was the UEFA Cup originally called?
2   In which year did the first tournament take place?
3   Who were England's representatives in that first final?
4   When was the tournament first called the UEFA Cup?
5   Which country provided both teams for the 1998 final?
6   For most of its life the UEFA Cup final was played over two legs. When did this change?
7   Which was the last Scottish team to appear in the final?
8   Which was the last English team to win the trophy?
9   Who did they beat in the final?
10 Liverpool won a memorable final against which German team in 1973?
11 Which north-eastern team won the Fairs Cup against Ujpest Dozsa in 1969?
12 Who won the competition in 2000?
13 In which city do they play their football?
14 Who did they beat in the final?
15 Where was the 1999 final between Parma and Marseille played?
16 Which English city provided the finalists in both 1960 and 1961?
17 Which Argentinian scored for Napoli when they beat Stuttgart to win the 1989 tournament?
18 Which East Anglian club won the tournament in 1981?
19 In which year did the only all-English final take place?
20 When did Leeds last appear in the UEFA Cup final?

Answers

World Cup 98 (see Quiz 51)
1 USA. 2 Zero. 3 Spain. 4 Marcelo Salas. 5 Christian Vieri.
6 Scored an own goal. 7 Mexico's. 8 Laurent Blanc. 9 Diego
Simone. 10 Gabriel Batistuta. 11 Zinadine Zidane. 12 Croatia won
3-0. 13 Denmark. 14 Croatia. 15 Ronald De Boer. 16 Frank
Leboeuf. 17 Davor Suker. 18 Two. 19 Ronaldo. 20 Marcel
Desailly.

Quiz 50 West Ham United

Answers – see page 160

1 What was West Ham's original name?

2 Who did West Ham play in the 1923 'White Horse' FA Cup final?

3 In what year did West Ham first win the FA Cup?

4 Who took over from Ron Greenwood as manager in 1974?

5 Which former West Ham great played for Fulham against the Hammers in the 1974 FA Cup final?

6 Which Hammer scored a rare header to win the 1978 FA Cup final against Arsenal?

7 What is the official name of West Ham's home ground?

8 Which player holds the league appearances record?

9 Who is West Ham's most capped player?

10 Who was the assistant manager during the 2000-01 season?

11 What are West Ham's away colours?

12 How many times have West Ham won the FA Cup?

13 In what year did West Ham win the European Cup Winners' Cup?

14 Who did they beat in the final?

15 Who scored twice in that match?

16 How many times have West Ham reached the League Cup final?

17 Which Croatian striker did the Hammers sign for free from Arsenal in summer 2000?

18 Which tough defender left West Ham for Palace during summer 2000?

19 Who beat West Ham 6-0 in the 1990 Littlewoods Cup semi-final?

20 Where did West Ham finish in the Premier League in 1999-2000?

Non-League Football (see Quiz 52)
1 Stevenage. 2 Chester City. 3 Yeovil. 4 Kidderminster, Macclesfield or Stevenage. 5 Rushden and Diamonds. 6 Brighton. 7 Coventry City. 8 Chris Waddle. 9 Newcastle United. 10 Wimbledon. 11 Blyth. 12 Barnet. 13 Borough. 14 Town. 15 Victoria. 16 Returned to League after relegation. 17 Malcolm Christie. 18 Nigel Clough. 19 Ron Atkinson. 20 The Midlands.

1   Which team completed Group F in the finals along with Germany, Yugoslavia and Iran?

2   How many points did Japan get in their first round group?

3   In the best game of the first round Nigeria came back to beat which team 3-2?

4   Who scored two goals for Chile in their 2-2 first round draw with Italy?

5   Which Italian striker scored four times in the first round group stage?

6   Why will Tommy Boyd remember Scotland's opening game with Brazil?

7   Luis Hernandez was which country's blond World Cup star?

8   Who scored the first Golden Goal in World Cup history to eliminate Paraguay from the tournament?

9   Who did David Beckham kick out at to be sent off in the second round match against Argentina?

10   Who scored Argentina's penalty after five minutes of the match against England?

11   Which French star was suspended for their second-round game?

12   What was the score of Germany's quarter-final with Croatia?

13   Who shocked Brazil by scoring after two minutes in their quarter-final, but eventually lost 2-3?

14   Who did France meet in the semi-final?

15   Which Dutch player missed the deciding penalty in their semi-final?

16   Who replaced the suspended Laurent Blanc in the French final team?

17   Who won the Golden Boot with a goal in the third place play-off match?

18   How many of France's goals did Zidane score in the final?

19   Which Brazilian was passed fit only 45 minutes before the final?

20   Which Frenchman was sent off in the final?

Answers

The UEFA Cup (see Quiz 49)
1 The Inter-Cities Fairs Cup. **2** 1958. **3** London. **4** 1972.
5 Italy. **6** 1998: it became a one-off match. **7** Dundee United in 1987. **8** Spurs in 1984. **9** Anderlecht. **10** Moenchengladbach.
11 Newcastle United. **12** Galatasaray. **13** Istanbul. **14** Arsenal.
15 Moscow. **16** Birmingham. **17** Diego Maradona. **18** Ipswich Town. **19** 1972. **20** 1971.

Quiz 52 Non-League Football

Answers – see page 158

1   Which non-League club had a dispute with Newcastle United when they chose to play at their own ground in the FA Cup in 1998?

2   Which League team were relegated to the Conference in 2000?

3   Which non-League team were once notorious for their sloping pitch?

4   Name one of the three Conference champions who were denied promotion to the Football League because their ground was inadequate.

5   Which shining non-league team's FA Cup run in 2000 ended in a penalty shoot-out defeat by Sheffield United?

6   Which South Coast team were beaten on penalties by Sudbury Town in the 1997 FA Cup?

7   Which First Division team were beaten by Sutton in the FA Cup only two years after they had won it?

8   Which future England player was discovered playing for Tow Law Town?

9   Hereford United, then in the Southern League, earned a famous victory over which team with a Goal of the Season from Ronnie Radford?

10 Who won the FA Cup only 11 years after joining the Football League?

11 Which Spartans are a famous North East non-league club?

12 Which club did manager Barry Fry take into the Football League in 1981?

13 Nuneaton and Stevenage have which club name in common?

14 Complete the non-league team name: Hednesford ..?

15 Complete the non-league team name: Northwich ..?

16 What feat did Halifax Town and Lincoln City achieve?

17 Which current Derby County forward came from non-League football?

18 Which famous manager's son is in charge at Burton Albion?

19 Which retired flamboyant manager spent his playing days skippering Oxford United from the Southern League to the Second Division?

20 The Dr Marten's League centres on which region of the country?

1 Which English club won the European Cup in 1980?

2 For how long were English clubs banned from European competitions after the Heysel tragedy?

3 Who won the World Cup in 1986?

4 Which camera company sponsored the football league during the 1980s?

5 Who won the European Championship in 1988?

6 Who scored five goals for Ipswich as they beat Southampton 5-3 in a league match in 1982?

7 In which country was the 1982 World Cup played?

8 Which three brothers all appeared for Southampton in a league game in 1988?

9 Which 80s manager claimed referees were 'intimidated' at Anfield?

10 Which manager grabbed, punched and kissed some fans in 1989?

11 Who did Arsenal beat with an injury time-goal to win the league championship in 1989?

12 Which Spurs keeper became a hero when his two penalty saves won them the UEFA Cup in 1984?

13 When were the last Home Internationals held?

14 Who scored a memorable goal as England beat Brazil in Rio in 1984?

15 Who became England manager in June 1982?

16 When did Barclays Bank start sponsoring the Football League?

17 Who won the League Cup in 1989?

18 Who beat Arsenal in 1988 to win the League Cup for the first time in their 98-year history?

19 Who won the league and FA Cup double in 1986?

20 Who banned away fans from their Kenilworth Road ground in 1985?

Answers

Overseas Grounds (see Quiz 55)
11 Maracana. **2** AS Monaco. **3** Stadium of Light. **4** The Rose Bowl, Pasadena. **5** Nou Camp, Barcelona. **6** Bayern Munich. **7** Bernabeu. **8** San Siro. **9** Moscow. **10** Poland. **11** Sampdoria and Genoa. **12** England 0 USA 1 **13** Santiago. **14** Heysel. **15** Estonia. **16** Chile. **17** Charleroi. **18** Copenhagen. **19** Ajax. **20** Stade de France.

Quiz 54 German Football

LEVEL 2

1 What is the name of the German league?

2 Who did Bayern beat in the 1974 European Cup final?

3 How many times in a row did Bayern win the European Cup during the 1970s?

4 Which former Leeds striker currently plays for Hamburg?

5 For which German team does Djorkaeff play?

6 Which Norwegian star joined Munich 1860 in summer 2000?

7 What is Andy Moller's nickname?

8 Whose penalty helped West Germany beat England in the quarter-finals of the 1972 European Championships?

9 Who scored a penalty before West Germany had even touched the ball in the 1974 World Cup final?

10 Who defeated West Germany in the 1982 World Cup final?

11 Who scored West Germany's two goals in the 1986 World Cup final?

12 Who scored Germany's winner from the penalty spot in Italia 90?

13 How many Argentinian players were sent off in that final?

14 Who memorably defeated Germany in the quarter-finals of the 1994 World Cup?

15 Who scored against them that day?

16 Which was the last German club to win the European Cup?

17 Who scored twice in the final that year and then went on to play for Liverpool and Fulham?

18 Which German club did Chelsea beat in the 1998 European Cup Winners Cup final?

19 Which other teams were in Germany's Euro 2000 group?

20 Who took over as team manager after that tournament?

Answers

Hat-Tricks (see Quiz 56)
1 Henrik Larsson. 2 Paul Scholes. 3 Luxembourg. 4 Manchester City. 5 Luther Blissett. 6 Real Madrid's. 7 Matt Le Tissier. 8 Poland. 9 Marco Van Basten. 10 Alan Shearer. 11 Stan Collymore. 12 Patrick Kluivert. 13 Robbie Fowler. 14 One. 15 Michael Bridges. 16 Charlton Athletic. 17 Paul Gascoigne's. 18 Nwankwo Kanu. 19 Eric Cantona. 20 Rangers.

Quiz 55 Overseas Grounds

Answers – see page 161

LEVEL 2

1   In which ground do Brazil host most international matches?

2   Which French team play at the Louis II stadium?

3   Which Lisbon ground shares its name with a Premier League stadium?

4   Which stadium hosted the 1994 World Cup final in USA?

5   Where did Manchester United win the 1999 European Cup Final?

6   Which German team play at the country's national stadium?

7   What is the name of Real Madrid's famous stadium?

8   Which ground is home to Milan and Internazionale?

9   The Luzhniki Stadium, originally Spartak's ground but now home to Torpedo, is in which city?

10   Which country play most their matches at the Stadion Slaski in Katowice?

11   Which two clubs share the Luigi Ferraris stadium in Italy?

12   What famous match took place at Belo Horizonte in 1950?

13   The match between Chile and Italy in 1962, which was dogged by foul play and serious violent conduct became known as the Battle of..?

14   Which stadium was rebuilt after a tragedy and renamed the Stade de Roi Baudouin?

15   Who were Scotland meant to be playing in the Kadriorg Stadium in 1996 when they kicked off with no opposition?

16   Which South American country used their National Stadium as a prison and execution centre after a right-wing coup in 1973?

17   Which city's Euro 2000 ground was deemed by many experts to be unsafe because of its steep temporary terracing?

18   In which city did Arsenal play the 2000 UEFA Cup final?

19   Which Dutch team moved to the country's national stadium in 1996?

20   Which ground was built for the 1998 World Cup?

Answers

The 80s (see Quiz 53)
1 Nottingham Forest. **2** Five years, 1985-90. **3** Argentina.
4 Canon. **5** Holland. **6** Alan Brazil. **7** Spain. **8** Danny, Rodney and Ray Wallace. **9** Alex Ferguson. **10** Brain Clough.
11 Liverpool. **12** Tony Parks. **13** 1984. **14** John Barnes.
15 Bobby Robson. **16** 1987. **17** Nottingham Forest. **18** Luton Town. **19** Liverpool. **20** Luton Town.

Quiz 56 Hat-Tricks

Answers – see page 162

1   Who scored a hat-trick for Celtic against Rangers in August 2000?

2   Who scored a hat-trick for England against Poland in 1999?

3   Who did Alan Shearer score a hat-trick against at Wembley in 1999?

4   Tony Adcock, Paul Stewart and David White all scored hat-tricks in whose 10-1 defeat of Huddersfield Town in 1987?

5   Which Watford player scored a hat-trick on his England debut in 1982?

6   Puskas and Di Stefano both scored hat-tricks in whose 7-3 European Cup final victory over Eintracht Frankfurt?

7   Who scored a hat-trick for Southampton in 86 when only eighteen?

8   Who did Gary Lineker scored a hat-trick against in the 86 World Cup?

9   Who scored a hat-trick against England in Euro 88?

10   Who scored a hat-trick for Southampton in 88 when only seventeen?

11   Who scored a hat-trick in 1999 after being 'rescued' by Leicester City?

12   Who scored a hat-trick for Holland against Yugoslavia in Euro 2000?

13   Who scored a hat-trick in five minutes against Arsenal in 1994?

14   How many of Geoff Hurst's World Cup hat-trick came in the 90 minutes?

15   Which Leeds signing scored a hat-trick in his second game in 1999?

16   Clive Mendonca scored a play-off hat-trick at Wembley in 1998 to send which team to the Premier League?

17   Whose hat-trick for Tottenham included two free-kicks floated past Derby keeper Peter Shilton in 1990?

18   Whose sensational hat-trick in the last 20 minutes enabled Arsenal to come back from 0-2 to beat Chelsea in 1999?

19   Who scored a hat-trick for Leeds United against Liverpool in the 1992 Charity Shield?

20   Gordon Durie scored a hat-trick for which club in a 1996 Cup final?

Answers

German Football (see Quiz 54)
1 The Bundesliga. 2 Atletico Madrid. 3 Three times, 1974, 75 and 76. 4 Tony Yeboah. 5 Kaiserslautern. 6 Erik Mykland.
7 'Cry Baby'. 8 Gunter Netzer. 9 Johan Neeskens for Holland.
10 Italy. 11 Rummenigge and Völler. 12 Andreas Brehme.
13 Two. 14 Bulgaria. 15 Stoichkov and Letchkov. 16 Borussia Dortmund in 1997. 17 Karlheinz Reidle 18 Stuttgart.
19 England, Portugal and Romania. 20 Rudi Völler.

Quiz 57 Everton

LEVEL 2

1 What was Everton's original name?

2 What is Everton's motto?

3 What is Everton's training ground called?

4 Who is the most successful captain in Everton's history?

5 From whom did Everton sign Peter Reid in 1982?

6 Who is the club's top post-war goalscorer?

7 Who scored the famous winning goal for Everton in the Merseyside derby in October 1978?

8 Which Everton keeper was known as 'Handbag' by Liverpool fans?

9 Who scored twice for the Toffees in the 1966 FA Cup final?

10 Who famously played in white boots for Everton in the late 1960s?

11 Which dazzling striker signed for Everton from Anderlecht in 1976 but left for Chelsea two years later?

12 Who won £10,000 from the *Daily Express* for scoring 30 goals during the 1977-78 season?

13 Which Republic of Ireland player crossed Stanley Park from Liverpool to Everton in 1982?

14 Which striker scored a hat-trick on his league debut against Newcastle, in 1988?

15 Who scored 20 goals in his first season for Everton, in 1990-91?

16 In which year did Everton win a European trophy?

17 What colour shirts comprise Everton's away strip in season 2000-01?

18 To whom did Everton sell John Spencer in 1998?

19 Have Everton ever won the League Cup?

20 Where did Everton finish in the Premier League in 1999-2000?

Answers

Transfers (see Quiz 59)
1 Mo Johnston. **2** Pierre Van Hooijdonk. **3** Duncan Ferguson.
4 Coventry City. **5** Alan Ball. **6** Nothing. **7** Paul Gascoigne.
8 Frank and Ronald de Boer. **9** Paul Ince. **10** Edu. **11** Tony
Cascarino. **12** Christian Vieri. **13** Chris Sutton. **14** Thierry Henry.
15 Jaap Stam. **16** John Hartson. **17** Barcelona. **18** Winterburn
and Suker. **19** Robbie Keane. **20** Duncan Ferguson.

1   Which French club knocked Celtic out of the 2000 UEFA Cup?

2   What is Celtic's nickname?

3   What did Fergus McCann do at Celtic in 1994?

4   In what year did Celtic hero Kenny Dalglish join Liverpool?

5   Which striker did Celtic sign from Chelsea in 2000?

6   Which manager was sacked after their Cup humiliation against Inverness in January 2000?

7   Who took over as manager temporarily until Martin O'Neill's appointment?

8   From which English Premier League club did Celtic sign Bobby Petta?

9   How many championships did Celtic win consecutively from 1966?

10 Which 90s Celtic hero joined Sheffield Wednesday and then West Ham?

11 Who did Celtic beat to win the European Cup final in 1967?

12 Which Celtic forward went on as Scotland's substitute in both Euro 2000 play-off games with England?

13 Which year did Celtic win the championship and prevent Rangers winning 'ten in a row'?

14 Where did Celtic play in 1994-95 while Celtic Park was being rebuilt?

15 Which Scottish international midfielder won 76 caps for Scotland between 1984 and 1997?

16 Which Champagne Charlie rejoined Celtic in 1990?

17 Which member of Celtic's 1953-54 double-winning team engineered their rennaissance in 1965?

18 Which English team did Celtic beat in the European Cup in 1970?

19 Celtic's leading scorer in 1999-2000 left the club at the end of the season. Who was he?

20 Which Channel Four Italian football expert played for Celtic?

Answers

Hard Men (see Quiz 60)
1 Tommy Smith. **2** Norman Hunter. **3** Ron Harris. **4** Vinnie Jones.
5 Graeme Souness. **6** Harald Schumacher. **7** John Fashanu.
8 John Hartson. **9** David Cross. **10** Dean Saunders. **11** Patrick Vieira. **12** Nicky Butt. **13** Manchester United. **14** Leeds United.
15 Vinnie Jones. **16** Leeds and Spurs. **17** Terry Butcher.
18 Celtic v Rangers. **19** Ron Harris. **20** Roy Keane.

Quiz 59 Transfers

Answers – see page 165

LEVEL 2

1   Whose transfer from Watford to Rangers in 1989 caused uproar ?

2   Who joined Vitesse Arnhem in June 1999 after refusing to play for Nottingham Forest ever again?

3   Who rejoined Everton from Newcastle in August 2000?

4   Who spent £1m on Arsenal youth player Jay Bothroyd in 2000?

5   Who did Arsenal break the existing British transfer record for in 1971?

6   How much did German international Markus Babbel cost Liverpool?

7   Whose price was reduced by £3.5m after he was injured in 1991?

8   Which brothers joined Barcelona for a combined fee of £14m in 1999?

9   Which West Ham player angered fans by appearing in a Manchester United shirt before signing for them in 1989?

10 Which Brazilian was set to join Arsenal in the summer of 2000, but arrived with an invalid passport?

11 Which Ireland striker reputedly cost Gillingham a set of tracksuits?

12 Which Italian forward went to and returned from Spain in deals amounting to over £50m?

13 Who did Chelsea sell for £6m in 2000 – exactly a year after paying out £10m for him ?

14 Who did Arsenal buy from Juventus for £10.5m in 1999?

15 Who was Manchester United's most expensive signing out of Andrew Cole, Fabien Barthez and Jaap Stam?

16 Which Wimbledon player did Tottenham back out of buying at the last minute in 2000?

17 Who sold Ronaldo for £18m in 1997?

18 Which players went on free transfers from Arsenal to West Ham in 2000?

19 Who replaced Lee Bowyer as Britain's most expensive teenager in 1999?

20 Who moved to Rangers in 1994 for a record Scottish fee?

Quiz 60 Hard Men

LEVEL 2

Answers – see page 166

1 Which Liverpool player wrote a book entitled *The Hard Way*?

2 Which Leeds player was said to 'bite yer legs'?

3 Which Chelsea defender 'dealt with' Eddie Gray in the 1970 FA Cup final?

4 Who deliberatley hurt Steve McMahon with an early tackle in the 1988 FA Cup final?

5 Who was sent off in his first match as player-manager of Rangers in 1986?

6 Which German keeper committed a horrendous foul on France's Patrick Battiston in the 1982 World Cup semi-final?

7 Which Wimbledon player's elbow broke Gary Mabbutt's cheekbone?

8 Who kicked Eyal Berkovic in the head during a West Ham training session?

9 Which West Ham striker was known as 'Psycho'?

10 Whose tackle ended Chelsea defender Paul Elliott's professional career?

11 Which Arsenal player was sent off in both the first and second games of the 2000-01 season?

12 Which Manchester United player was sent off twice in September 1998?

13 Which club was criticised for intimidating referees during 1999-2000?

14 Which club had players arrested and charged with GBH during 1999-2000?

15 Which player was fined for his part in the release of a video called *Soccer's Hard Men* in 1992?

16 Which two teams were fined for a brawl during a league game in the 1999-2000 season?

17 Which Rangers player was fined £500 for kicking a door after a match against Aberdeen in 1988?

18 Which match featured 3 sendings off and 8 other bookings in May 1999?

19 Which Chelsea defender earned the nickname 'Chopper' for his combative performances?

20 Who was sent off during the 2000 Charity Shield match?

Answers

Celtic (see Quiz 58)
1 Lyon. 2 The Bhoys. 3 Bought 51% of the club. 4 1977.
5 Chris Sutton. 6 John Barnes. 7 Kenny Dalglish. 8 Ipswich Town.
9 Nine. 10 Paulo Di Canio. 11 Inter Milan. 12 Mark Burchill.
13 1998. 14 Hampden Park. 15 Paul McStay. 16 Charlie
Nicholas. 17 Jock Stein. 18 Leeds United. 19 Mark Viduka.
20 Paul Elliott.

Quiz 61 The North

LEVEL 2

1   Who replaced Paul Jewell as Bradford City manager in 2000?

2   In which colour shirts do Grimsby Town play?

3   Which Yorkshire team reached the FA and League Cup finals in 1993?

4   Which current non-league Yorkshire team became the first to be promoted automatically from the Conference in 1997?

5   Which Yorkshire side used to play at Leeds Road?

6   Which manager exchanged Sheffield Wednesday for Leeds in 1988?

7   Which club does Steve Bruce manage?

8   Which Yorkshire team became the only visiting side to win at Old Trafford in season 1995-96, when a 3-0 victory knocked Manchester United out of the Coca-Cola Cup?

9   Which mecurial Italian joined Bradford City from Aston Villa in 2000?

10 In which colour shirts do Sheffield United play?

11 Which Yorkshire team play at Boothferry Park?

12 David Pleat, Ron Atkinson and Trevor Francis have all managed which team?

13 Jimmy Adamson, Jimmy Armfield and George Graham have all managed which northern team?

14 Which team regained their league status in 1998 after five years in the Conference?

15 Scunthorpe, Scarborough or Doncaster – which is the League team?

16 Which Party's MPs put Sheffield Wednesday under pressure to sack manager Danny Wilson in 2000?

17 Which hot midfielder joined Leeds from Sheffield United in 1976?

18 For which team does Belgian international Gilles de Bilde play?

19 Allan Clarke returned to Leeds after managing which Yorkshire side?

20 Which Yorkshire city's teams took part in an FA Cup semi-final at Wembley?

Answers

World Cup 94 (see Quiz 63)
1 He was assassinated. 2 Sweden. 3 Saudi Arabia. 4 Greece.
5 Ray Houghton. 6 New York. 7 Hristo Stoichkov. 8 Five. 9 USA.
10 Holland. 11 Gianfranco Zola. 12 Bebeto. 13 Diego Maradona.
14 Jurgen Klinsmann. 15 Roberto Baggio's. 16 Bulgaria.
17 Sweden. 18 Franco Baresi. 19 Roberto Baggio. 20 Romario.

Quiz 62 Italia 90

Answers – see page 172

1   Who won the tournament?
2   Which Italian striker hit the headlines with his goals?
3   Who sensationally beat Scotland in their opening game?
4   On which island did the English fans camp during the first phase of the tournament?
5   Who did England play in their opening game?
6   Who did the Republic of Ireland beat in the second phase?
7   Who famously scored their winning penalty in that match?
8   Who put Brazil out of the tournament with a 1-0 win in the second phase?
9   Where was England's second phase match against Belgium played?
10 Who scored England's winner in that match?
11 Who did England play in the quarter-finals?
12 What was unique about their opponents in that match?
13 Whose singing dominated Italia 90?
14 What was unique about the semi-finals?
15 Who did England play in their semi-final?
16 Which England player wept when he was booked in the semi-final?
17 Who missed England's penalties in the semi-final shoot out?
18 In which city was the Argentina v Italy semi-final played?
19 How was the final decided?
20 Who top scored at Italia 90?

LEVEL 2

1 What was the ultimate consequence of Andreas Escobar's own goal against the USA?

2 Which team had Thomas Ravelli in goal during the tournament?

3 Which Middle-Eastern team beat Belgium in round one?

4 Which European team scored none and conceded ten in three games?

5 Whose goal for the Republic of Ireland defeated Italy in the opening Group E game?

6 In which city did Ireland play Italy?

7 Which Golden Boot winner scored in every round up to the semi-final?

8 How many goals did Oleg Salenko score in Russia's 6-1 victory over Cameroon in the first round group match?

9 Which team's line-up included Wynalda, Dooley and Lalas?

10 Which country beat the Irish 2-0 to send them home?

11 Which future Chelsea player was sent off when Italy met Nigeria in the second round?

12 Which Brazilian initiated a cradle-rocking goal celebration after his goals in the tournament?

13 Which legendary player was thrown out of the tournament after failing a drugs test in the competition?

14 Which striker scored five goals for Germany in the tournament?

15 Which Italian's last-minute goal eliminated Nigeria?

16 Who knocked Germany out of the competition in the quarter-finals?

17 Which country lost to Brazil in the semi-final?

18 Who was Italy's captain in the final and missed their first penalty?

19 Who missed Italy's fifth penalty and lost them the final?

20 Which striker scored five goals for Brazil and converted his penalty in the final shoot-out?

Quiz 64 Nationwide 2

LEVEL 2

Answers – see page 170

1   Which club used to play at Teignmouth Road?

2   Who was Southend United's first international?

3   In which year did Port Vale reach the FA Cup semi-final?

4   What was Norwich City's highest finish in the Premier League?

5   In what year were York City formed?

6   Manchester United have played in the Nationwide League. True or False?

7   Which club did Bruce Rioch take over as manager of in June 2000?

8   In which year did Cambridge United play their first Football League game – 1900s, 1940s or 1970s?

9   Which Division did Notts County win in 1997-98?

10 Which club did Peter Shilton manage between 1992 and 1995?

11 How many times did Sunderland win the Division 1 championship in the 1990s?

12 Which Nationwide League team gave their manager to the country in 1999?

13 Which Nationwide team are known as the Red Imps?

14 Who took over from Graham Taylor at Watford in 1984?

15 Which club were formed in 1889 but did not turn professional until 1964?

16 What is Bournemouth's full name?

17 Non-League clubs are allowed to enter the League Cup – true or false?

18 Which teams contested the Auto Windscreens Shield Final in 2000?

19 Who won?

20 Which team won the Division 3 Championship in 1981?

1   When was the 'Champions League' proper introduced?

2   How was the new competition different from the old?

3   Who won the competition in 1992?

4   Where was the final played that year?

5   Which current Chelsea star scored for AC Milan in the 1994 final?

6   Which team appeared in the 1993, 1994 and 1995 finals?

7   Which Italian team appeared in the 1996, 1997 and 1998 finals?

8   How many of those three finals did they win?

9   Which current Arsenal star played for Ajax in the 1996 final?

10 Who beat Manchester United in the quarter-finals of the 1997 competition?

11 How did the competition change in 1998?

12 Who won the competition that year?

13 Who did they beat in the final?

14 Who did Manchester United play in the first match of the 1998-99 competition?

15 Which country do they come from?

16 Who else were in Manchester United's group?

17 What was the result of United's quarter-final first leg against Inter?

18 Who scored United's semi-final winner?

19 Who did United defeat in the final?

20 How did the competition change in 1999?

Quiz 66 Name That Team

LEVEL 2

Answers – see page 176

1 Hopkin, Petrescu, Carbone?

2 Tome, Phillips, Hutchison?

3 Beasant, Scimeca, Harewood?

4 Boa Morte, Collins, Saha?

5 Ardley, Euell, Gayle?

6 Page, Helguson, Hyde?

7 Hinchcliffe, Booth, Sibon?

8 Savage, Lennon, Elliott?

9 Bogarde, Cudicini, Stanic?

10 Blake, Duff, Jansen?

11 Roberts, Llewellyn, Bellamy?

12 Pollett, Ndah, Akinbiyi?

13 Thomas, Little, Payton?

14 Greening, May, Rachubka?

15 Barmby, Arphexad, Diomède?

16 Fox, Suker, Kanouté?

17 Scales, Johnson, Wright?

18 Chettle, Shipperley, Ward?

19 Ndlovu, Adebola, Sonner?

20 Furlong, Kiwomya, Breacker?

Quiz 67 The 90s

Answers – see page 173

LEVEL 2

1   Who had spells in charge of Brighton and Celtic in the 90s?

2   Which Blackburn chairman's millions bought them success in the 90s?

3   In which colour shirts did Manchester United play for one half in 1996?

4   Who made his club and international debut in 1991 at the age of 17?

5   Which two other names did the Coca-Cola Cup go under in the 90s?

6   What occurred at Leeds in 1995 that hadn't happened since 1966?

7   Which boxing promoter took over Leyton Orient in 1995?

8   Who left Leicester City to take over at Aston Villa in 1995?

9   Who scored Scotland's only goal in Euro 96?

10   Who won the PFA Footballer of the Year award twice in the 90s?

11   *Left Foot Forward* and *Left Foot in the Grave* are whose soccer memories?

12   Who finished Premier League runners-up despite holding a 12-point lead in January?

13   Which club reached a League Cup final and two FA Cup semi-finals in the decade before being relegated in 1994?

14   Who is the only African to win the World Footballer of the Year award?

15   Which 90s manager was allegedly involved in brown-paper-bag bungs?

16   Which international played for Derby County, Liverpool, Aston Villa, Galatasary and Nottingham Forest in the 90s?

17   Which England international spent four years in the early 90s playing for three Italian teams?

18   Which Bulgarian won four Spanish Championships, a European Cup and helped his country to a World Cup semi-final in the 90s?

19   In the 90s, who became the first player to win back-to-back championships with different clubs?

20   Which Scouser played in two 90s World Cup finals while in his 30s?

Champions League (see Quiz 65)

Answers

1 1992. **2** It was no longer exclusively a knockout competition.
3 Barcelona. **4** Wembley. **5** Marcel Desailly. **6** AC Milan.
7 Juventus. **8** One. **9** Kanu. **10** Monaco. **11** Runners-up were allowed in as well as champions. **12** Real Madrid. **13** Juventus.
14 LKS Lodz. **15** Poland. **16** Barcelona and Bayern Munich.
17 2-0 to United. **18** Andy Cole. **19** Bayern Munich. **20** More teams and a second group stage were added.

Answers – see page 174

1   Who scored a hat-trick on his home debut for Man City in 2000?

2   Which team scored three late goals to draw with Slovenia in Euro 2000

3   Who equalled Frank Stapleton's Republic of Ireland scoring record with a goal against South Africa in 2000?

4   Who signed Celtics' top scorer in the 2000 close season?

5   David Johnson was which team's leading goalscorer in 1999-2000?

6   Who did Holland knock six goals past in Euro 2000?

7   Who beat Tottenham 6-1 in an FA Cup replay in 1999?

8   For which club did Man United's Andy Cole score 41 goals in 93-94?

9   Iwan Roberts was which club's leading goalscorer in 1999-2000?

10 Which England veteran won the BBC Goal of the Season with a crackin volley for Fulham in 1974?

11 Andy Payton was the Division Two leading scorer in 1999-2000 with 2 goals for which club?

12 How many goals did Chris Sutton score in his season at Chelsea?

13 In 1999-2000 which Belgian striker joined Coventry City on loan and immediately scored goals?

14 Who scored 50 goals for Tottenham Hotspur in 1986-87?

15 Who beat Yugoslavia 4-3 in Euro 2000 to knock Norway out of the tournament?

16 Who scored England's goal against France in 2000 in Paris?

17 Who scored Germany's only goal in Euro 2000?

18 Who scored eight goals in his first eight games for Coventry City in 1994?

19 Which centre-half won the 2000 Worthington Cup for Leicester City wit two headed goals?

20 Which Liverpool player has scored the most goals in FA Cup Finals?

Quiz 69 **Euro 2000**

Answers – see page 179

1   Which city hosted the opening game of the finals?
2   Which team in the quarter-finals qualified for Euro 2000 through the play-offs?
3   Who were the only team to win all of their qualifying matches?
4   Sergio Conceicao scored a hat-trick against Germany. For which team?
5   Nils Johan Semb's team went out after the first stage. Who are they?
6   Who scored England's second goal against Portugal?
7   Who was awarded a penalty in the eighty-ninth minute and so won their first match?
8   In which town did England play Germany?
9   What was the result when Holland met France in Group D?
10 Who scored two goals in Holland's 6-1 demolition of Turkey?
11 Who was sent off in the quarter-final between Romania and Italy?
12 From whose cross did Alan Shearer head England's winning goal against Germany?
13 Who won their semi-final after being awarded a penalty in extra-time?
14 Who missed a last-minute penalty for Spain to give France a 2-1 quarter-final victory?
15 Members of which team received long international suspensions for their ugly protests at a refereeing decision?
16 Which Italian forward missed two gilt-edged chances in the final?
17 Who scored France's winning goal in the final?
18 Frank de Boer missed one of Holland's penalties in normal time of the semi-final – who missed the other?
19 Which player conceded a late penalty to Romania to end England's participation in the tournament?
20 Which two teams scored 13 goals in the finals?

Quiz 70 **Euro Champs Pre-1992**
LEVEL 2

Answers – see page 180

1   What was the original name of this tournament?

2   What is the actual name of the trophy?

3   In which year was the trophy first won?

4   Who won that first tournament?

5   How often is the tournament held?

6   When did England first join the competition?

7   How was the 1968 semi-final between Italy and USSR decided?

8   Who won the 1972 tournament?

9   Where was the 1984 competition held?

10 Who did France beat in the final that year?

11 What is the furthest England have gone in the competition?

12 How many points did England get in the group stage of the 1988 tournament?

13 Where was the tournament held that year?

14 Who won that tournament?

15 Who did they beat in the semi-final?

16 Who did they play in the final?

17 In which city was the final held?

18 Where was the 1976 tournament held?

19 Who won that tournament?

20 Which is the only final ever to have gone to a replay?

Quiz 71 Holland and Belgium

LEVEL 2

Answers – see page 177

1   Who won the Belgian league in 1999-2000?

2   In which city are they based?

3   At which Belgian club's ground did England play two matches in Euro 2000?

4   In which city do Feyenoord play?

5   With which electrical company are PSV Eindhoven associated?

6   Which Englishman managed PSV between 1990 and 1992?

7   Which Dutch team won the European Cup in 1995?

8   Which Belgian team appeared in both the 1983 and 1984 UEFA Cup finals?

9   Which two Dutchmen played for Ipswich against AZ 67 in the 1981 UEFA Cup final?

10 Which Belgian team did Liverpool defeat to win the 1975 UEFA Cup?

11 The 1988 European Cup Winners Cup final was contested by a team from Holland and a team from Belgium. Who were they?

12 Who won the European Cup three years running at the beginning of the 1970s?

13 Who scored both goals for Ajax in the 1972 final against Inter?

14 Who won the Dutch league in 1999-2000?

15 How many goals did Belgium score in Euro 2000?

16 In which round were Holland eliminated from Euro 2000?

17 From which club did Aston Villa sign Belgian Luc Nilis in summer 2000?

18 Dutch star Winston Bogarde joined Chelsea from which club in August 2000?

19 Who holds the appearances record for Holland?

20 In which city do Ajax play?

Answers – see page 178

1   Which African country are called 'The Elephants' and have never played in a World Cup?

2   Who became the first African side to qualify for the World Cup in 1970?

3   Which African country won the Olympic gold in 1996?

4   Which African team are known as 'the Black Stars'?

5   Which country won the 2000 African Cup of Nations?

6   Which African country beat West Germany in the 1982 World Cup?

7   Which country's team are called 'the Indomitable Lions'?

8   Who won their 1986 World Cup group ahead of England, Poland and Portugal?

9   Where did Nigeria finish in both their 1994 and 1998 World Cup final groups?

10   Which country knocked Cameroon out of the 1990 World Cup?

11   Which country knocked Nigeria out of the 1994 World Cup with a last-gasp goal?

12   Which country's team are nicknamed 'Bafana Bafana' (The Boys)?

13   In which colour shirts do Nigeria play?

14   Which country had most their team killed in a plane crash in 1993?

15   How many games did Cameroon lose in the 1982 World Cup?

16   Which African country did Scotland beat 2-0 in the 1974 World Cup?

17   Which African country did England beat 1-0 in the 1990 World Cup?

18   Who hosted and won the 1996 African Cup of Nations?

19   Including the 2000 competition, which two teams have both won the African Cup of Nations four times?

20   Which African country did England beat 2-0 in the 1998 World Cup?

Answers

Euro Champs Pre-1992 (see Quiz 70)
1 European Nations Cup. 2 The Henri Delaunay Cup. 3 1960.
4 USSR. 5 Every four years. 6 1964. 7 Toss of a coin. 8 West Germany. 9 France. 10 Spain. 11 Semi-finals. 12 0. 13 West Germany. 14 Holland. 15 West Germany. 16 USSR 17 Munich. 18 Yugoslavia. 19 Czechoslovakia. 20 1968, Italy v Yugoslavia.

Quiz 73 Rest of the World

Answers – see page 183

LEVEL 2

1   Who won the Turkish league in 1999-2000?

2   In which city do Boca Juniors play?

3   If you watched the Rio derby, which two teams would you see?

4   What is the nickname of the Australian national team?

5   Which Brazilian club did Manchester United defeat to win the Toyota Inter-Continental Cup in 1999?

6   Who were the champions of Brazil in 1999?

7   What is the nationality of the footballing Flo brothers?

8   Which is the longest-running international football competition?

9   In which city do River Plate play?

10   For whom did Pele play his club football?

11   Who won the Greek league in 1999-2000?

12   What is the North American football league called?

13   In which year did New Zealand make its only appearance in the World Cup finals?

14   What is the Copa Libertadores?

15   In which year was the World Cup last held outside Europe?

16   In which city do Vasco Da Gama play?

17   Liverpool's Brad Friedel is what nationality?

18   Brazilian Mario Jardel left Portuguese club Porto for which other club in summer 2000?

19   Who won the Libertadores Cup in 2000?

20   In which country do Rayos Del Nacaxa play their football?

London (see Quiz 75)

Answers

1 Millwall. 2 QPR. 3 (Woolwich) Arsenal. 4 Wimbledon. 5 Inter Milan. 6 Yes (1962-63). 7 Irish. 8 Brentford. 9 Gerry Francis. 10 Brentford. 11 West Ham United. 12 British. 13 Republic of Ireland. 14 QPR. 15 Sergei Rebrov (with Dynamo Kiev in Ukraine). 16 Thierry Henry. 17 France. 18 Wycombe Wanderers. 19 Crystal Palace. 20 Fulham.

Quiz 74 The Midlands

LEVEL 2

1 Which club demolished their Trinity Road stand in the summer of 2000?

2 Which team's late-70s brown away kit is widely accepted as the ugliest in history?

3 Which Zimbabwean forward left Coventry City for Birmingham City?

4 Which manager was dismissed as England Under-21 boss in 1999 and is now at home in the Midlands?

5 Which 'troublesome' Leicester City forward was fined for fire extinguisher japes in Spain shortly after being signed in 2000?

6 Colin Lee is in the hot seat at which Midlands club?

7 Which club saw Karren Brady become the first female managing director?

8 Former Liverpool midfielder Mike Marsh has been an important part of which team's recent success?

9 Which English team play at Gay Meadow and have won the Welsh Cup six times?

10 Which club did Barry Fry successfully take to the play-offs in 2000?

11 Who was John Sillet's FA Cup winning managing-director partner?

12 Which Wolves forward joined Leicester City in 2000?

13 Which Midlands club gets called the Throstles or the Baggies?

14 Which team missed doing 'the double' in 1959-60 by one point?

15 Spink, Cowans and Morley helped win which club's greatest prize?

16 In which colour shirts do Notts County play?

17 Who is Leicester City's Scottish international centre-half?

18 Which Midlands club sold both their top two 1999-2000 scorers at the end of the season?

19 In how many of England's 1990 World Cup games did Wolves' Steve Bull play?

20 In what year did Trevor Francis take over as Birmingham City manager?

Answers

Manchester City (see Quiz 76)
1 Ardwick FC. 2 'The Citizens'. 3 Moss Side. 4 Alan Oakes.
5 Blackburn Rovers. 6 Colin Bell. 7 Lee Bradbury. 8 Joe Mercer.
9 Malcolm Allison. 10 Manchester United. 11 Tony Book.
12 Neil Young. 13 Th European Cup Winners Cup. 14 West
Bromwich Albion. 15 Francis Lee. 16 Denis Law. 17 Wolves.
18 Rodney Marsh. 19 Dennis Tueart. 20 Steve Daley.

Quiz 75 London

Answers – see page 181

LEVEL 2

1   Which London club has had its ground closed by the Football Association more than any other in the League?

2   Which London club had an artificial pitch in the 1980s?

3   Which London club dropped their first name when they moved grounds in 1913?

4   Cunningham, Ardley and Leaburn play in which London team's line-up?

5   Arsenal signed Kanu and Bergkamp from which Italian team?

6   Have Leyton Orient ever played in the top flight?

7   What nationality is Charlton skipper Mark Kinsella?

8   Which London club play in red and white stripes?

9   Which former England captain is manager of QPR?

10   Apart from QPR, for which other London club did Stan Bowles appear?

11   Which London club played a cup-tied player in the Worthington Cup quarter-final causing the game to be replayed?

12   Which is the largest nationality group in the 2000-01 Chelsea squad?

13   Charlton keeper Dean Kiely has represented which country?

14   Morrow, Wardley and Kiwomya play for which London team?

15   Which member of the Spurs team has won the championship every year from 1993-2000?

16   Which Arsenal player scored on his last seven Premiership appearances in the 1999-2000 season?

17   West Ham's Frederic Kanoute hails from which country?

18   The deliciously named Jermaine McSporran plays for the Chairboys. Who are they?

19   Malcolm Allison, Terry Venables and Steve Coppell have all managed which London side?

20   Which club did Kevin Keegan manage before taking charge of England?

Answers

Rest of the World (see Quiz 73)
1 Galatasaray. 2 Buenos Aires, Argentina. 3 Flamengo and Fluminense. 4 The Socceroos. 5 SE Palmeiras. 6 Corinthians. 7 Norwegian. 8 The Copa America. 9 Buenos Aires. 10 Santos. 11 Olympiakos. 12 Major League Soccer. 13 1982. 14 The South American Club Cup. 15 1994, in the USA. 16 Rio. 17 American. 18 Galatasaray. 19 Boca Juniors. 20 Mexico.

Quiz 76 Manchester City

Answers - see page 182

1 What was Manchester City's original name?

2 Apart from 'The Blues' what is Manchester City's other nickname??

3 In which part of Manchester is Maine Road situated?

4 Who holds the appearances record for the club?

5 Who did Manchester City beat in April 2000 to clinch promotion to the Premiership?

6 Who is Manchester City's most capped player?

7 Who did Manchester City sign from Portsmouth for £3m in July 1997?

8 Who took over as manager of the club in 1965?

9 Who joined him as his assistant soon after?

10 Who did City pip for the First Division Championship in 1967-68?

11 Who led City up the steps at Wembley to receive the FA Cup in 1969?

12 Who scored the only goal of that game?

13 In 1970 they won a double; the League Cup and which other trophy?

14 Who did City beat to win the League Cup that year?

15 Which City player was the First Division's top scorer in season 1971-72?

16 Which former United favourite scored for City to relegate his former club in 1974?

17 City lost the League Cup final that year. Who did they lose to?

18 Which City player refused to collect his loser's tankard after that match?

19 City won the League Cup again in 1976. Who scored a spectacular winner that day?

20 City shattered the British transfer record in 1979 when they signed which player from Wolves?

Quiz 77 The North West

Answers – see page 187

LEVEL 2

1 Which is the most north westerly team in the football league?

2 What is the name of their ground?

3 In what county do they play?

4 In which division do Carlisle currently play?

5 Who are their nearest league neighbours to the south?

6 Who is Blackpool's most famous player?

7 Who did Blackpool beat in the 'Matthews Final'?

8 When did Matthews leave Blackpool?

9 How old was he?

10 What did he do next?

11 How old was he when he retired?

12 In which division do Blackpool currently play?

13 What is the name of their ground?

14 What is the name of Blackburn's ground?

15 Who left Manchester United to take over as manager at Blackburn in December 1998?

6 How many managers did they have during the 1999-2000 season?

7 Which two Cumbrian towns had teams in the football league, but no longer do so?

8 In which year did Barrow lose their place in the football league?

9 To whom did Workington lose their place in 1977?

0 What is the name of Burnley's ground?

Quiz 78 Who Did What? 2

LEVEL 2

Answers – see page 188

1   Who changed sponsors from JVC to Dreamcast?

2   Who scored for Chelsea in the 1997 and 2000 FA Cup finals?

3   Who promised that Rangers would sign Catholics in 1985?

4   Whose reign as Wales manager ended when they failed to qualify for the 1994 World Cup?

5   Who wrote an autobiography called *The Good, the Bad and the Bubbly*?

6   Dave Bassett managed which club for three days in 1984?

7   Who was fined £45,000 for spitting at Neil Ruddock?

8   Which European trophy did Newcastle win in 1969?

9   Who counted himself out of England's Euro 2000 squad in an attempt to get fit to play for Tottenham?

10 Which Wolves striker played for England while in the Third Division?

11 Who was the first black player to captain England?

12 Who scored a UEFA Cup semi-final hat-trick for Arsenal against Werder Bremen in 2000?

13 Who came from Malaysia to score 13 goals for Leicester in 1999-2000?

14 Which former England striker joined Burnley from Celtic in 1999 and retired a year later?

15 Which team-mate scrapped with David Batty during a Blackburn Rovers European tie in 1995?

16 Who was the first man to captain and coach a World Cup-winning team?

17 Who won the Charity Shield for four consecutive years in the 80s?

18 Which Everton forward scored for England in the under 21's Euro 2000?

19 Which silver-haired Italian joined Middlesbrough in 1996?

20 Who supplied four players when England played France at Wembley in 1999?

Answers

The 60s (see Quiz 80)
1 Match fixing. 2 Manchester City. 3 Pat Jennings. 4 Swindon Town. 5 Geoff Hurst. 6 Celtic. 7 Alf Ramsey. 8 Spurs. 9 John White. 10 Ian St John. 11 Ron Springett. 12 Celtic. 13 Dave Mackay. 14 Two. 15 Everton. 16 Real Madrid. 17 January 1960 18 9-3 to England. 19 West Bromwich Albion. 20 Geoff Astle.

Quiz 79 Sent Off!

Answers – see page 185

1   Which England player was sent off against Argentina in the 98 World Cup?
2   Which disgraced Rangers, WBA and Scotland winger was sent off 21 times in his first-class career?
3   Who was the Argentinian sent off against England in 1966?
4   Who was sent off for the first time in his 671st League game in 1993?
5   Who was sent off in a 1998 World Cup semi-final?
6   Who was sent off in Leeds United's 1999 UEFA Cup defeat at Roma?
7   Alan Mullery became the first England player to be sent off, When?
8   Which West Ham player was sent off in the '93 FA Cup semi -final?
9   Who were Manchester United playing when a dismissed Eric Cantona attacked an abusive supporter?
10 Which great Romanian international was sent off in the 2000 UEFA Cup final against Arsenal?
11 Who was sent off playing for Wales against Georgia in 1995 and 10 other times in domestic competition?
12 What happened after Francis Lee and Norman Hunter's dismissal in 1974?
13 Which Blackburn Rovers goalkeeper was sent off after only 72 seconds against Leeds United in 1995?
14 Who was sent off for England in the Euro 2000 qualifier against Sweden?
15 For and against whom were Mark Walters, Terry Hurlock and Mark Hateley sent off in one match in 1991?
16 Who was sent off twice within three days of the 2000-01 season?
17 Who was sent off in the 2000 Charity Shield?
18 Who had a player sent off in each of their Euro 2000 Group C matches?
19 Who was sent off along with David Beckham when Manchester United met Necaxa in the 2000 World Club Championship in Brazil?
    Who was sent off in the 1985 FA Cup Final?

1   What kind of scandal rocked English football in 1963?

2   Who won the league championship in 1968?

3   Which keeper scored for Spurs against Manchester United in the 1967 Charity Shield?

4   Which Third Division team beat Arsenal in the 1969 League Cup final?

5   Who scored six when West Ham beat Sunderland 8-0 in 1968?

6   Which Scottish club won the European Cup in 1967?

7   Who was the manager of Ipswich Town when they won the First Divsion title in 1962?

8   Who became the first English team to win a European trophy when they beat Atletico Madrid in 1963?

9   Which Spurs player was killed when struck by lightning in 1964?

10 Who scored Liverpool's winner in the 1965 FA Cup final and then went on to be a successful TV pundit?

11 Which England keeper kept goal for Sheffield Wednesday in the 1966 FA Cup final?

12 Who won the Scottish treble in 1969?

13 Which Derby player was joint Footballer of the Year with Tony Book in 1969?

14 How many World Cups were there in the 1960s?

15 Mike Trebilcock scored two goals for which '60s FA Cup winning side?

16 Who did Manchester United beat to reach the 1968 European Cup final?

17 When was the footballers' maximum wage law abolished?

18 What was the score in the annual England v Scotland fixture at Wembl in April 1961 ?

19 Which Midlands club won the FA Cup in 1968?

20 Who scored the winning goal?

At which club did Teddy start his league career?

Which manager signed him in 1992?

Which current Premier League manager was his first boss?

With which Republic of Ireland striker did he form a deadly partnership?

What was controversial about his transfer to Tottenham in 1993?

Which manager signed Teddy for Spurs?

Against which country did Teddy score two goals in Euro 96?

In what year did Teddy win his first professional trophy?

Which overseas striker did Sheringham form a partnership with at Tottenham?

Where was Teddy involved in a incident involving a dentist chair and Flaming Lamborghinis?

Who was Sheringham bought to replace at Manchester United?

Did Sheringham score from a penalty in the Euro 96 semi-final shoot out against Germany?

Against which team did Sheringham score in a FA Cup final?

Which number shirt does Teddy hold at Old Trafford?

At which of his clubs is Teddy the all-time top goalscorer?

Who did Teddy replace in the opening minutes of the 1999 FA Cup final?

In which year did Teddy win the Premiership Golden Boot?

Did Sheringham score the first or second of Manchester United's 1999 European Cup Final goals?

Who did Sheringham replace when brought on as substitute in the 1999 European Cup Final?

Which team does Teddy claim to hate with every bone in his body?

Premiership Stars (see Quiz 83)
1 Wes Brown. 2 Stan Collymore. 3 Ipswich Town. 4 Olivier Dacourt. 5 Mark Kennedy. 6 Liverpool. 7 Luton Town.
8 Republic of Ireland. 9 Sunderland. 10 Chelsea.
11 Middlesbrough. 12 Fumaca. 13 Derby County. 14 Coventry City. 15 Chelsea. 16 Southampton. 17 Malcolm Shotton.
18 Aston Villa. 19 Bradford City. 20 West Ham United.

Quiz 82 England

Answers – see page 192

LEVEL 2

1   Who did England play in their first match after Euro 2000?

2   What was the score in that match?

3   What was the score of the previous meeting between the two sides?

4   Which other teams are in England's World Cup 2002 qualifying group?

5   Where is the World Cup 2002 going to be held?

6   Apart from England, how many other teams have won the World Cup?

7   When did England first lose to European opponents?

8   When did England first lose at Wembley to European opponents?

9   How many people are thought to have watched England's friendly against Argentina before Euro 2000?

10   In which year was the last Home International Championship held?

11   Who did England play in their last fixture of the Championship?

12   Why was the Championship discontinued?

13   Against whom did England lose their first match after winning the World Cup in 1966?

14   Where did England first play their home games?

15   Where was England's abandoned match against the Republic of Irela played in Feburary 1995?

16   When did England last beat France in an international match?

17   Who was England's official goalkeeping coach in Euro 2000?

18   Which keeper gave away two penalties when playing for England against Malta in a warm-up game for Euro 2000?

19   Where did England play their opening fixture of Euro 2000?

20   Who were England's first opponents in the qualifying group for World Cup 2002?

Answers

Pot Luck 5 (see Quiz 84)
1 USA. 2 None. 3 Germany. 4 Two. 5 Rangers and Spurs.
6 Uzbekistan. 7 1972. 8 Tottenham Hotspur. 9 Barcelona.
10 Arsenal. 11 Opta. 12 None. 13 MLS (Major League Soccer).
14 Southend Utd. 15 Leicester City. 16 Chester City. 17 False
(Dakar). 18 Chelsea. 19 Kingstonian. 20 Kenny Miller.

190

Quiz 83 Premiership Stars

LEVEL 2

1 Which young Manchester United defender missed the whole of the 1999-2000 season through injury?

2 Which controversial Leicester striker broke a leg at Pride Park shortly after signing for the club?

3 For which Premiership team does Titus Bramble play?

4 Who did Leeds sign from Lens for £7.2m during summer 2000?

5 After unhappy spells at Liverpool and Wimbledon, who started the 2000-01 Premiership season with Manchester City?

For which Premiership team does Stephane Henchoz play?

From whom did Arsenal sign Matthew Upson?

Charlton's Dean Kiely plays for which international side?

Steve Bould left Arsenal for which other Premier League team in summer 1999?

10 For which Premiership team does Jody Morris play?

11 Of which club is Steve Gibson the chairman?

12 According to Newcastle fans, who is 'the only Brazilian on earth who can't play football'?

13 For whom will 'Kinky' Kinkladze be terrorising defences in 2000-01?

14 Peruvian international Ysrael Zuniga plays for which Midlands club?

15 From whom did Glenn Hoddle sign Paul Hughes on a free transfer in 1999?

Defender Joe Tessem plies his trade for which south coast club?

Who was appointed assistant manager at Bradford in summer 2000?

Where does England left back Gareth Barry play his club football?

Which Premiership club plays at Valley Parade?

For which Premier League team does Michael Carrick play?

Quiz 84 Pot Luck 5

Answers – see page 190

LEVEL 2

1. In which county was the NASL?
2. How many times have Scotland reached the second round of an international tournament?
3. In which country did Cha Bum-Kun play most of his club football?
4. How many league rounds were there in the Champions League in 1999-2000?
5. John Hartson failed fitness tests preventing his transfer to which two clubs?
6. Which team won the Asian Cup in 1994?
7. In what year was the first UEFA Cup?
8. Who won it?
9. Who were the first Spanish League champions?
10. Which club has not been out of the top division since 1919?
11. Who are the official statisticans of the Premier League?
12. Which league club plays home games at the Stade de France in Paris?
13. What replaced the NASL?
14. Which team plays at Roots Hall?
15. Which club found itself in trouble over tickets for the Worthington Cup final in 1999?
16. Which club had Adewale Ajetunmobi on their books in 2000?
17. Patrik Vieira was born in France – true or false?
18. Which club's first manager was John Tait Robertson?
19. Which Nationwide Conference team are nicknamed the K's?
20. Who was Scottish Young Player of the Year in 2000?

Quiz 85 Supporters

Answers – see page 195

1   Whose fans 'only sing when they're fishing'?

2   Whose fans sing an aria from *Rigoletto*?

3   Where do they sing 'The Blaydon Races'?

4   What is Chelsea's theme song?

5   For which team do the 'Pompey Chimes' ring out?

6   Which fans allegedly get to eat the nicest pies?

7   Whose fans used to stand in 'the jungle'?

8   Which team had more fans arrested than any other during 1999-2000?

9   Where are you most likely to hear the song 'Bubbles'?

10   Whose fans sit at the Gladwys Street end?

11   Whose fans greeted their team's FA Cup victory in 1965 with a chorus of 'Ee-ay-addio, we won the Cup'?

12   Whose fans used to stand in the original Spion Kop?

13   Who sang the unforgettable 'Ozzie's going to Wembley'?

14   Whose fans carried out a 'pants' protest in the mid-1990s?

15   Whose fans are featured on the Pink Floyd LP *Meddle*?

16   Whose fans are likely to be reading *A Kick Up the Rs*?

17   Whose fans will no longer be singing 'He's French, he's quick, his name's a porno flick'?

18   Whose fans have nicknamed their new player 'Ralph' Lauren?

19   Whose fans were voted worst dressed by a men's magazine in 1999-2000?

20   Whose fans are likely to be reading *Heroes and Villains*?

Answers

Substitutes (see Quiz 87)
1 1965. **2** One substitute could replace an injured player.
3 Charlton's Keith Peacock. **4** David Fairclough. **5** Dennis Clarke of West Brom in 1968. **6** Bobby Charlton. **7** Ricky Villa. **8** They couldn't afford a 13th man. **9** Ian Wright. **10** Gary Lineker.
11 Teddy Sheringham. **12** Rudi Völler. **13** Gianluca Vialli.
14 Brian McClair. **15** Teddy Sheringham and Ole Gunnar Solskjaer.
16 Gianfranco Zola. **17** Majeta Kezman of Yugoslavia went on as a sub after 87 minutes against Norway and was sent off 44 seconds later.
18 Ole Gunnar Solskjaer. **19** Up to seven. **20** Five named, three used.

Quiz 86 Family Connections LEVEL 2

Answers – see page 196

1 Which team does the son of England goalkeeper Ray Clemence play for?

2 Graham and Ray Wilkins played together at which club?

3 True or False: Phillip and Gary's father is named Neville Neville?

4 What relation is Ian Harte to his Leeds teammate Gary Kelly?

5 Which brothers played together for Manchester United in the 1977 FA Cup final?

6 Which brothers played together at Leeds but never for Scotland?

7 Which Nottingham Forest manager gave his son his debut?

8 True or False: Robbie and Roy Keane are cousins?

9 Which father and son both played for Nottingham Forest and Scotland?

10 Ian Wright's son Shaun Wright-Williams made his Premiership debut in 2000 for which team?

11 The footballing Milburns are related to which famous brothers?

12 Three brothers played for Southampton, two of them for Leeds and one of them for Rangers. Which family?

13 Cyril Knowles' brother Peter left Wolves to become what in 1969?

14 Les, Paul, Clive, Martin and Bradley are from which footballing family?

15 Which Manchester United player chose to have his first name rather than his famous father's surname on his back?

16 Which brothers Rene and Willy played in the 1978 World Cup final?

17 Which brothers signed together for Barcelona in 1999?

18 True or False: Scottish manager Craig Brown and football commentator Jock Brown are brothers?

19 Who is former Norwich and Everton boss Mike Walker's footballing son?

20 Which Fashanus played for Norwich and Wimbledon respectively?

Answers

Northern Ireland (see Quiz 88)
1 Windsor Park, Belfast. **2** Sammy McIlroy. **3** 1986. **4** Knocked out in the group stage. **5** 1984, the last year it was played.
6 1-0, May 1999. **7** Malta. **8** 1-0 to Northern Ireland.
9 Bulgaria, Czech Republic, Iceland and Denmark. **10** Steve Lomas.
11 Quarter-finals in 1958. **12** Bertie Peacock. **13** Billy Bingham.
14 Terry Neill. **15** Danny Blanchflower. **16** Norman Whiteside.
17 1-0 to Northern Ireland. **18** Gerry Armstrong. **19** France.
20 1-0 to Northern Ireland.

Quiz 87 Substitutes

Answers – see page 193

LEVEL 2

1   When were substitutes first introduced to English league football?

2   What was the first rule?

3   Who was the first substitute in English football?

4   Which Liverpool player was known as 'supersub' during the 1970s?

5   Who was the first substitute to be used in an FA Cup final?

6   Who did Ramsey take off with England 2-1 up against Germany in 1970?

7   Who broke down in tears after being substituted in the 1981 FA Cup final and then scored twice in the replay to win it for Spurs?

8   Why was the Football League's 1982 plan to allow two subs rejected?

9   Who went on as a substitute and scored twice for Crystal Palace in the 1990 FA Cup final?

10   Who was substituted in his last match for England in 1992 and denied the opportunity of equalling Bobby Charlton's England scoring record?

11   Who went on as a substitute for Roy Keane and scored Manchester United's first goal in the 1999 FA Cup final?

12   Who went on as a sub for West Germany and equalised against Argentina in the 1986 World Cup final?

13   Who played two minutes of the 1997 FA Cup final for Chelsea and went on to win the trophy as manager three seasons later?

14   Which Manchester United substitute scored their fourth goal in the 1994 FA Cup final?

15   Which two subs scored for Man Utd to win the 1999 European Cup?

16   Who came off the sub's bench to win the 1998 Cup Winners' Cup?

17   Which player had the shortest time on the field during Euro 2000?

18   Who went on for Man Utd after 72 minutes and scored four in 1999?

19   How many subs can be named for a Champions League game?

20   How many subs can be named and used in the Premiership in 2000-01?

Quiz 88 Northern Ireland

LEVEL 2

1 Where do Northern Ireland traditionally play their home games?

2 Who took over from Lawrie McMenemy as manager of Northern Ireland in 2000?

3 When was the last time Northern Ireland played in the World Cup finals?

4 How far did they get in that tournament?

5 When was the last time Northern Ireland won the Home International Championship?

6 When was the last time Northern Ireland beat the Republic?

7 Who did Northern Ireland play in their opening match of the 2002 World Cup qualifiers?

8 What was the score in that match?

9 Who are the other teams in the group?

10 Who captains the team for the World Cup 2002 campaign?

11 What is the furthest Northern Ireland have ever gone in the World Cup?

12 Which manager gave George Best his first taste of international football?

13 Who took over from that manager?

14 Who scored Northern Ireland's winning goal against England at Wembley in 1972?

15 One of Northern Ireland's greatest results was 2-2 against the 'total football' Dutch in 1976. Who was in charge for that match?

16 Which Northern Ireland player became the youngest ever to play in a World Cup match in Spain in 1982?

17 What was the result of the final group game against Spain that year?

18 Who scored for Northern Ireland?

19 Who did Northern Ireland lose to in the second round?

20 What was the score when World Cup runners-up West Germany visited Belfast in November 1982?

1   Who is the most capped player for the Republic?

2   Who is the Republic's record goalscorer?

3   What is the Republic's record victory?

4   In 1994 the Republic won their first ever game in the World Cup finals. Who did they beat?

5   Who scored the winner that day?

6   Who scored two goals against Malta in 1989 to send the Republic to the World Cup finals for the first time?

7   In which year did Jack Charlton become the Republic's manager?

8   Who did the Republic beat in the opening game of the 1988 European Championships?

9   Who was the first black player to play for the Republic?

10 Who became the Republic's first player-manager, in 1973?

11 Who was the first Republic of Ireland player sent off in an international?

12 Which player has captained the Republic more than any other?

13 Which other teams are in the Republic's World Cup 2002 group?

14 Which player captained the Republic in the 2002 qualifying campaign?

15 Which Irish sensation was transferred to Inter in summer 2000?

16 Who took over in 1996 as the Republic's team manager?

17 Who did the Republic play in their opening game of the 2002 World Cup campaign?

18 What was the score in that match?

19 The Republic played a European Championships play-off against which team at Anfield in 1995?

20 What was strange about the Republic not qualifying for the 1992 European Championships?

Quiz 90 **Michael Owen**

LEVEL 2

Answers – see page 200

1   In which year was Michael Owen born?

2   Where was he born?

3   Against whom did he make his Liverpool debut?

4   In what year was that?

5   What happened in that match?

6   How many goals did he score in total in his first season?

7   Which award did he win at the end of that season?

8   Against whom did he make his debut for England?

9   Against whom did he score his first goal for England?

10 Later that season Michael scored a wonder goal. What was the occasion?

11 Which award did he win later that year?

12 In September 1998 Michael gave Dave Beasant a big surprise. What was it?

13 How many goals did he score in total that season?

14 In 1999-2000 Michael suffered a serious injury. What went wrong?

15 How many appearances did he make that season for Liverpool?

16 How many goals did he score?

17 How many games did he play at Euro 2000?

18 How many goals did he score?

19 What does Michael list as his hobbies?

20 Against whom did Michael score in England's first match after Euro 2000?

Quiz 91 England 2

Answers – see page 197

1   Who was the first English player to be sent off in a Wembley international?

2   Which England manager gave Carlton Palmer his first cap?

3   Who replaced Gary Lineker in England's 1992 defeat by Sweden?

4   Who was made captain for the 1990 third-place play-off after 124 games for his country?

5   What was the result of the match against Poland at Wembley that England needed win to qualify for the 1974 World Cup?

6   Which World Cup record did Bryan Robson set in 1982 against France?

7   Who in 1955 became the youngest England player of the 20th century?

8   Which Liverpool player won his first cap against Ukraine in 2000?

9   Against which team did a late David Platt goal save England from a penalty shoot-out in the 1990 World Cup?

10 What did England win in the 1990 World Cup?

11 After a 1-1 draw in Saudi Arabia what manager was the target of the newspaper headline "In the Name of Allah Go?"

12 What was the England v Portugal half-time score in Euro 2000?

13 Which was the only country England managed to beat away from home in their Euro 2000 qualifying group?

14 Which team beat England in their Euro 2000 qualifying group?

15 Who scored most goals for England: Gascoigne, Beardsley or Sheringham?

16 Which England player failed to complete a full game in Euro 2000?

17 Which Leicester City player won his only cap in 1999?

18 Who made his England debut in 1995 and won his eighth cap in 2000?

19 Which Southampton and Manchester City striker scored 21 goals for England in the 70s?

20 Did Glenn Hoddle win more than 50 England caps?

Answers

Republic of Ireland (see Quiz 89)
1 Paul McGrath. 2 Frank Stapleton. 3 8-0 v Malta in 1983. 4 Italy.
5 Ray Houghton. 6 John Aldridge. 7 1986. 8 England. 9 Chris Hughton. 10 Johnny Giles. 11 John Dempsey. 12 Andy Townsend.
13 Holland, Portugal, Cyprus, Andorra, Estonia. 14 Roy Keane.
15 Robbie Keane. 16 Mick McCarthy. 17 Holland. 18 2-2.
19 Holland. 20 They did not lose any of their qualifying games.

Quiz 92 Who Did What? 3

LEVEL 2

Answers – see page 198

1   Who scored the winner for Scotland against Latvia in a World Cup qualifier in September 2000?

2   Which Dutch defender moved from Barcelona to Chelsea in August 2000?

3   Who managed Scotland during the 1998 World Cup?

4   Which French defender scored twice in the 1998 World Cup semi-final?

5   Who managed Barcelona to the 1986 European Cup final?

6   Who was arrested in Colombia for stealing an emerald bracelet in 1970?

7   Who headed the ball out of Gordon Banks' hands and scored for Ireland in 1971, although the goal was disallowed?

8   Who was sacked as manager of Manchester United in 1977?

9   Which keeper saved two penalties for Spurs in a game at Anfield in 1973?

10   Who attempted a takeover of Manchester United in 1990?

11   Who made a 'V' sign at his team's fans when they booed Arsenal's Charlie Nicholas in a league game in 1987?

12   Which Scotland manager died at pitchside shortly after seeing his team play Wales in 1985?

13   Who resigned as manager of Liverpool in February 1991?

14   Where does Jason McAteer play his club football?

15   Which keeper was sent off for the first time in his career in his 971st league game?

16   Who was the first Rangers manager to sign a catholic player?

17   Who became the first paid director in football in 1981?

18   Who was sacked as manager of Spurs in 1993?

19   Who resigned as Spurs manager after allegations of kerb-crawling came to light?

20   Who scored for the Republic of Ireland against Holland in Amsterdam September 2000?

Answers

Michael Owen (see Quiz 90)
1 1979. 2 Chester. 3 Wimbledon. 4 1997. 5 He scored in a 1-1 draw. 6 21. 7 Young Player of the Year. 8 Chile. 9 Morocco 10 World Cup eighth final v Argentina. 11 BBC Sports Personality of the Year. 12 He scored four in a game against Forest. 13 23. 14 Hamstring. 15 30. 16 12. 17 Three. 18 One. 19 Golf and snooker. 20 France.

Quiz 93 Short Players

Answers – see page 203

1 Which Brazilian star's name means 'Little Man' in Portuguese?

2 Which Tottenham winger is often smaller than the young mascot?

3 Which terrier-like Leeds' skipper took on many men taller than his five feet, four inches?

4 Who is Aston Villa's diminutive full back?

5 Which Stoke City and Everton player was nicknamed 'Inchy'?

6 Which tempestuous Italian brought his five feet and six inches to Aston Villa and Bradford City?

7 Which Aston Villa forward is a full six inches shorter than Dion Dublin?

8 Who's the tallest Blue out of Deschamps, Wise, Zola and Morris?

9 Tiny England forward Wilf Mannion was a hero at which League club?

10 Which Leeds and Wales' pocket battleship is now managing Wrexham?

11 Who is Derby County's smallest and possibly most skilful player?

12 Which small but perfectly formed playmaker managed to outjump Peter Shilton (six foot one) to a high ball in the 1986 World Cup?

13 Which small striker has seen Manchester City through the divisions?

14 Which Premier League pocket-sized winger played for Birmingham City as a teenager?

15 Which World Cup winning shorty managed Swindon Town, West Bromwich, Newcastle and Tottenham?

16 Who is the tallest Hammer out of Joe Cole, Nigel Winterburn and Steve Potts?

17 Which English League-based Spaniard stands at five feet and six inches?

18 Who is the smallest out of Scholes, Barmby and Owen?

19 For which club did impish winger 'Jinky' Johnstone play?

20 Which diminutive German midfielder won a World Cup winners medal in 1990 and a European championship winners medal in 1996?

Nicknames 2 (see Quiz 95)
1 Hibernian. 2 Torquay. 3 Mansfield Town. 4 Darlington.
5 Forfar Athletic. 6 Clyde. 7 Shrewsbury Town. 8 Wrexham,
Cheltenham Town or Swindon Town. 9 Morton. 10 Hull City.
11 Lincoln City. 12 Rochdale. 13 Bournemouth. 14 Dunfermline.
15 Stirling Albion. 16 Exeter City. 17 Crystal Palace. 18 Cardiff
City. 19 Barnsley. 20 Partick Thistle.

1   How many penalties does each side take before 'sudden death'?

2   In which year was the first major cup final settled on penalties?

3   Which tournament was it?

4   What happened in the Final?

5   When was the first World Cup penalty shootout?

6   Spurs won a major European trophy in a penalty shootout in 1984. Who did they beat?

7   That same year Liverpool had the same success in a different competition. What year was that?

8   Which competition did Liverpool win?

9   Terry Venables' Barcelona beat Gothenburg on penalties to qualify for the 1986 European Cup Final. Who did they play?

10   What was the score at the end of the match?

11   Who set a record in the shootout?

12   When did the FA first decide to settle the FA Cup final on penalties?

13   In which World Cup were both semi-finals decided on penalties?

14   Who won them?

15   Who were the first First Division side knocked out of the FA Cup on penalties?

16   How many penalties were there in all in the England 1998 World Cup game against Argentina?

17   Which two England players misssed that night?

18   Antonin Panenka's penalty won teh European Championship for which nation?

19   Which was the first World Cup settled on penalties?

20   Which country missed five penalties (in the match and the shootout) crash out in the semi-finals of Euro 2000?

Quiz 95 Nicknames 2

Answers – see page 201

LEVEL 2

1   The Hibees?
2   The Gulls?
3   The Stags?
4   The Quakers?
5   The Loons?
6   The Bully Wee?
7   The Shrews?
8   The Robins?
9   The Ton?
10   The Tigers?
11   The Red Imps?
12   The Dale?
13   The Cherries?
14   The Pars?
15   The Binos?
16   The Grecians?
17   The Eagles?
18   The Bluebirds?
19   The Colliers?
20   The Jags?

Answers

Short Players (see Quiz 93)
1 Juninho. 2 Jose Dominguez. 3 Billy Bremner. 4 Alan Wright.
5 Adrian Heath. 6 Benito Carbone. 7 Julian Joachim.
8 Deschamps. 9 Middlesbrough. 10 Brian Flynn. 11 Georgi
Kinkladze. 12 Diego Maradona. 13 Paul Dickov. 14 Jose
Dominguez. 15 Osvaldo Ardiles. 16 Nigel Winterburn. 17 Albert
Ferrer. 18 Paul Scholes. 19 Celtic. 20 Thomas Hassler.

Quiz 96 **Kenny Dalglish**

LEVEL 2

1   In which year was Kenny Dalglish born?

2   Where was he born?

3   For which club did he sign first?

4   Which manager signed him?

5   In which year did he play his first international?

6   How many caps did he get for Scotland during his career?

7   How many goals did he score in those games?

8   He is top equal top scorer for Scotland with which other player?

9   When did Kenny move to Liverpool?

10 Who did he replace as 'King of the Kop'?

11 In 1978 he scored the winner for Liverpool to win the European Cup against which team?

12 How many goals did Kenny score when Liverpool won the league that same season?

13 What role did Kenny play at Liverpool during the double-winning 1985-86 season?

14 How many league titles did Kenny win as Liverpool manager?

15 What was Dalglish's last trophy as Liverpool boss?

16 Why did Dalglish resign as manager?

17 With which club did he get back into football management?

18 In which year did he win the title again?

19 What was his next club?

20 When did Dalglish give up his interest in Celtic?

Answers

Penalty Shootouts (see Quiz 94)
1 Five. **2** 1980. **3** European Cup Winners Cup. **4** Arsenal lost 5-4 to Valencia. **5** 1982, West Germany v France, semi-final. **6** Anderlecht. **7** 1984. **8** European Cup. **9** Steaua Bucharest. **10** 0-0. **11** Helmut Ducadam saved four penalties for Steaua. **12** The 1990 FA Cup final replay. **13** 1990. **14** West Germany and Argentina. **15** Manchester United in 1992. **16** Twelve. **17** Paul Ince and David Batty. **18** Czechoslovakia. **19** Brazil v Italy, 1994. **20** Holland.

Quiz 97 Dennis Wise

LEVEL 2

Answers – see page 206

1 In which year was Dennis Wise born?
2 For which club did Dennis Wise originally sign as an apprentice?
3 Who was his first manager?
4 How many league appearances did he make for Wimbledon?
5 When did he move to Chelsea?
6 Against whom did he make his Chelsea debut?
   Against whom did he score his first Chelsea goal?
   Which was the first trophy Dennis Wise lifted as Chelsea captain?
   By what nickname is he known?
10 What was his nickname for Ruud Gullit?
11 Wise scored a crucial goal in one of the world's great stadiums in
   October 1999. Where was that?
12 What is Wise's best goal haul in any one season for Chelsea?
13 When did Dennis Wise make his England debut?
14 How many goals had Dennis Wise scored for England by Euro 2000?
15 Who did he score against?
16 After being left out for some years, Keegan brought Wise back to play
   for England in 2000. Who was that against?
   How many appearances did he make for England during Euro 2000?
18 Who did Chelsea play in Dennis Wise's testimonial?
   How many league appearances did he make for Chelsea in season
   1999-2000?
   How many league goals did he score in the same season?

Chairmen and the Board (see Quiz 99)
1 Alan Sugar. 2 Rangers. 3 Arsenal. 4 Manchester United.
5 Ken Bates. 6 Harry Redknapp (West Ham). 7 Leicester City.
8 Aston Villa. 9 Norwich City. 10 Manchester City (Francis Lee).
11 AC Milan. 12 Leeds United. 13 It was blank. 14 Tottenham.
15 Chairmen-managers. 16 Jimmy Hill. 17 Terry Venables.
18 Newcastle United. 19 Elton John. 20 Chelsea.

Quiz 98 Players' Nicknames
LEVEL 2

Answers – see page 207

1   What was Paul Ince's self-proclaimed nickname?

2   Who was known as the Gentle Giant?

3   Who was Manchester United's Sparky?

4   Which Nottingham Forest and England defender was the original 'Psycho'?

5   Who at Tottenham is known as 'Shaggy' or 'Sicknote'?

6   Who was Chelsea's 70s Chopper?

7   Which Tottenham, Liverpool and West Ham defender earned the epithet 'Razor'?

8   Which of the 'Magnificent Magyars' was nicknamed 'The Galloping Major'?

9   Which Everton and Leeds player was 'The Little General'?

10 Who was known as 'Captain Marvel'?

11 Which Englishman was known as 'Mighty Mouse' when he played in Germany?

12 Which long-serving winger was called 'The Wizard of Dribble'?

13 Which ex-Manchester United Czech star was nicknamed 'the Express Train'?

14 Who was known as the Preston Plumber?

15 Which Russian was the Black Panther?

16 Who was 'The Lion of Vienna'?

17 Who was Der Bomber?

18 Which manager was called The Doc?

19 Which player's nickname stemmed from his fondness for chips?

20 Which Italian is known as 'the Divine Ponytail'?

Quiz 99 Chairmen and the Board
LEVEL 2
Answers – see page 205

1   Who is Tottenham's cheap computer salesman chairman?

2   David Murray is chairman at which Scottish club?

3   David Dein is in charge of business at which club?

4   Where did it look like the Sky was the limit for Martin Edwards?

5   Which chairman is a famous farmer at Chelsea?

6   Who threatened resignation when his board sold Andy Impey to Leicester without telling him?

7   Barrie Pierpoint made Martin O'Neill's life interesting at which club?

8   Which is the 'Deadly' Doug Ellis club where no manager is safe?

9   With Delia among them which club has the tastiest board meetings?

10 Who 'benefitted' from their 70s goalscoring hero taking over in 1994?

11 Which Italian club is run by a former Prime Minister and head of the country's biggest media network?

12 Chairman Peter Risdale became high profile when his club had Turkish problems. Which is his club?

13 What was odd about the chapter in Len Shackleton's autobiography entitled 'What directors know about football'?

14 Now on the board at Nottingham Forest, Irving Scholar previously had troubled times at which club?

15 What kind of chairman are/were Noades, Knighton and Reames?

16 Which football pundit has been on the board at Fulham and Coventry?

17 Which player, manager, pundit has been on the board at QPR, Tottenham and Portsmouth?

18 Which club's fans saw their chairman resign after comments he made about their centre-forward and the attractiveness of local women?

19 Which rock star chairman cried when his side lost the 84 Cup final?

20 Whose board member Matthew Harding died in a helicopter crash?

The Hard Questions

If you thought that this section of the book would prove to be little or no problem, or that the majority of the questions could be answered and a scant few would test you, then you are sorely mistaken. These questions are the *hardest* questions ever! So difficult are they that any attempt to answer them all in one sitting will addle your mind and mess with your senses. You'll end up leaving the pub via the window while ordering a pint from the horse brasses on the wall. Don't do it! For a start there are 1,000 of them, so at 20 seconds a question it will take you over five hours and that's just the time it takes to read them. What you should do instead is set them for others – addle your friends' minds.

Note the dangerous nature of these questions though. These are your secret weapons, so use them according, unless, of course, someone or some team is getting your back up. In which case you should hit them hard and only let up when you have them cowering under the bench whimpering "offside".

These questions work best against league teams, they are genuinely tough and should be used against those people who take their pub quizzes seriously. NEVER use these questions against your in-laws.

Which referee sent off Hamaan, McAllister and Vieria when Liverpool played Arsenal in August 2000?

Which Scot refereed two Euro 2000 matches?

Which Italian refereed the Euro 2000 final?

Which referee got in hot water in 1999 for apparently celebrating a Liverpool goal?

Who was the first black referee on the Premier League list?

Which referee was knocked over by Paolo Di Canio?

Which referee is a Harrow schoolmaster?

Who was the first woman to referee a professional national-league match?

What is the retirement age for referees in the Football and Premier Leagues?

Which famous match did Gottfried Dienst referee?

Which English referee awarded a penalty in the opening minutes of the 1974 World Cup final?

Which Welsh referee was involved in a series of controversial decisions in the 70s and 80s?

What did referee Rob Harris mistakenly allow Tranmere to do in 1999?

Which Bristol referee failed to caution Gazza for his 1991 FA Cup final exploits?

Who was the 70s larger-than-life bald smiling referee?

What happened to both Uriah Rennie and Paul Alcock in May 2000?

What monumental decision did Peter Willis make in 1985?

Which referee did Emmanuel Petit push to receive a suspension in 1997?

What was significant about Kidderminster Harriers home tie with Nuneaton Borough in the 1999 Vauxhall Conference?

What did Ian Wright call referee Robbie Hart?

Quiz 2 Goalkeepers

Answers – see page 212

LEVEL 3

1   In addition to van der Saar, who else kept goal for Holland in Euro 200

2   Which club did Charlton goalkeeper Simon Royce join in summer 200

3   From which country does Everton goalkeeper Steve Simonsen hail?

4   For which country did Quim play as a substitute goalkeeper in Euro 20

5   For which club does Italy's Francesco Toldo play?

6   Which goalkeeper was South American Footballer of the Year in 199

7   Which goalkeeper scored with a drop kick for Hibernian in 1988?

8   Which goalkeeper became player-manager at Plymouth in 1992?

9   In 2000 which goalkeeper completed his 23rd season at a Nationwi
    League club?

10 Which former international goalkeeper was sacked as coach of Fortu
    Koln at half-time in their 1999 match with Waldhorf Mannheim?

11 In 1995 which goalkeeper played for Manchester City in the Premie
    League at the age of 43?

12 Which goalkeeper saved eight of ten penalties he faced in 1977-78

13 Which goalkeeper was fined for giving a Nazi salute at White Hart L

14 Who is Dundee United's Scotland under 21 goalkeeper?

15 Who plays in goal for Wigan Athletic and Northern Ireland?

16 Which former Arsenal, Coventry and Wolves striker's goalkeeping so
    made his international debut in 1999?

17 Which keeper made his international debut in 1999 at the age of 3

18 Dave Beasant was Player of the Year at which club in 1999-2000?

19 Finnish international goalkeeper Tuevo Moilanen plays at which
    British club?

20 Which two goalkeepers played in all their team's Premiership games
    1999-2000?

Quiz 3 Bobby Moore

Answers – see page 209

LEVEL 3

1   In which year was Bobby Moore born?

2   Apart from West Ham, which was Moore's only other English club?

3   Which two American clubs did he play for?

4   How many England caps did he win?

5   Which two cup winner's medals did he win with West Ham?

6   Which number shirt did he usually wear for West Ham?

7   In which year did he win his first England cap?

8   Who were England playing that day?

9   Where was that match played?

10   How many goals did he score for England?

11   In which year did Moore lead a team out in the FA Cup final against West Ham?

12   For what alleged offence was Moore arrested in Colombia in 1970?

13   In which year did Moore make his last England appearance?

14   Who were England playing that day?

15   Where was that match played?

16   What was the score?

17   Against which opposition did Moore make his 100th appearance for England?

18   What was the score in that match?

19   In which year did he die?

20   What caused his death?

Quiz 4 Football Awards

Answers – see page 210   LEVEL 3

1   For what is 'The Golden Boot' awarded?

2   What do the letters PFA stand for?

3   What are English football's two major seasonal awards?

4   What major monthly awards are made?

5   Which organisation elects the World Footballer of the Year?

6   Which player won both major English awards in 2000?

7   When was the English Football Writers' Footballer of the Year title first awarded?

8   Who was the first recipient of the award?

9   Who was both the PFA and the Football Writers' Player of the Year in 1999?

10 Who was he playing for at the time?

11 Who won both of the Scottish equivalent awards that year?

12 Who was both European and World Footballer of the Year in 1998?

13 Which club was he playing for at the time?

14 Who was FIFA World Footballer of the Year in 1996?

15 Who was European Footballer of the Year in 1966?

16 Who was the English Football Writers' Player of the Year in 1997?

17 Who was FIFA's World Footballer of the Year in 1995?

18 Which Englishman was the Scottish Footballer of the Year in 1996?

19 Which German was the English Football Writers' Player of the Year in 1995?

20 Which Welshman was the European Golden Boot award winner in 1984?

Quiz 5 Wanderers
Answers – see page 215

1   Who scored three goals for Bolton Wanderers in their 2000 play-off semi-finals against Ipswich?

2   Which Wanderers are in the Jewson Eastern Counties League: Ipswich, Lowestoft or Clacton?

3   Which Wanderers were founded under the name 'Forest'?

4   Which former England international midfielder plays at Wolves?

5   Which two Premier League club managers began their careers at Wycombe Wanderers?

6   Which brothers temporarily saved Wolverhampton Wanderers from extintion in 1982?

7   Who is Bolton Wanderers Icelandic international defender?

8   Which Wanderers won the FA Cup in three successive seasons?

9   Which Wanderers are in the Eircom League Division One: Bray, Monaghan or Cobh?

10   Riodairibord Wanderers are a leading club in which country?

11   In which country have The Wanderers won the League four times?

12   Who is the manager at Wycombe Wanderers?

13   On which condition did the Wanderers hand the FA Cup back in 1878?

14   How much did Wolverhampton Wanderers receive for Robbie Keane in August 1999?

15   Who was Wycombe Wanderer's leading scorer in 1999-2000?

16   Who defeated Bolton Wanderers in the 1999 play-offs?

17   In which year were The Wanderers disbanded?

18   What did Wycombe Wanderers win in 1991 and 1993?

19   Which Wanderers were founded under the name Christ Church FC?

20   How many Wanderers were among the original 12 Football League teams?

LEVEL 3

1   Which team are associated with the violent Inter-City Firm?

2   What is the name given to groups of club-sponsored fans travelling to Italian games?

3   Which teams supporters were credited with starting taking inflatables to matches in the 90s?

4   Which team is the focus of The Ugly Inside fanzine?

5   Which team's fans gained a reputation for taking celery to matches?

6   Left on the Shelf was a pressure group formed by which team's supporters?

7   In the 90s which club's supporters formed a political party and polled 14, 838 votes?

8   Which team's supporters left an unlit petrol bomb by chairman David Kohler's home?

9   A demonstration by which team's supporters led to the abandonment of their 1996 match against York City?

10   www.squareball.co.uk is a website dedicated to which team?

11   One Nil Down... Two One Up was which club's successful 90s fanzine?

12   Which club's supporters voted their hippo mascot seventh in their best player poll of 1997-98?

13   The City Gent fanzine is dedicated to which team?

14   Of which club is the famous half-naked Tango Man a supporter?

15   Which film theme does the band inspire travelling England fans to sing?

16   What is the name given to groups of loyal supporters in Italy?

17   Which supporters' unofficial anthem is Blue Moon?

18   Which team were encouraged by their fans sounding of the chimes?

19   Which team's fans took a bull to grounds on their 90s FA Cup run?

20   Which team's fanzine is called Brian Moore's Head Looks Uncannily Like the London Planetarium?

Answers

Scandals (see Quiz 8)
1 Eric Cantona. 2 Bruce Grobbelaar. 3 Diego Maradona. 4 Paolo Rossi. 5 Marseille. 6 Bernard Tapie. 7 Torino. 8 George Graham. 9 Brian Clough. 10 Vinnie Jones. 11 Peter Swan and Tony Kay. 12 Brazil. 13 Leeds City. 14 Dennis Wise. 15 Roma. 16 Hungary. 17 Lou Macari. 18 Swindon Town. 19 Terry Venables 20 Arsenal and Manchester United.

LEVEL 3

1   Who won the Full Members Cup in 1986?

2   Who won the only Screen Sport Super Cup ever played?

3   Who won the Anglo-Scottish Cup in 1976?

4   Who won the Texaco Cup in both 1974 and 1975?

5   Who won the Anglo-Italian Cup in 1974?

6   Which West Country club won the Anglo-Italian Cup Winners' Cup in 1969 and the Anglo-Italian Cup in 1970?

7   Who won the Anglo-Italian Cup in 1996?

8   Who won the Watney Cup in 1970?

9   Who won the Zenith Data Systems Cup in 1990?

10 Who won the only Football League Group Cup ever played?

11 How many Anglo-Italian Cup competitons were played?

12 Who won the Texaco Cup in 1971 and the Sherpa Van Trophy in 1988?

13 Which is the only Scottish club to have won the Anglo-Scottish Cup?

14 Who won the Full Members Cup in 1987?

15 Who took over sponsorship of the Sherpa Van Trophy in 1990?

16 Who won the trophy that season?

17 Who currently sponsors that trophy?

18 Who won the Simod Cup in 1988?

19 Who won the Anglo-Italian Cup in 1975?

20 Who won the Football League Trophy in 1983?

Quiz 8 Scandals

Answers – see page 214

LEVEL 3

1 Who was given 120 hours community service for attacking a fan in 1995?

2 Which goalkeeper was at the centre of a match-fixing scandal in 1994?

3 Who was arrested in Argentina in 1991 on drugs charges?

4 Which Italian striker was banned from playing in 1980 for illegal betting?

5 Who had the European Cup taken away from them in 1993 for bribery?

6 Who was their president jailed for his part in the affair?

7 Which Italian club was accused of procuring prostitutes for match officials in 1994?

8 Who was dismissed by Arsenal in 1995 for receiving 'bungs'?

9 Which manager was fined by the FA for striking a fan in 1989?

10 Who was banned after biting a reporter's nose in a Dublin bar in 1994?

11 Which two England players were banned for life for match fixing in 1965?

12 In which country were four club directors and five referees arrested for match fixing in 1994?

13 Who was expelled from the league for making illegal payments to players?

14 Who was sentenced to prison for assaulting a taxi driver in 1995?

15 Which Italian club was banned when its president was arrested for trying to bribe the referee before a European Cup semi-final in 1986?

16 In which country were 40 players and officials arrested for their part in match fixing in 1988?

17 Which Swindon manager was fined £7,500 for betting on his team's FA Cup tie against Newcastle in 1990?

18 Which club was demoted to Division Three after winning a Second Division Play-off in 1990?

19 Who was the first manager to be involved in 'bung' speculation in 1993

20 Which two clubs had points deducted in 1990 as a result of a mass brawl between the two sets of players?

Quiz 9 Continental Coaches

LEVEL 3

1 Who did Jo Bonfrere coach in the 2000 African Cup of Nations?

2 Which World Cup team did Tele Santana coach in 1982 and 1986?

3 Who became Germany's caretaker manager after Euro 2000?

4 Which Italian was the first foreign manager to win the Bundesliga?

5 Which coach of Bulgaria was also their most-capped player and highest scorer?

6 Who was appointed as Spain's coach in 1992?

7 Which great player took charge of Charleroi in 2000?

8 Who did Fatih Terim manage after taking Turkey to Euro 96?

9 Euro 2000 managers Camacho and Boskov had been player and manager respectively for which championship-winning team?

10 Which Dutch manager is credited with creating 'total football'?

11 Which manager filled Barcelona's 2000 team with Dutchmen and won the double?

12 Which two-time Soviet Union manager scored four goals in the 1970 World Cup?

13 Who took over as French coach from Gerard Houllier in 1993?

14 Which manager led West Germany to at least third place in four World Cup finals?

15 Swedish skipper Nils Liedholm later became a coach in which country?

16 Which midfielder coached Hungary after winning 100 caps for them?

17 Which Argentinian World Cup winning captain later became their coach?

18 Which coach of Italy was previously president of Lazio?

19 Jamaica's 1998 World Cup manager Rene Simoes is from which country?

20 Who was Denmark's triumphant Euro 92 coach?

Quiz 10 Pot Luck

Answers – see page 220

LEVEL 3

1   Which team supplied the most Writers Footballer of the Years in the 90s?

2   Which Aston Villa full-back was the subject of a rejected compensation claim by Brighton?

3   Which team's goalkeeper scored in the last seconds to keep them in the Football League in 1999?

4   Which Italian club are nicknamed the Rossoneri?

5   Which Tottenham player fled from a This is Your Life performance?

6   In which year did Italy re-allow foreign players in their league?

7   Who were the first club to win the FA Cup without an Englishman?

8   The Thames Valley Royals was a proposed merger of which two teams?

9   In France what is a Semaine Anglaise?

10 Which country won the first three FIFA Futsal (indoor football) World Championships?

11 Whose ground's official name is the Stadio Giuseppe Meazza?

12 Which Hughie was Scotland's pre-war goalscoring hero?

13 Who is Spain's most capped player?

14 Since 1980 where has the World Club Cup been played?

15 How does a team earn two points in a J-League game?

16 Which team has appeared the most times in the Women's FA Challenge Cup final?

17 Which Scottish ground supposedly means 'dungheap' in Gaelic?

18 Who was the first player born after 1966 World Cup to play for England?

19 What is English about AC Milan and Athletico Bilbao?

20 Who was the first Nigerian to play in the Premiership?

Answers

Family Connections (see Quiz 12)
1 Steffen Iversen. 2 First siblings on referees list. 3 Steve Gatting.
4. Fritz and Otmar Walter (1954). 5 David O'Leary. 6 The Nevilles.
7 The Morgans. 8 Two. 9 The Koemans. 10 The Laudrups.
11 Kenny Dalglish. 12 Coventry. 13 Newcastle Utd. 14 Nicky
Summerbee. 15 Cyrille Regis. 16 Baresi. 17 Mpenza.
18 Jeff and Jim Whitley. 19 Wrexham. 20 Ron and Allan Harris.

1   What is the record score in British football?

2   What is England's record victory?

3   What is the record score in English football?

4   What is the Premier League's highest score?

5   What is the highest score in a League Cup match?

6   What is the highest score in a World Cup match?

7   What is the record score in an FA Cup final?

8   What is the highest number of goals scored by one player in an English league match?

9   Which player scored the most goals in any one season?

10   Which player scored the most hat-tricks in a season?

11   Which keeper scored the most goals in a season?

12   What is the record score in a Scottish league match?

13   What is the record score in the European Cup final (apart from penalties)?

14   Which team has scored the most goals in a Premiership season?

15   How many goals did they score that season?

16   Which season was that?

17   Which player holds the record for penalties scored in a season?

18   What is the highest number of penalties awarded in any one game?

19   What is the greatest number of goals scored by one player in a Scottish Cup match?

20   What is the record score in a European Championship match?

Quiz 12 Family Connections

LEVEL 3

Answers – see page 218

1. Which of Britain's Scandinavian contingent had a international goalscoring father?
2. How did Graham and David Laws make history in 1996-97?
3. Which brother of an England cricket captain played in the 1983 FA Cup final?
4. Who were the first brothers to play in a World Cup winning team?
5. Which Arsenal defender appeared in the same international team as his brother?
6. Whose sister is an England international netball player?
7. Which brothers were wingers for Tottenham and QPR in the 70s?
8. How many of Liam Brady's brothers played for English or Irish league clubs?
9. Who are the only siblings to have won European championship medals?
10. Which two brothers were in FIFA's 1998 World Cup all-star squad?
11. Which famous player and manager's son plays for Norwich City?
12. Which English club have two of their manager's sons in their squad?
13. Gary and Stephen Caldwell are in which Premier League team's 2000-01 squad?
14. Which son of a Manchester City legend is a Sunderland player?
15. Who is Bristol Rovers forward Jason Roberts's former England-goalscoring uncle?
16. Which brothers Guiseppe and Franco played against each other in 80s Milan derbies?
17. Name the brothers who played for Belgium in Euro 2000?
18. Which Manchester City brothers are Northern Ireland internationals?
19. For which team does Sir Alex Ferguson's son play?
20. Which brothers played in the 1967 FA Cup final?

Answers

Pot Luck (see Quiz 10)
1 Tottenham. 2 Gareth Barry. 3 Brazil. 4 AC Milan. 5 Danny Blanchflower. 6 1980. 7 Liverpool in 1986. 8 Oxford United and Reading. 9 A mid-week match. 10 Bobby Moore. 11 Inter and AC Milan's. 12 Gallacher. 13 Andoni Zubizarretta. 14 Tokyo. 15 A Golden Goal win. 16 Doncaster Belles. 17 Pittodrie. 18 Tony Adams. 19 Both have anglicised names. 20 Efan Ekoku.

What did the acronym SUAM stand for in 1999?

London ticket agent Stan Flashman was chairman of which club in the 90s?

Manchester United were 385p, Tottenham were 100p – what price were Millwall floated at?

Which former Everton owner is Tranmere's chairman?

At which club is Geoffrey Richmond chairman?

What was the name of the media group that took over Leeds United in 1996?

What was the name of the family who ran Chelsea from 1905 until the 1970s?

'He's fat, he's round, he's never at the ground.' To which chairman or owner were Oxford and Derby supporters referring?

Who 'bought' Crystal Palace in 1998?

At which club was Ken Bates chairman before he bought Chelsea?

At which club is Freddy Shepherd currently chairman?

David Sheepshanks is chairman at which club?

At which club did Belotti and Archer manage to unite the whole of football against them?

Which club did Rodney Marsh aim to help turn into 'the Macclesfield of the South?'

Who has the big chair in the Middlesbrough boardroom?

The Hill-Wood family have long been connected with which club?

Peter Kenyon took over from which high-profile chief executive?

Bryan Richardson rules the roost at which Premier League club?

Steve Archibald bought which club in 2000?

From which former QPR chairman did Terry Venables buy a 51% stake of Portsmouth for £1 in 1996?

Manchester United (see Quiz 15)
1 Parma. 2 Barnet 3 20p. 4 Peter Johnson. 5 Bradford City.
6 Caspian. 7 Mears. 8 Robert Maxwell. 9 Mark Goldberg.
10 Oldham Athletic. 11 Newcastle United. 12 Ipswich Town
13 Brighton and Hove Albion. 14 Ashford Town. 15 Steve Gibson.
16 Arsenal. 17 Martin Edwards. 18 Coventry. 19 East Fife.
20 Jim Gregory.

Quiz 14 Who Did What?
LEVEL 3

1   Who scored Scotland's opening goal in the 1998 World Cup in France?
2   Who scored for Internazionale in both the 1997 and 1998 UEFA Cup finals?
3   Who scored 1,281 goals for Brazil?
4   Who won the Division One championship in 1966-67?
5   Who scored for Leeds in the 1965 FA Cup final against Liverpool?
6   Who was the first £1m player?
7   Which player holds the record for goals scored during the final stages a single World Cup?
8   Which club provided 11 players for Belgium in an international agains Holland in 1964?
9   Who started the World Cup?
10 Who scored a hat-trick for England against Poland in the 1986 World Cu
11 Who kept goal on more than 100 occasions for Sweden?
12 Who scored twice for Norwich against Bayern Munich in their 1993-9 UEFA Cup tie?
13 Who won the Scottish Premier League title in 1997-98?
14 Who went unbeaten for 42 matches between November 1977 and November 1978?
15 Who was the Premiership's leading scorer in 1994-95 and 1995-96?
16 Which non-league team has beaten more league teams in FA Cup tie: than any other?
17 Who scored Wimbledon's winner against Liverpool in the 1988 FA Cup final?
18 Who currently sponsors the FA Cup competition?
19 Who won the first FA Cup final?
20 Who won the League Cup in 1966?

Answers

Extra Time & Penalties (see Quiz 16)
1 30 minutes. **2** 1934. **3** Royal Engineers v Old Etonians, 1875
4 1996. **5** 1991. **6** 1984, Liverpool v Roma. **7** Valencia.
8 Spurs. **9** 1983. **10** Aberdeen. **11** England 2 West Germany
12 Seven. **13** 1877. **14** Three. **15** 1-1. **16** Euro 96.
17 Oliver Bierhoff. **18** David Trezeguet. **19** Five. **20** Brazil beat Italy on penalties.

From which club did United sign Jesper Blomquist?

From which club did United sign Peter Schmeichel?

Who was Manchester United's Player of the Year in 2000?

Which United midfielder was at Tottenham as a junior?

Which United player was signed from Turkish club Besiktas?

How many goalkeepers did Manchester United use in 1999-2000?

Who 'damned' United's 1995-96 season by saying 'You don't win anything with kids?'

Who knocked United out of the 1997 Champions League?

How much did Manchester United lose buying and selling Massimo Taibi?

Who did Manchester United sell to Blackburn Rovers in the summer of 2000?

Who was the only member of Manchester United's 1999 FA Cup final team without an international cap?

For what were Manchester United fined £50,000 in 1990?

Who stopped BskyB's takeover of United in 1998?

Who scored United's goals in their 1992 Cup Winners Cup final victory?

Who did Solksjaer replace in the 1999 European Cup final?

Which former player missed United's 1999 European Cup final goals after leaving the stadium early?

Who played in both of United's 90's European finals?

Who played in United's 1977, 1983 and 1985 FA Cup final victories?

How many penalties were given against United at Old Trafford between 1993 and 2000?

Which United player's European appearance record did Dennis Irwin break in 1999?

The Boardroom (see Quiz 13)
1 Supporters United Against Murdoch. **2** Barnet **3** 20p.
4 Peter Johnson. **5** Bradford City. **6** Caspian. **7** Mears.
8 Robert Maxwell. **9** Mark Goldberg. **10** Oldham Athletic.
11 Newcastle United. **12** Brighton and Hove Albion.
13 Ashford Town. **14** Ashford Town. **15** Steve Gibson. **16** Arsenal.
17 Martin Edwards. **18** Coventry. **19** East Fife . **20** Jim Gregory.

1   How long is a normal period of extra time?

2   In which year did the first World Cup final go to extra time?

3   Which was the first FA Cup final to go to extra time?

4   When was the 'Golden Goals' rule first introduced?

5   When did the FA decide to settle the FA Cup final on penalties after one replay?

6   When was the first European Cup final settled after penalties?

7   Arsenal lost the European Cup Winners' Cup final in 1980 after extra time and penalties. Who beat them?

8   Despite being two-legged, the 1984 EUFA Cup final went to extra time and penalties. Who won it?

9   Which was the last European Cup Winners' Cup final settled after extra time?

10 Which Scottish club won the tournament that year?

11 What was the score after 90 minutes of the 1966 World Cup final?

12 How many matches involving England have gone to extra time?

13 In which year did the first Scottish FA Cup final go to extra time?

14 How many goals did Manchester United score during extra time in the 1968 European Cup final?

15 What was the score after 90 minutes of England's World Cup semi-final against Germany in the 1990 World Cup?

16 What was the first major tournament involving Golden Goals?

17 Which player scored the winner in that final?

18 Who scored the Golden Goal winner for France in the Euro 2000 final?

19 How many goals were scored during extra time in the 1970 World Cup semi-final between Italy and West Germany?

20 How was the 1994 World Cup final settled?

1 Club Deportivo Los Millonarios, Atlético Junior and América de Cali play in which country?

2 In which South American country did Liverpool finish third in the league on three occasions in the early 70s?

3 From which club did Tottenham sign Ossie Ardiles?

4 The Copa CONMEBOL is equivalent to which European competition?

5 Which player did Newcastle United sign from Boca Juniors?

6 1981 Copa Libertadores runners-up Cobreloa are from which country?

7 1997 Copa Libertadores runners-up Sporting Cristal are from which country?

8 In which colours do Santos play?

9 From which club did PSV sign Ronaldo?

10 Danubio, Bella Vista and Defensor Sporting play in which country?

11 In which city are Vasco de Gama based?

12 Which Argentinian team play in the 'Chocolate Box'?

13 Which country's clubs have won the Copa Libertadores the most?

14 Who did Barcelona buy from Boca Juniors for £3 million in 1982?

15 Kempes, Batistuta and Ruggeri all played for which South American club?

16 Which South American team won the 2000 World Club Championship?

17 Which veteran Brazilian star scored twice for Vasco de Gama against Manchester United in the 2000 World Club Championship?

18 Which two Urugayan teams play home games at the national stadium?

19 Which club did Juninho and Denilson leave to play in Europe?

20 From which Argentinian team did Lazio buy Marcelo Salas?

Quiz 18 Liverpool

Answers – see page 228

LEVEL 3

1   What is the fewest number of goals conceded by Liverpool in a league season?

2   What is Liverpool's longest unbeaten league sequence?

3   Against which team did Liverpool play their first match with Bill Shankly as manager?

4   Who were the first team to beat Liverpool at Anfield in the European Cup?

5   How many times have Liverpool been relegated from the top flight?

6   Against which team did Robbie Fowler score his first hat-trick?

7   What nationality is Jorgen Nielsen?

8   How many times was Bob Paisley named Manager of the Year?

9   Which former Liverpool player was also a junior volleyball international?

10 Against which team did Michael Owen make his 100th Liverpool appearance?

11 Against which club did Emile Heskey score his first goal for the Reds?

12 Who made most appearances for Liverpool in the 1999-2000 season?

13 What is Titi Camara's real first name?

14 Where was Emile Heskey born?

15 Who runs the Liverpool reserve team?

16 Prior to 2000-01, when was Liverpool's last victory against Manchester United?

17 Who scored Liverpool's winner against Chelsea at Anfield in 1999-2000?

18 Whose goal denied Liverpool a place in the 2000-01 Champions League?

19 From which team did Gérard Houllier sign Bernard Diomede?

20 Who is Liverpool's first-team coach?

Answers

John Gregory (see Quiz 20)
1 Northampton Town. 2 Brighton. 3 Terry Venables. 4 Derby County.
5 Assistant manager at Portsmouth. 6 Alan Ball. 7 January 1990.
8 Seven years. 9 Wycombe Wanderers. 10 1998. 11 Liverpool.
12 Stan Collymore. 13 Mark Bosnich. 14 Seventh.
15 Savo Milosevic. 16 Alan Thompson. 17 36 hours.
18 Dwight Yorke. 19 Paul Merson. 20 Bolton Wanderers.

Quiz 19 Stranger than strange

LEVEL 3

Answers – see page 225

1 Who played for Wales and Bayern Munich on the same day in 1988?

2 What was strange about Barnet's 5-4 win over Torquay in 1993?

3 Which strange Chelsea and Coventry goalkeeper appeared on Wogan?

4 What allegedly did the referee ask West Ham to do in their 1999 UEFA Cup tie with Steaua Bucharest?

5 Who announced his football retirement on a US chat show in June 2000?

6 Who did Real Madrid sack eight days after winning the European Cup in 1998?

7 Which unusual event occurred in both the 1946 and 1947 FA Cup finals?

8 Which former Wimbledon and Chelsea player broke a toe when trying to break the fall of a bottle of salad cream with his foot in 1990?

9 Which goalkeeper appeared with a full head of hair at Reading having been bald in the 1994 World Cup?

10 Which international goalkeeper designed his own multi-coloured shirts?

11 Which team's reserve was sent off after two minutes in Euro 2000?

12 Which tiny footballing nation beat Austria 1-0 in 1990?

13 Which Scottish captain was born in Scandinavia?

14 Which scorpion-kicking goalkeeper was jailed for his role in a kidnapping?

15 Which commentator ran the line in a 1972 first division match?

16 Which manager appeared on TV as a teenage pigeon-fancier?

17 Who used to turn up to England matches in a top hat, a Union jack waistcoat and red hunting jacket?

18 What record did Dean Gibb set in a penalty shootout in an FA Cup match for Bedlington Terriers?

19 Which 1969 European Footballer of the Year became an Italian Member of Parliament?

20 For what reason did Argentinian keeper Carlos Roa turn down a contract at Real Mallorca?

Answers

South America (see Quiz 17)
1 Colombia. 2 Uruguay. 3 Huracan. 4 UEFA Cup. 5 Nolberto Solano. 6 Chile. 7 Peru. 8 White. 9 Cruzeiro. 10 Uruguay. 11 Rio de Janeiro. 12 Boca Juniors. 13 Argentina. 14 Maradona. 15 River Plate. 16 Corinthians. 17 Romario. 18 Peñarol and Nacional. 19 Sao Paulo. 20 River Plate.

Quiz 20 John Gregory

Answers – see page 226 **LEVEL 3**

1 Which club originally signed John Gregory as a player?

2 Which was his next club?

3 Who signed him for QPR?

4 Which was Gregory's last club as a player?

5 What was Gregory's first managerial position?

6 Who was in charge of the club at the time?

7 When was Gregory sacked by Portsmouth?

8 How long was it before Gregory got back into football management?

9 With which club did he make his management comeback?

10 When was he appointed manager at Villa?

11 Who did Villa play in his first match in charge?

12 Who scored twice in that match to bring a smile to Gregory's face and three points for Villa?

13 Who was Villa's keeper when Gregory took over?

14 Where did Villa finish in the table in Gregory's first season in charge?

15 Who was Gregory's first major sale at Villa?

16 Who was his first major purchase?

17 For how long was David Unsworth a Villa player?

18 Who did Gregory sell to Manchester United at the start of the 1998-99 season?

19 Which ex-Arsenal player did Gregory sign from Middlesbrough in September 1998?

20 Who did Villa beat in the FA Cup semi-final in April 2000?

1   'It's not like it said in the brochure.' Part of which manager's threat to quit in 1992?

2   Which Premier club vice-president died in '96 after 57 years with the club?

3   Who shocked Brazil beating them 1-0 in the 1998 Concacaf Gold Cup?

4   Who lasted 32 days in charge of Manchester City in 1996?

5   Which Tottenham player became the first player to be suspended for feigning an injury in 1992-93?

6   Who did USA beat on penalties in the 1999 Women's World Cup final?

7   Who was sacked for eighth time at the same club in 1993?

8   Which team resigned from the Football League in 1992?

9   Which Leicester City player scored ninetieth minute own goals on two occasions in 1998-99?

10 Which Reading player was the League's top scorer in 1993-94?

11 Who inflicted England's first home World Cup defeat in 1997?

12 What was memorable about Oxford United's game against Sunderland in February 1999?

13 Who retired in 1993 after managing the same club for 21 years?

14 In which year was the Republic of Ireland against England match abandoned due to supporter violence?

15 Who beat Vitesse Arnhem and Bayern Munich in the UEFA Cup in '93-94?

16 Who was Liam Brady's assistant manager at Celtic?

17 Who was fined after calling German football officials 'brainless' in 1994?

18 Who beat the Maldives 17-0 in a World Cup qualifier in 1997?

19 Which team missed a last-minute penalty that would have won them the 1993-94 Spanish League?

20 Which League experimented with kick-ins rather than throw-ins in '93-94?

Quiz 22 Leeds United

Answers – see page 232

LEVEL 3

1 In which season did Norman Hunter and Billy Bremner depart from Elland Road?

2 In which season did John Charles score 42 goals?

3 At what age did Peter Lorimer make his Leeds United debut?

4 Which Leeds substitute scored a hat-trick in nine minutes against Walsall in the FA Cup in 1995?

5 Who was sent off in Leeds 2000 UEFA Cup semi-final at Elland Road?

6 An on-pitch brawl with which club landed Leeds a hefty fine in 2000?

7 Who was sacked for the eighth time at the same club in 1993?

8 Who knocked Leeds out of the 1998-99 UEFA Cup?

9 Whose eight goals in 1996-97 made him Leeds top goalscorer that season?

10 To whom did Leeds offer the manager's job when George Graham left?

11 From which club did Duncan McKenzie sign for Leeds?

12 Whose wild challenge on Stephen Clemence precipitated a mass brawl in 1999-2000?

13 Who hit two hat-tricks in 11 days for Leeds in 1995?

14 Who did Leeds sign from Liverpool in 1996?

15 Which team did Leeds beat on the day they won the championship in 1992?

16 Which club did Jack Charlton leave Leeds for in 1973?

17 How many of Eric Cantona's 17 Leeds goals came in Europe?

18 Who did Leeds beat to win the Fairs Cup in 1971?

19 Who scored the winning goal in Leeds' 1968 League Cup final victory?

20 Who was the only Leeds player to appear in Euro 2000?

Quiz 23 Nicknames
Answers – see page 229

LEVEL 3

1 Southend United?

2 Alloa Athletic?

3 Stockport County?

4 Queen's Park?

5 Montrose?

6 Darlington?

7 Crewe Alexandra?

8 Albion Rovers?

9 Falkirk?

10 Stenhousemuir?

11 Macclesfield Town?

12 Oxford United?

13 Rotherham United?

4 Bristol Rovers?

5 Chesterfield?

6 Barnet?

7 Ayr United?

8 Forfar Athletic?

9 Stirling Albion?

0 Burnley?

The 90s (see Quiz 21)
1 Kevin Keegan. 2 Bob Paisley. 3 USA. 4 Steve Coppell.
5 Gordon Durie. 6 China. 7 Barry Fry. 8 Maidstone. 9 Frank Sinclair.
10 Jimmy Quinn. 11 Italy. 12 First pay-per-view match.
13 Jim McLean (Dundee Utd). 14 1995. 15 Norwich City.
16 Joe Jordan. 17 Franz Beckenbauer. 18 Iran.
19 Depotivo La Coruña. 20 Diadora.

Quiz 24 Chelsea

Answers – see page 230

1   Who holds the record for most consecutive appearances for Chelsea?

2   Who was Chelsea's 'chess expert'?

3   What was manager Bobby Campbell's nickname?

4   Who took 'the worst penalty in the world' for Chelsea against Manchester City?

5   Who was Chelsea's first Jamaican international?

6   Which Norwegian defender was signed by Chelsea from Bayern Munich in 1989?

7   Which Chelsea keeper was known as 'The Cat'?

8   Whose long throw was such a feature for Chelsea in the late 1960s and early 1970s?

9   Who is the only Spanish-born player ever to have played for Chelsea?

10   Who was Chelsea captain the day they won the Full Members Cup at Wembley in 1986?

11   Who did Tommy Docherty succeed as Chelsea boss in 1962?

12   Who scored Chelsea's winner against Bolton in 1983, a win that saved them from Third Division football?

13   Which Chelsea striker was known as 'Mary'?

14   Who gave away a penalty in the closing minutes of a League Cup match drawn 4-4 against Sheffield Wednesday at Hillsbrough in 1985?

15   Who signed from Lazio in June 1988 but played only 15 games before injury ended his career?

16   Who scored the most penalties in one season for Chelsea?

17   From which club did Ruud Gullit join the Blues?

18   In which country was Tony Dorigo born?

19   How many managers have Chelsea had in their history?

20   Which Chelsea player went on to be Terry Venables's assistant manger at Barcelona?

Quiz 25 Everton

Answers – see page 235

LEVEL 3

1   What is Everton's record league victory?

2   Who was Everton's manager between 1961 and 1973?

3   For how many matches did Everton go undefeated in 1984-85 to set a club record?

4   What were Everton's first colours?

5   What nickname did those colours earn for the team?

6   What is the record number of league goals Everton have scored in one season?

7   What is Everton's record attendance?

8   Who is the youngest player ever to have played for Everton?

9   What is Everton's record league defeat?

10   Who is Everton's leading goalscorer in European competitions?

11   How many managers have Everton had in their history?

12   Who scored on his debut for Everton against Newcastle on the first day of the 1996-97 season?

13   How many league goals did Gary Lineker score in season 1985-86?

14   Who was sent off in the 1980 FA Cup semi-final against West Ham shortly after scoring a penalty?

15   Whose first goals came in 1995 in a 2-1 win against Liverpool at Anfield?

16   Who did Everton beat 7-1 in the league at Goodison in November 1996?

17   Against which team did Everton need three replays to progress in the FA Cup in 1988?

18   Who did Everton beat 5-0 at Goodison in a league game in December 1999?

19   In which round were Everton knocked out of the FA Cup in 1999-2000?

20   Where did Neville Southall go when he left Everton in 1999?

Name of Quiz (see Quiz 27)
1 Arsenal. **2** Tottenham. **3** Brentford. **4** Crystal Palace.
5 West Ham United.   **6** Leyton Orient. **7** The club was formed by workers at an arms factory. **8** West Ham. **9** Wimbledon.
10 Charlton Athletic. **11** Crystal Palace. **12** Fulham. **13** Leyton Orient. **14** Millwall. **15** Wimbledon. **16** West Ham. **17** Spurs, 5-1 v Atletico Madrid, ECWC, 1963. **18** QPR. **19** Millwall. **20** Charlton Athletic.

Quiz 26 Gianluca Vialli
LEVEL 3

1   In which year was Vialli born?

2   In which Italian city was he born?

3   With which club did he win the Serie A title in Italy in 1991?

4   How many international goals did he score?

5   Who said of Vialli, 'I used to take him out for a few beers and he just couldn't handle it'?

6   Whose underpants did Vialli sprinkle with pepper before he put them on?

7   How many Italian caps did he win?

8   In 1992 he became the world's most expensive player. Who bought him?

9   For whom did he make his Italian league debut?

10 What was the last trophy Vialli won as a player in Italy?

11 Which was the first medal he won as a player at Chelsea?

12 When did he take over as manager of Chelsea?

13 When Vialli led Chelsea to European glory in 1998, how many years was it since they had done such a thing?

14 Against which club did Vialli score twice to help Chelsea to a 4-2 victory in the 1996 FA Cup?

15 Against who did he make his Chelsea debut as a player?

16 Against who was his first match as Chelsea manager?

17 Which European trophies did Vialli win as a player?

18 How many World Cups did Vialli play in?

19 How many trophies did he win as a player and manager at Chelsea?

20 When was he sacked as manager of Chelsea?

Quiz 27 London

Answers – see page 233   **LEVEL 3**

1   Which was the first London team to beat Manchester United in the 2000-01 league season?

2   Which London club was managed by Gerry Francis between 1994 and 1997?

3   Whose ground is situated in Braemar Road?

4   Which London club were runners up in the 1990 FA Cup competition?

5   Which London club have only ever had eight managers?

6   Of which London club is Barry Hearn the chairman?

7   Why are Arsenal known as 'The Gunners'?

8   Which London club's top scorer is Vic Watson?

9   Which London club is owned by a Norwegian business consortium?

10   Which London club used to play at Siemen's Meadow?

11   Of which London club was Attilio Lombardo player/manager in 1998?

12   For which London club does Chris Coleman play?

13   Which London club started life in 1881 as Glyn Cricket and Football Club?

14   Current Republic of Ireland manager Mick McCarthy managed which London club between 1992 and 1996?

15   For which London club does Alan Cork hold the appearances record?

16   Which London club lost 2-8 at home to Blackburn Rovers in a league game in 1963?

17   Which London club holds the record for the biggest victory in a European final?

18   Which London club was managed by Tommy Docherty in 1968 and 1979-80?

19   Of which London club is Theo Paphitis the chairman?

20   For which London club does Sam Bartram hold the most league appearances record?

Quiz 28 The Midlands

Answers – see page 234   **LEVEL 3**

1 Sky Sports presenter Richard Keys is a supporter of which Midlands team?

2 Who was Aston Villa's goalkeeper in the 1982 European Cup final?

3 In which year did West Bromwich Albion win the League Championship?

4 Which former Welsh international is Shrewsbury's manager?

5 Blackpool, York City and Barnet have been giant-killing victims of which Midlands Conference team?

6 Who were Leicester City's first opponents in the 2000-2001 UEFA Cup?

7 Mark McGhee left Leicester City to take over whixh club as manager?

8 Which club's winger Jon McCarthy broke a leg twice in 1999-2000?

9 Which former Aston Villa hero is manager at Walsall?

10 Which other Midlands clubs has Coventry City's Stephen Frogatt played?.

11 Leicester signed both Robbie Savage and Neil Lennon from which club?

12 Which Aston Villa star was born in Ghana?.

13 Which Derby player made his debut for the Republic of Ireland in 1998?

14 Which Aston Villa youngster played in the 2000 European Under 21 Championship?

15 Which West Bromwich Albion international joined Sunderland in the 1999-2000 season?

16 Sam Allardyce took which Midlands club to the 1998 Third Division championship?

17 Which Notts County teenager controversially signed for Arsenal in 1999?

18 Which Aston Villa player was sent off in the 2000 Worthington Cup semi-final at Wembley?

19 Which player won the League Championship with Aston Villa and Nottingham Forest?

20 Which Midlands club won the old First, Second, Third and Fourth Division championships?

---

1   Who scored Sunderland's winning goal in the 1973 FA Cup final?

2   Which former Hartlepool player won his first cap for Scotland in 1999?

3   Which future Premier League manager took Darlington back to the Football League in 1990?

4   Which FA Cup giant-killing Geordies beat Preston North End and Scarborough in 1990?

5   Which FA Cup giant-killing Geordies beat Stoke City in 1978?

6   Which former League team from the North East folded in 1973?

7   Next to Shearer who scored the most goals for Newcastle in 1999-2000?

8   In which year was Peter Reid appointed Sunderland manager?

9   Who was Middlesbrough's top scorer in 1999-2000?

10 Which club prevented Newcastle from reaching a third consecutive FA Cup final in 2000?

11 Who scored four goals for Sunderland in 1999-2000 despite only ever appearing as a substitute?

12 Which club bought Brian Clough from Middlesbrough in 1961?

13 How many of Newcastle's 1998 FA Cup final team played in the 1999 final?

14 Which former England international scored twice for Hartlepool in '98-99?

15 Which well-travelled forward left Darlington for Northampton in the summer of 2000?

16 Who left Middlesbrough for WBA in a British record transfer in 1979?

17 Which North East team have scored three goals against Manchester United on three occasions in the Premier League?

18 Which 1999 signing set Sunderland's record transfer fee?

19 From which club did Newcastle sign Nikos Dabizas?

20 Which club has a fanzine called Fly Me to the Moon?

Quiz 30 Republic of Ireland
LEVEL 3
Answers – see page 240

1 Who is credited with introducing football to Ireland?

2 In which year did Irish football split in a north/south divide?

3 In which year did FIFA accept the Irish Free State as an international team?

4 When and where did they play their first international match?

5 Against who did the Irish Free State win their first international match?

6 When was the Irish Free State's first World Cup match?

7 In which year was the Irish Free State team first called Ireland?

8 When was the team first called the Republic of Ireland?

9 In 1956 Ireland beat the World Champions 3-0 in a friendly. Who were their victims?

10 Who were the first League of Ireland team to play in the European Cup?

11 In November 1966 who beat the Republic to deny them a place in the World Cup finals?

12 Who scored four goals for the Republic against Turkey in October 1975?

13 In 1978 the Republic played Northern Ireland for the first time. What was the score?

14 Which club failed to reach the European Cup quarter-final after losing to Celtic in 1979?

15 What is the Republic's record victory?

16 What was the score when the Republic met England in the 1990 World Cup?

17 Against which opponents did Frank Stapleton score in 1990 to set a new goalscoring record for the Republic?

18 Who scored the Republic's first ever goal at Windsor Park in 1993?

19 In which American city did Ireland lose to Holland in the 1994 World Cup finals?

20 What is the name of the projected new stadium in Dublin in which the Republic will play their games from 2002?

1 Who scored for Leeds Utd in their Champions League home tie with AC Milan in September 2000?

2 Who won the Tennent's Scottish Cup in 1997?

3 Which team has made the highest number of FA Cup semi-final appearances?

4 Who scored a hat-trick for Newcastle in a European Cup match against Barcelona in 1997-98?

5 Who holds the record for most goals in one World Cup match?

6 Who was the leading goalscorer in the 1998 World Cup?

7 Who won the Scottish League Cup in 1995?

8 Who is Southampton's highest goalscorer?

9 Who is the Republic of Ireland's most capped player?

10 Who took over from Graham Taylor as England manager?

11 Who holds the league appearances record for Blackburn Rovers?

12 Which Italian team won the European Cup in 1989?

13 Which player won a Scottish Cup winner's medal with both Rangers and Celtic?

14 Who won the first Football League title in 1888-89?

15 Which team has appeared in most FA Cup finals?

16 Who won the European Cup Winners' Cup in 1972?

17 Who managed Scotland during the 1998 World Cup?

18 Which 42-year-old played for England v Denmark in May 1957?

19 Which Third Division team beat Arsenal to win the League Cup in 1969?

20 Who were the first sponsors of the Football League?

Quiz 32 Tottenham Hotspur
LEVEL 3

Answers – see page 238

1   Which Norwegian goalkeeper did Tottenham sell to Watford in 2000?

2   Who two Spurs played in England's under 21 Euro 2000?

3   Which Tottenham midfielder started his career at Portsmouth?

4   In which year were Spurs originally banned from the FA Cup?

5   Which Tottenham player has won an English championship medal?

6   Before Rebrov who was Tottenham's record signing?

7   Which popular figure at White Hart Lane is Tottenham's president?

8   Which Tottenham player made his debut for the Republic of Ireland in the 2000 Toulon tournament?

9   Who scored the equalising goal against Anderlect in the 1984 UEFA Cup final at White Hart Lane?

10 For what tactics were Arthur Rowe's 1950s Tottenham team renowned?

11 Who scored Tottenham's goal in the 1999 Worthington Cup final?

12 Which Tottenham player was sent off in the 1999 Worthington Cup final

13 Which two Tottenham players were in England's 1970 World Cup team against West Germany?

14 Who did Tottenham pay Newcastle £4.2 million for in July 1997?

15 Who scored two goals in Tottenham's 1991 FA Cup semi final victory over Arsenal?

16 Which team did Spurs beat 7-2 in the 1999-2000 season?

17 Who is missing from the Ossie Ardiles 'famous five': Barmby, Klinsmann, Sheringham, Anderton..?

18 Which two players did George Graham sign from Wimbledon in 2000?

19 How much did Tottenham pay Dynamo Kiev for Sergei Rebrov?

20 Which two former Spurs were Premier League managers in the 2000-2001 season?

Answers

Republic of Ireland (see Quiz 30)
1 John McAlery. 2 1921. 3 1923. 4 1926, Turin. 5 Belgium.
6 1934. 7 1936. 8 1954. 9 West Germany.
10 Shamrock Rovers. 11 Spain. 12 Don Givens. 13 0-0.
14 Dundalk. 15 8-0 v Malta, 1983. 16 1-1. 17 Malta.
18 Alan McLoughlin. 19 Orlando. 20 The Arena.

Quiz 33 Spain

Answers – see page 243

LEVEL 3

1   For which club does Raul play?

2   Which club play at the Vicente Calderon stadium?

3   What colour shirts do Barcelona play in?

4   Which is Spain's oldest club?

5   In which year did Spain win their first major trophy?

6   In which year did Barcelona first win the European Cup?

7   Who won the Spanish League title in 2000?

8   What nationality is Deportivo's Roy Makaay?

9   Who did Valencia sign in 2000 to replace Claudio Lopez?

10 Which club has Jose Manuel Mane as their coach?

11 Who is the pichichi?

12 What nationality is Barcelona's Rivaldo?

13 Which Madrid team was relegated from the top flight in 2000?

14 For which team does keeper Iker Casillas play?

15 Which other Spanish team did Real Madrid play in the 2000 Champions League final?

16 Which player opened the scoring in that match?

17 Who took over from Johan Cruyff as manager of Barcelona?

18 For which club does striker Joseba Etxeberria play?

19 From which club did Internazionale buy defender Francisco Farinos in summer 2000?

20 For which club do Russian internationals Karpin and Mostovoi play?

Quiz 34 Pot Luck 2

Answers – see page 244

LEVEL 3

1   Before Chelsea's win in October 1999 who were the last team to beat Manchester United 5-0?

2   What non-league team did Bulgarian international Bontcho Guenchev play for in 1999?

3   Which Premier League team scored the most headed goals in 1999-2000?

4   From which country does Colchester's Lomana Lua Lua hail?

5   Which former England international played for Ross County in 1999?

6   Who scored a hat-trick after betting on his own team to beat Barnsley in 2000?

7   Daniel Amokachi was the first what since Cliff Marshall?

8   Which club's ground is featured in LS Lowry's painting Going to the Match?

9   Which player's portrait hangs in the Scottish Portrait Gallery?

10 What was the name of England's 1966 World Cup mascot?

11 Gordon McQueen is first-team coach at which club?

12 What role did Archibald Leitch play in British football?

13 Which university runs a course of Football Industries?

14 In which competition did Nicolas Anelka score his first goal for Real Madrid in 2000?

15 Which team were called the Manchester United of Division Three in 1999?

16 Which Premier League player completed the most crosses in 1999-2000?

17 According to The Times which West Ham player was the dirtiest in the Premier League in 1999-2000?

18 Willie Donachie is first-team coach at which club?

19 For which country did Nandor Hidegkuti play?

20 Which club had the lowest average Premiership attendance from 1997 to 2000?

Answers

Terry Venables (see Quiz 36)
1 Sir Alf Ramsey. 2 The Nou Camp. 3 Thingummywigs.
4 They Used to Play on Grass. 5 Steve Archibald. 6 Allan Harris.
7 Anthony Newley. 8 Play at all levels. 9 Chief Executive. 10 Iran.
11 1985. 12 The League Cup (1965). 13 Malcolm Allison.
14 Crystal Palace. 15 Peter Beardsley. 16 Terry Fenwick.
17 Arsenal. 18 Rest of the World. 19 Panorama. 20 Nayim.

1   Who plays in the city of Bergamo?

2   Who won the Italian league in 2000?

3   What is the name of Parma's ground?

4   In which Italian city do Fiorentina play?

5   For which club does Brazilian Cafu play?

6   Which club have Ronaldo and Christian Vieri as their strike force?

7   How many clubs are there in Serie A?

8   Who scored Italy's goal in the Euro 2000 final?

9   For which club does he play?

10   For which club does Matias Almeyda play?

11   Why did Serie A not start until 1 October in 2000?

12   Which is the leading Sardinian club?

13   Which two Italian teams contested the 1998 UEFA Cup final?

14   Which was the last Italian club to win the European Cup?

15   When did Italy last win the World Cup?

16   How many times have they won the trophy altogether?

17   Who managed Parma during the 1999-2000 season?

18   Which Italian politician owns AC Milan?

19   Which two Italian teams contested the 1995 UEFA Cup final?

20   Which Italian coach was known as 'Il Mago' (the Magician)?

Quiz 36 Terry Venables

Answers – see page 242   **LEVEL 3**

1. Venables grew up in the same town as which other England manager?
2. Portentously, where was Venables last appearance in a Chelsea shirt?
3. What were the names of the hats with attached wigs that Venables marketed in the 60s?
4. What was the name of the novel Venables co-wrote in 1971?
5. Who did Venables sign to replace Maradona at Barcelona?
6. Who was Venables managerial assistant from Crystal Palace to Barcelona?
7. Who did Venables impersonate on TV's Celebrity Stars in their Eyes?
8. Venables was the first to do what as an England player?
9. What was his job title when he and Alan Sugar took over at Tottenham?
10. Who did his Australia team lose to in the 1998 World Cup qualifying play-offs?
11. In which year did Venables become the first Briton to be named World Manager of the Year?
12. In which competition did Venables score a Cup final goal?
13. Who was manager when Venables joined Crystal Palace as coach in 1976?
14. Which is the only English club Venables has managed but has had no financial interest in?
15. Which player did Venables bring back from international wilderness in his first England match?
16. Which defender played under Venables at Palace, QPR and Tottenham?
17. For which club did Venables sign a contract to take over at the beginning of the 1986-87 season?
18. Which team did Venables manage in the Football League Centenary Match
19. Which TV series first raised allegations about Venables's financial dealings
20. Which Barcelona player did Venables bring to Tottenham when he took charge?

Answers

Pot Luck 2 (see Quiz 34)
1 Newcastle (1996). 2 Hendon. 3 Newcastle United. 4 Zaire.
5 Mark Hateley. 6 Steve Claridge. 7 Black player at Everton.
8 Bolton Wanderers. 9 Danny McGrain. 10 World Cup Willie.
11 Middlesbrough. 12 Stadium architect. 13 Liverpool. 14 World
Club Championship. 15 Peterborough 16 Nolberto Solano. 17 Paulo
Wanchope. 18 Manchester City. 19 Hungary. 20 Southampton.

Quiz 37 Germany

Answers – see page 247

LEVEL 3

1 What is the name given to a derby game in Germany?

2 For which club does German international Oliver Neuville play?

3 Which East German side entered the reunified Bundesliga with Hansa Rostock in in 1990?

4 For which German team did Mark Hughes play?

5 Which German World Cup winner was on the bench for Real Madrid in their 2000 Champions League final?

6 Who were relegated in 1998-99?

7 Sebastian Deisler plays for which German club?

8 Which German club won the 1992 European Cup Winners Cup?

9 Who is Bayern Munich's manager?

10 Which German team won the 1997 UEFA Cup?

11 Who was Bayern Munich's leading scorer in their 1999-2000 Champions League campaign?

12 Who scored Germany's only goal in Euro 2000?

13 Which Scot played for Bayern Munich in the 1990 European Cup semi finals?

14 What is or who are the DFB Pokal?

15 Which German was European Footballer of the Year in 1980 and 1981?

16 Which German side play in white shirts with red and black flashing?

17 Which player did Liverpool buy from Borussia Munchengladbach in 1996?

18 Who was Germany's manager in Euro 2000?

19 Who are the only country to have beaten Germany in a penalty shoot-out in a major competition?

20 Which 'non-German' club has won the German League ?

Who Did What? 3 (see Quiz 39)

Quiz 38 Literary Football
Answers – see page 248 **LEVEL 3**

1   *The Glory Game* was Hunter Davies's classic study of which club?

2   Which Millwall and Republic of Ireland player's diary is *It's Only A Game*?

3   *This One's On Me* was which troubled 50s and 60s star's autobiographical account

4   *Left Foot in the Grave* is Gary Nelson's account of life at which club?

5   *Flat Back Four* is which pundit's guide to tactics?

6   *Manchester United Ruined my Life* is written by a supporter of which team?

7   What collection forms the annual book entitled *The Wrong Kind of Shirts*?

8   *The Greatest Footballer You Never Saw* was about which Reading and Cardiff player?

9   Who is the subject of Dave Hill's *Out of his Skin*?

10   *Strikingly Different* is which England forward's autobiography?

11   *Football is My Passport* is which England captain's account?

12   What is the subject of John Sampson's *Awaydays*?

13   *The Soccer Tribe* was whose anthropological study of football supporters?

14   Who wrote the classic entitled *The Football Man*?

15   What was the subject of Pete Davies's *All Played Out*?

16   *Clown Prince of Soccer* was which England forward's autobiography?

17   Whose *World Cup Diary* upset some of England's players in 1998?

18   Which event is the focus of *The Day Italian Football Died*?

19   Which team is the subject of David Winner's *Brilliant Orange*?

20   What is the title of Chris Hulme's account of a prison football team?

Answers

England (see Quiz 40)
1 Alan Shearer. 2 1985. 3 David Platt. 4 Jimmy Armfield.
5 7-1. 6 Ray Wilkins. 7 Cagliari. 8 2-0. 9 Steve Guppy.
10 Paul Gascoigne. 11 Richard Wright. 12 Clive Allen. 13 2-2.
14 Paul Ince. 15 Paul Parker. 16 David Batty. 17 Kevin Keegan.
18 Nick Barmby. 19 Don Revie. 20 Des Walker.

Quiz 39 Who Did What? 3

Answers – see page 245

LEVEL 3

1   Who sold Matt Jansen to Crystal Palace in 1997-98?

2   Who scored a total of 10 goals with none conceded in two games at Valley Parade in 1999 and 2000?

3   Which England player received a three-match international ban in 1999?

4   Who bought Birmingham City in 1993?

5   Who won the Euro 2000 under 21 tournament?

6   Who scored for Scotland against Latvia in their opening World Cup 2002 qualifying match?

7   Neil Grayson is the star of which Nationwide League team?

8   What was Ryan Giggs's surname when he played for England schoolboys?

9   Chris Morgan was which team's Player of the Year in 1999-2000?

10   Who were the only visiting team to win at Ibrox in the 1999-2000 Premier League?

11   Who won the PFA Fair play trophy seven times (1994-2000)?

12   Which Ipswich Town defender previously played for Wolverhampton Wanderers?

13   Which manager became recognisable by his fedora headwear?

14   Which manager was recognisable by an old green sweatshirt?

15   Which former Charlton player was coach of the Faroe Islands in their Euro 2000 qualifiers?

16   Which chairman tried to erect an electric fence at his ground in 1985?

17   Who took over as Wigan Athletic's manager in June 2000?

18   In which 1999-2000 final was Thomas Solberg sent off?

19   What is the name of Stuart Cosgrove's account of sex and scandal in Scottish football?

20   Who was Manchester United's leading goalscorer in their 1999-2000 Champions League campaign?

Quiz 40 England

Answers – see page 246

LEVEL 3

1   Who was the only England player booked in their final Euro 2000 match?

2   In what year did Gary Lineker score his first goal for England?

3   Which player was controversially brought down by Ronald Koeman in England's World Cup qualifier in Rotterdam in 1993?

4   Who was appointed as the FA's headhunter when Graham Taylor resigned?

5   What was the score when England played San Marino in November 1993?

6   Who was the most capped player under Ron Greenwood?

7   Where did England play all of their group matches in the 1990 World Cup?

8   What was the half-time score in England's Euro 2000 qualifying play-off at Hampden?

9   Which left-sided player made his debut against Belgium in 1999?

10   Who did Graham Taylor controversially leave out of his first England team?

11   Which Euro 2000 squad member was the only player to be dropped in Kevin Keegan's first post tournament squad?

12   Which striker made his debut as an England substitute against Brazil in Rio in 1984?

13   What was the half-time score in England's Euro 2000 tie against Portugal?

14   Who earned England's penalty against Romania in Euro 2000?

15   Who deflected Brehme's free-kick to give Germany the lead in the 1990 World Cup semi-final?

16   Who was sent off playing for England in Warsaw in 1999?

17   Who did Bobby Robson controversially leave out of his first England team?

18   Who played his first game for five years against Brazil in 2000?

19   Which manager introduced bingo sessions and carpet bowls to England training camps?

20   Who brought down Marc Overmars to give Holland an equalising penalty at Wembley in 1993?

Literary Football (see Quiz 38)

Answers

1 Tottenham. 2 Eamonn Dunphy. 3 Jimmy Greaves. 4 Torquay United. 5 Andy Gray. 6 Manchester City. 7 Quotations. 8 Robin Friday. 9 John Barnes. 10 Gary Lineker. 11 Billy Wright. 12 England hooliganism. 13 Desmond Morris. 14 Arthur Hopcraft. 15 England 1990. 16 Len Shackleton. 17 Glenn Hoddle. 18 Torino air disaster. 19 Holland. 20 Manslaughter United.

Quiz 41 Scotland

Answers – see page 251

1 Who scored Scotland's winner in their Euro 96 match against Switzerland?

2 Which Scottish player and manager was known as the 'chocolate soldier'?

3 When did Scotland join FIFA?

4 Who was known as 'wee Bud'?

5 At which stadium did Scotland play Finland in 1998?

6 Who kept goal for Scotland during all three of their 1998 World Cup matches?

7 Who did Craig Brown take over from as Scotland manager?

8 Whose penalty goal against Wales secured Scotland a place in the 1986 World Cup in Mexico?

9 Which Scottish player won the 1964 European Footballer of the Year award?

10 Which Scottish player scored on his debut that day?

11 What was the score when Scotland beat Wales at Anfield in the 1978 World Cup qualifier?

12 Who were Scotland's first opponents in the 1978 World Cup Finals?

13 Who scored for Scotland that day?

14 Who did Scotland beat in their final match to qualify for Italia 90?

15 When did Scotland last qualify for the European Championships?

16 Who were their first opponents in that tournament?

17 Who defeated Scotland in their last match in the 1998 World Cup Finals?

18 How many Scottish caps did Pat Nevin win?

19 Where did the Scotland squad stay during the 1998 World Cup campaign?

20 Who scored Scotland's winner against Argentina at Hampden in 1990?

Quiz 42 Pot Luck 4

Answers – see page 252

LEVEL 3

1. Who is the 'Alexandra' in Crewe Alexandra?
2. Which England opponents substituted all eleven players in June 1990?
3. Who was the first foreign player to win the Scottish Footballer of the Year?
4. Which club was supported by the U-boat crew in the TV series Das Boot?
5. Which club were originally known as the Black Arabs?
6. Which is the only Scottish club to have had an artificial pitch?
7. Which English player was the UEFA Cup leading scorer in 1976-77?
8. For which two teams has the Sugar Puffs honey monster played?
9. What was the title of the ITV documentary about Graham Taylor?
10. Who were the only League club not to join a mass protest resignation from the FA in 1965?
11. 'You've beaten them once. Now go and do it again.' Whose extra time instructions?
12. Who was the last player from outside the top division to win the English writers Footballer of the Year award?
13. Who won championship medals with Blackburn and Everton?
14. Which innovation did FIFA experiment with in the USA and Egypt in the 2000-01 season?
15. Which was the first national newspaper to publish a Fantasy Football League?
16. Which country's supporters won the 1997 FIFA Fair Play Award?
17. Which ground apart from Wembley has twin towers?
18. 'When you get used to caviar, it's difficult to come back to sausages.' Said which Premiership manager?
19. In which season did British Rail stop running football specials?
20. Who said 'If Arsenal were playing in my back garden, I'd pull the curtains?'

Answers

Memorable Matches (see Quiz 44)
1 David Beckham. 2 USA. 3 Michael Owen. 4 Wrexham.
5 Bristol Rovers. 6 East Sterling. 7 Stan Bowles.
8 Sunderland. 9 France won 4-3 on penalties. 10 Denmark.
11 1997. 12 Michel Platini. 13 Frank Leboeuf. 14 6-1.
15 Germany. 16 Manchester United. 17 Internazionale. 18 Paul Ince and David Batty. 19 Rapid Vienna. 20 Sheffield Wednesday.

LEVEL 3

1   In which colours do the New Zealand team play?

2   For which Massachusetts club did Alexei Lalas play?

3   Which country has the fourth best record in World Cup qualifying games but has never reached the finals?

4   In which year did Canada reach the World Cup finals?

5   For which country has Soh Chin Aun been credited with 250 international appearances?

6   Which non-South American country played in the 1999 Copa America?

7   Which US team did Johan Cruyff join on leaving Barcelona?

8   Which Brazilian played for J-League team Kashima Antlers?

9   In which city is Australia's national football stadium?

10 Where were Pakistani players arrested for playing in shorts in 2000?

11 For which country does Barnet striker Ken Charlery play?

12 Which West Ham defender was born in the USA?

13 Al Saad, Al Wakra and Al Rayyan are successful teams in which country?

14 Ararat Yerevan won the Soviet 'double' in 1973. In which country do they now play?

15 Apart from Britain and the USA, in which other country have Bobby Moore and George Best played?

16 'Tonight the strong and arrogant opponent felt the bitter taste of defeat.' Which leader's official statement?

17 Masami Ihara was which country's World Cup finals captain?

18 What is the full name of Australia's Perth team?

19 Which country qualified for the finals of the Asian Cup of Nations every time it was held from 1984 to 1996?

20 Which United Arab Emirates team competed in the 2000 World Club Championship?

Scotland (see Quiz 41)
1 Ally McCoist. **2** Graeme Souness. **3** 1873. **4** Willie Johnston.
5 Easter Road. **6** Jim Leighton. **7** Andy Roxburgh. **8** Davie
Cooper. **9** Denis Law. **10** Jim McCalliog. **11** 2-0 to Scotland.
12 Peru. **13** Joe Jordan. **14** Norway. **15** 1996. **16** Holland.
17 Morocco. **18** 28. **19** St Remy. **20** Stewart McKimmie.

Quiz 44 Memorable Matches
LEVEL 3
Answers – see page 250

1   Ryan Giggs scored a wonder goal to help Man Utd beat Arsenal in the 1999 FA Cup semi-final replay. Who scored United's other goal?

2   Who did Iran defeat in the group stage of France 98?

3   Who scored England's goal when they lost to Romania in France 98?

4   Which Fourth Division team sensationally beat Arsenal 2-1 in the FA Cup in 1992?

5   Who did Bradford City defeat in the last match of the season to retain their Premiership status in May 2000?

6   Who won the 'Battle of Highbury' in 1934?

7   What was the score in the 1970 World Cup final in Mexico?

8   Norwich City won the Milk Cup in 1985. Who did they beat in the final?

9   Brazil and France clashed in the 1986 World Cup quarter-final. What happened?

10 Who defeated Germany in the European Championship final in 1992?

11 In which year did Roberto Di Matteo score his 43-second FA Cup final goal?

12 Who scored for Juventus in the match that followed the Heysel tragedy?

13 Who equalised for Chelsea in the last minute in a fourth-round FA Cup tie against Oxford in 1999?

14 Holland beat Yugoslavia in the quarter-finals of Euro 2000, by what score?

15 Who did Croatia beat in the quarter-final of the 1998 World Cup?

16 Which team scored twice in the last two minutes to beat Liverpool in a fourth-round FA Cup-tie in 1999?

17 Who did Celtic beat to win the European Cup final in 1967?

18 Which two England players missed penalties as they lost to Argentina the 1998 World Cup?

19 Who did Everton beat in the 1985 European Cup Winners' Cup final?

20 Who beat Manchester United to win the Rumbelows Cup in 1991?

LEVEL 3

Which French stars retired from international football after the friendly against England in 2000?

Who is France's leading goalscorer?

Which French club saw better days as European Cup runners-up in 1956 and 1959?

Which European Footballer of the Year was Just Fontaine's strike partner in the 1958 World Cup?

Which French club did Zidane help to the 1996 UEFA Cup final?

How many games did France win in normal time in Euro 2000?

Did the French Euro 2000 victors have more players playing in Italy or England?

How many games did France win in normal time in the 1998 World Cup?

Which ex-Premier League player scored for Marseilles against Chelsea in the 2000 Champions League?

Who is West Ham's French midfielder?

Which Frenchman played in the 2000 Champions League final?

Which French coach took them to Euro 2000 glory?

From which French club did Arsenal sign Gilles Grimandi?

Which French club did George Weah help win a League championship in 1994?

Which French champions became known as Matra Racing, then Racing '92?

Which city hosted the Brazil versus Holland 1998 World Cup semi-final?

Which team play at the Geoffroy-Guichard stadium?

Who was the only member of the France Euro 2000 winning team who was playing in France at the beginning of the 2000-01 season?

In which country was French international Patrick Vieira born?

Who did Liverpool sign from Lens in 1999?

African Football (see Quiz 47)
1 Mustapha Hadji. **2** Ghana. **3** Algeria. **4** Ivory Coast. **5** Argentina.
6 2-1 to Eire. **7** Sent off against Argentina (1990). **8** Albert
Johanneson. **9** Dele Adebola. **10** Lua Lua Lomana. **11** Nigeria.
12 Tunisia. **13** Mali. **14** Salif Keita. **15** Zaire. **16** Barcelona.
17 Cameroon. **18** Zimbabwe. **19** Victor Ikpeba. **20** Mali.

Quiz 46 Jack Charlton

LEVEL 3

Answers – see page 256

1   In which year was Jack Charlton born?

2   How many teams did he manage during his career?

3   How many England caps did he win?

4   In which year did he make his Football League debut?

5   In which year did he win his first England cap?

6   At which club did he take up his first managerial post?

7   What did he achieve in his first year as manager?

8   How many clubs did Jack Charlton play for during his career?

9   For how long was he manager of Newcastle?

10 In which year did he retire from playing?

11 When was he appointed manager of the Republic of Ireland?

12 In 1988 they qualified for the European Championships. Who were their most celebrated victims during that tournament?

13 Who granted Jack Charlton an audience during Italia 90?

14 How far did the Republic get during that tournament?

15 Whose scalp did the Republic famously take during the 1994 World Cu

16 Which other club did Charlton manage?

17 In which year was Jack Charlton voted Footballer of the Year?

18 In which year was he voted Manager of the Year?

19 For how long was he in charge at Sheffield Wednesday?

20 In which year did he retire from management?

Answers

The 80s (see Quiz 48)
1 Trevor Brooking. 2 Liverpool. 3 Everton. 4 Terry Venables.
5 Gary Mabbutt. 6 Sunderland. 7 Oxford United.
8 Diego Maradona. 9 Luton Town. 10 Chorley. 11 Everton.
12 Joe Miller. 13 1989. 14 Celtic. 15 Avi Cohen. 16 Aston Vi
17 West Ham. 18 Bob Paisley. 19 Gordon Smith of Brighton.
20 Liverpool won 3-1.

Which Spanish League player was the 1998 African Footballer of the Year?

Hearts of Oak, Asante Kotoko and Obuasi Goldfields play in which country?

Which African country beat West Germany in the 1982 World Cup?

From which country does the African Cup of Nations all time leading scorer Laurent Pokou hail?

Which country did Nigeria beat to win the Olympic gold in 1996?

What was the result when the Republic of Ireland played South Africa in the 2000 Nike Cup in the USA?

What place do Kana Byik and Massing have in Cameroon's World Cup history?

Which South African scored a hat-trick for Leeds United in the Fairs Cup in 1966?

Who is Birmingham City's Nigerian-born striker?

Which Nationwide League striker hails from Zaire?

In which African country did George Weah play after leaving Liberia?

Tarak Dhiab, Faouzi Rouissi and Adel Sellimi are footballing legends of which African country?

The Eagles is the nickname of which North African country?

Which St Etienne player was France Football magazine's first African Footballer of the Year in 1970?

PSV Eindhoven's Kalusha Bwalya hailed from which African country?

For which Spanish side did Nigerian Emmanuel Amunike play?

Jean Manga-Onguene was the coach of which 1998 World Cup finalists?

Black Aces, Black Rhinos and Wankie play in which country's league?

Whose shot was deemed not to have crossed the line in the 2000 African Cup of Nations final penalty shoot-out?

Where is the 2002 African Cup of Nations finals tournament to be played?

Quiz 48 The 80s

LEVEL 3

1 Who scored a rare header to win the FA Cup final for West Ham in 1980?

2 Who won the Milk Cup in 1984?

3 Which team lost the 1984 Milk Cup final but won the FA Cup the same year?

4 Who was Barcelona's manager when they lost the European Cup in 1986?

5 Who scored an own goal in the 1987 FA Cup final?

6 Who beat Chelsea in the Milk Cup semi-final in 1985 and sparked a riot as a result?

7 Which club won the Milk Cup for the only time in their history in 1986?

8 Who set up Argentina's winning goal in the 1986 World Cup final?

9 Which team was thrown out of the Littlewoods Cup in 1986 for refusing to allow away fans into their ground?

10 Which non-league team beat Wolves 3-0 in the first round of the FA Cup in 1987?

11 Who ended Liverpool's 29-match unbeaten run in March 1988?

12 Who scored Celtic's winner in the Old Firm Scottish Cup final in 1989?

13 In which year did Don Revie die?

14 Which Scottish team scored five goals in one match but were still eliminated from the 1990 European Cup Winners' Cup?

15 Who scored a goal and an own goal on his debut for Liverpool in 1980?

16 Which team used only 14 players during their championship-winning season in 1981?

17 Which team were ordered to play a Cup Winners' Cup match behind closed doors in 1980 following crowd trouble?

18 Who retired as manager of Liverpool after the 1983 Milk Cup final?

19 Who missed when he should have scored in the last minute of the 1983 FA Cup final?

20 Who won the first ever all-Merseyside FA Cup final in 1986?

Quiz 49 Arsenal

LEVEL 3

1   Which recent Arsenal signing was voted Player of the Tournament for the 2000 African Nations Cup?

2   Which former player is currently the coach of Arsenal reserves?

3   Which former England captain was manager of Arsenal between 1962 and 1966?

4   When did Arsenal move to Highbury?

5   Who did Arsenal beat 6-1 in a league game in April 1999?

6   From whom did Arsenal sign full-back Lee Dixon?

7   Where was David Seaman born?

8   Where did Christopher Wreh go on loan in 1998?

9   Who was manager of Arsenal when they won the double in 1971?

10   Which Arsenal striker was the First Division's joint top-scorer in 1977?

11   Who celebrated a goal against Coventry in 1979 by dropping his shorts in front of the crowd?

12   Who was man of the match for Arsenal in the 1979 FA Cup final?

13   Who scored Arsenal's first goal in the championship decider against Liverpool at Anfield in 1989?

14   Who top scored for Arsenal in the championship-winning 1990-91 season?

15   Where was Paulo Vernazza born?

16   Who are Arsenal's current sponsors?

17   What were Arsenal called between 1913 and 1927?

18   What was the score when Arsenal met Manchester United at Highbury in the league in September 1998?

19   What is Arsenal's record league victory?

20   Who is Arsenal's vice-chairman?

Quiz 50 Old Football

Answers – see page 260 **LEVEL 3**

1 Who did Arsenal break the transfer record for when signing him in 1938?

2 Who was the Italian manager when they won the World Cup in 1938?

3 In which year did the Pools Panel first sit?

4 Who lost the League Championship by 0.686 of a goal in 1964-65?

5 What kind of exhibition was the World Cup stolen from in 1966?

6 Who set a new transfer record when he moved from Swansea to Tottenham in 1958?

7 Whose fierce tackling in the FA Cup final brought them jeers from the crowd on their lap on honour in 1960?

8 Which England forward was interned in Germany during the Great War?

9 Who defied the Football League to enter the European Cup in 1956?

10 For which country did Josef Masopust, 1962 Footballer of the Year, play?

11 In 1965 who were the first Eastern bloc club to win a European cup?

12 Who was Berwick Rangers goalkeeper and manager when they sensationally knocked Rangers out of the FA Cup in 1967?

13 In 1959 who reached 100 League goals in fewer matches than any previous player?

14 Who scored in an FA Cup final, but watched his team win the match from his hospital bed?

15 How many England Internationals died in the 1958 Munich air disaster?

16 Which Yeovil player-manager later took Fulham to Wembley?

17 How many people watched the 1948 FA Cup final on television?

18 Players from which two teams were banned for match-fixing in the 1914-15 season?

19 Which manager took Northern Ireland to the 1958 World Cup finals?

20 Which team lost their League status at the end of the 1969-70 season

Quiz 51 West Ham United

Answers – see page 257

LEVEL 3

1 In which city was Paolo Di Canio born?

2 Who was manager of West Ham from 1961 to 1974?

3 Who is Harry Redknapp's assistant manager?

4 What is West Ham's record league victory?

5 When did West Ham move to the Boleyn Ground?

6 What is West Ham's longest sequence of league wins?

7 What are West Ham's away colours?

8 What is West Ham's record goal tally for a league season?

9 From which club did West Ham sign Paolo Di Canio?

10 In which year did Harry Redknapp take over as manager of the club?

11 Who did West Ham beat 5-1 in a league game in April 1999?

12 When did West Ham last win the FA Cup?

13 From which club did West Ham buy Neil Ruddock?

14 How many England caps did Martin Peters win in his career?

15 Who knocked the Hammers out of the Cup Winners' Cup in 1981?

16 Why did Ron Greenwood leave West Ham?

17 What was the score in the match between West Ham and Castilla of Spain that was played behind closed doors in 1980?

18 How many times have West Ham reached the FA Cup semi-final stage?

19 Who scored West Ham's opening goal in the FA Cup semi-final replay against Everton in 1980?

20 Who said 'If my head had been a ball, it would have ended in the top corner of the net'?

Quiz 52 Nationwide League

LEVEL 3

Answers – see page 258

1 Which former British Davis Cup captain bought Hull City in 1997?

2 Who won their first 11 games in the First Division in 1992-93?

3 Which Darlington striker was the top Third Division scorer in 1999-2000?

4 Which Reading midfielder was chosen in the 1999-2000 PFA Divisional Team of the Season?

5 Which former Wimbledon striker scored the winner for Peterborough in the 2000 Third Division play-off final?

6 Which Nationwide club are sponsored by Brittania Building Society?

7 Hanging on the Telephone is a fanzine of which Nationwide League club?

8 The Nationwide sponsor which Nationwide League team?

9 Paul Devlin was which Nationwide team's player of the year in 1999-2000?

10 Which Third Division team had the highest average attendance in 1999-2000: Millwall, Stoke City or Preston N.E.?

11 Which Nationwide team play in blue and amber striped shirts?

12 Who did Luton Town dismiss as their boss in 2000?

13 Slumberland sponsor which Nationwide League team?

14 Steve Claridge was player of the year at which Nationwide club in 1999-2000?

15 Who went from the First Division to the Third in consecutive years from 1996-98?

16 Which manager won play-offs with Notts County and Huddersfield Town?

17 From which club did Oxford United sign Joey Beauchamp?

18 Which Second Division team sacked their joint-managers in September 2000?

19 Who played their last game at Elm Park in 1998?

20 Which Lancashire team regularly used to kick off home matches at 3.15pm?

Answers

Old Football (see Quiz 50)
1 Bryn Jones. 2 Vittorio Pozzo. 3 1963. 4 Leeds United. 5 Stamp.
6 Cliff Jones. 7 Wolves. 8 Steve Bloomer. 9 Manchester United.
10 Czechoslovakia. 11 Ferencvaros. 12 Jock Wallace.
13 Brian Clough. 14 Roy Dwight. 15 Four. 16 Alec Stock.
17 One million. 18 Liverpool and Man. Utd. 19 Peter Doherty.
20 Bradford Park Avenue.

Quiz 53 Manchester City

Answers – see page 263

LEVEL 3

1   Who is head coach at the club?
2   Which former City player was manager at the club between 1974 and 1979?
3   In which city was Paul Dickov born?
4   From which club did City buy Shaun Goater?
5   Who were the opponents in City's last European match?
6   From whom did City buy defender Spencer Prior in 1999-2000?
7   What is City's record league victory?
8   Who scored City's first goal in the 1976 League Cup final?
9   Who did City beat in their last match of the season to win the league championship in 1968?
10 Who top scored for City that season?
11 How much did Joe Mercer pay for Colin Bell?
12 What is City's longest sequence of league games without a win?
13 At which club did Malcolm Allison first meet Tony Book?
14 How many England caps did Mike Summerbee win?
15 Who did City beat in the final of the European Cup Winners' Cup in 1970?
16 In which city did they play that match?
17 Who is the youngest player ever to play for City?
18 Who took over from Brian Horton as City manager in 1995?
19 Who is the current reserve team manager at City?
20 Who is City's highest league scorer?

Quiz 54 The West Country

LEVEL 3

Answers – see page 264

1   The Evening Herald sponsor which West Country team?

2   Which Ashton Gate team did Bristol City merge with in 1900?

3   Which West Country team released all of their players in the summer of 2000?

4   Bristol Rovers are nicknamed the Pirates but what do their fans call them?

5   Whose love of Scotland inspired Plymouth's name Argyle?

6   Which former Bristol City striker is in Manchester City's 2000-01 squad?

7   Which West Country club replaced Aberdare Athletic in the Football League in 1927?

8   Which West Country club play in red and white striped shirts?

9   Which West Country club sold their two 1999-2000 leading scorers by September 2000?

10   Who won the Anglo-Italian League Cup-winners Cup in 1970 and 1971?

11   Which 2000 England striker enjoyed an earlier spell at Ashton Gate?

12   Who was Swindon Town's manager when they won promotion in 1992-93?

13   Who joined Man. United from Torquay United for £180,000 in 1988?

14   From which West Country side did Tony Book join Manchester City?

15   How many seasons did Bristol City spend in the top flight in the 70s?

16   In what colour shirts do Plymouth play?

17   From which club did Derby County sign Dean Sturridge?

18   Who followed his father into the Bristol Rovers side and later played for England?

19   Who had the highest average attendance in 1999-2000: Plymouth, Exeter or Torquay?

20   Billy Mercer was which West Country club's Player of the Year in 1999-2000?

Jody Morris (see Quiz 56)

Answers

1 Hammersmith. 2 1978. 3 FA School of Excellence.
4 December 1995. 5 February 1996. 6 Middlesbrough.
7 5ft 5 ins (165cm). 8 Blackpool. 9 One. 10 Oldham Athletic.
11 Luxembourg. 12 Manchester United. 13 Galatasaray.
14 Richmond. 15 Four. 16 Southampton. 17 Young Player of the Year. 18 Arthur Bell. 19 30. 20 Pending court case.

Quiz 55 East Anglia & Essex
LEVEL 3
Answers – see page 261

1 In which year did Ipswich Town win the Texaco Cup?

2 Who is Norwich City's highest goalscorer?

3 What is the name of Colchester United's ground?

4 Where did Norwich City first play?

5 Which FA Cup winner was manager at Southend between 1986 and 1987, and 1988 and 1992?

6 Who did Ipswich Town defeat to win the UEFA Cup in 1981?

7 In which year did Colchester United win the FA Trophy?

8 Who is Southend's most capped player?

9 Who holds the league appearances record for Ipswich Town?

10 Who is the current director of football at Norwich City?

11 What club record did Ipswich set in March 1999?

12 What is the furthest that Southend have ever gone in the League Cup?

13 What nationality is Colchester's Lomano Lua Lua?

14 Where was Ipswich's Titus Bramble born?

15 What is Norwich City's best finishing position in the Premier League?

16 Who is Ipswich Town's most capped player?

17 What is Southend's longest sequence of league wins?

18 Which Italian giants visited Carrow Road in November 1993 for a UEFA Cup tie?

19 Who scored twice in Colchester's legendary FA Cup victory against Leeds in 1971?

20 Who was the Ipswich Town manager between 1990 and 1994?

Quiz 56 Jody Morris

Answers – see page 262

LEVEL 3

1 Where was Jody born?

2 In which year was that?

3 From which famous football school did he graduate?

4 When did he sign for Chelsea?

5 When did make his first team debut?

6 Who were Chelsea playing that day?

7 How tall is Jody?

8 Against which club did Jody score his first goal for Chelsea?

9 How many goals did Jody score in the 1998-99 season?

10 Against which club did Jody make his FA Cup debut?

11 Jody was sent off in an England Under 21 game in 1998. Who were the opponents that day?

12 In October 1999 Jody scored in a 5-0 victory. Who were the opposition that day?

13 Against which club did Jody make his full debut in the Champions League?

14 Where did Jody go to school?

15 How many yellow cards did Jody pick up during 1999-2000?

16 Jody scored in a Coca-Cola Cup fourth round match in November 199? Who were the opponents?

17 What Chelsea honour did Jody win in 1996?

18 Who were Jody's kit sponsors during the first few years of this career?

19 How many league appearances did Jody make in 1999-2000?

20 Why was Jody not considered for the England Under 21 team for the 2000 European Championship?

Who is Aberdeen's most capped player?

When did Dundee last win the Scottish League Cup?

Who is Hibernian's highest goalscorer?

What colour shirts do Kilmarnock play in?

What is the name of Clyde's stadium?

Who is the manager of Morton?

Which European competition did Raith Rovers play in during 1995-96?

Who is Celtic's most capped player?

Which Scottish Premier League team play in maroon shirts?

Who won the Scottish Cup in 1991?

Who is Dundee's highest goalscorer?

Who is Rangers' assistant manager?

In which town do Queen of the South play?

What is the capacity of East Fife's Bayview Stadium?

Which Frenchman opened the scoring for Rangers in the 1999 Coca-Cola Cup final?

What did Stenhousemuir achieve in 1999?

Why was the Scottish Cup not awarded in 1909?

How many teams play in Falkirk?

Up to 2000, how many times have Rangers appeared in the Scottish League Cup final?

In which town do Ross County play?

Bad Boys (see Quiz 59)
1 Gary Croft. **2** Peter Storey. **3** George Graham. **4** Dwight Yorke and Andy Cole. **5** Ray Parlour. **6** Faustino Asprilla. **7** Match fixing. **8** Ian Wright. **9** Jim Baxter. **10** George Best. **11** Edmundo. **12** Babb and Kennedy. **13** Simon Garner. **14** Sammy Nelson. **15** Paolo Rossi. **16** Jamie Lawrence. **17** Terry Fenwick. **18** Wimbledon. **19** Zvonimir Boban. **20** Eric Cantona.

Quiz 58 Local Rivals

Answers – see page 268

LEVEL 3

1   Which team changed their nickname in the 80s to emulate their rivals?

2   Which local rivals shared a ground and were both relegated in 1980-81?

3   Which city hosts the derby game between Piroozi and Esteghlal?

4   In which country does the derby game between Olimpia and Club Guarani take place?

5   Who plays Boca Juniors in the Buenos Aires derby?

6   Who are Ayr United's local rivals?

7   Which side play St Pauli in their derby match?

8   Marler Estates tried to merge which rival clubs in 1987?

9   Who was the first player to win an FA Cup with Rangers and Celtic?

10 Which local rivals were the Faroe Islands' only opponents from 1930-69?

11 Who are Schalke 04's local rivals?

12 Has there been more Liverpool wins, Everton wins or draws in the history of the Merseyside derby?

13 Which city has the closest League football stadiums in Britain?

14 Which local rivals of Linfield left the league in 1949?

15 Which rival side did Graeme Souness infuriate by planting his team's flag in their pitch?

16 Who are Burnley's local rivals?

17 Who are East Fife's neighbouring side?

18 For which rivals do Cambridge United reserve their greatest contempt?

19 In which city are UNAM and America local rivals?

20 Which team are Barcelona's nearest if not fiercest rivals?

Quiz 59 Bad Boys

Answers – see page 265

Answers – see page 265

LEVEL 3

1 Who received a sentence for driving while disqualified and trying to pass himself off as the son of snooker star Dennis Taylor?

2 Who received a six-month sentence for running a brothel in 1979?

3 Whose 1998 temporary downfall was attributed to Rune Hauge?

4 According to the *News of the World* which Manchester United players were involved in a 'three-in-a-bed love romp' in 1999?

5 Who in his wild days was fined after an altercation with a rickshaw driver while on a Far East tour?

6 Which former Premier League star fired a gun in a crowded bar?

7 Why were England players Tony Kay and Peter Swan jailed in 1965?

8 Who trashed the referee's changing room after getting sent off in 1999?

9 Which Scot was accused of stealing the Scottish FA Cup final ball?

10 Who was arrested for drink driving outside Buckingham Palace?

11 Which Brazilian got himself in trouble for giving beer to chimps?

12 Which Irish stars were arrested for damaging a police officer's car?

13 Which Blackburn Rovers goalscorer was sent to prison for disposing of cash held as matrimonial assets?

14 Who was banned for two matches for dropping his shorts to supporters?

15 Who became a hero shortly after serving a ban for match-fixing?

16 Whose criminal record led them to be banned from playing for Jamaica.

17 Which Tottenham and England defender received a four month jail sentence in 1992 for drink-driving offences?

18 Which club were fined when nine of their players dropped their shorts in a testimonial match?

19 Which Croatian international went on the run after being accused of assaulting a Serb policeman?

20 Who was arrested after a row with an 1994 World Cup official?

1   Who was originally banned for life for his part in the Bulgarian Cup Final brawl in 1985?

2   Who changed their name to Ujpesti Torna Egylet in 1990?

3   Kosice, Spartak Trnava and Tatran Presov play in which country's league?

4   For which 2000 Champions League team did Slovenian Zahovic play?

5   Which country did Maribor Teatanic represent in the 1999-2000 Champions League?

6   Which Romanian defender announced his retirement from international football after Euro 2000?

7   FK Obilic surprisingly won the 1998 league title in which country?

8   Who were the Ukrainian team drawn in Arsenal's 2000-2001 Champions League group?

9   Which East European team play at the Crvena Zvezda stadium?

10 For which West European team did Poland's Zbigniew Boniek play?

11 Who were the last team to win the East German league championship?

12 Which Soviet Union goalscoring legend became manager of Olympiakos and then a Ukrainian MP?

13 Which Yugoslavian international scored in the 1994 European Cup final?

14 Which Polish captain played for Manchester City?

15 Which Dynamo Kiev striker joined AC Milan in 1997?

16 Which legendary player scored against Manchester United for Croatia Zagreb in the 1999-2000 Champions league?

17 What relation is Gica Popescu to Georghe Hagi?

18 Which Romanian played in the 2000 Champions League final?

19 Tomas Rosicky is which team's teenage playmaker?

20 Which veteran Yugoslav captain plays in Japan's J-League?

In which year did Sol make his England debut?

What is the name Sol short for?

In which city was Campbell born?

Which Premier League player played in the same boys' district team as Sol?

How many England under 21 caps did Sol earn?

Against which team did Sol score two goals to earn a 2-2 draw at White Hart Lane in 1998-99?

Which pop star did the Daily Star suggest Sol had unsuccessfully asked out?

Against which country in World Cup '98 did Sol have a goal disallowed?

In which position did Sol play for England against France in September 2000?

How many minutes did Sol play for against Scotland in Euro '96?

From where did Spurs sign Campbell?

Against which team did a Campbell own goal knock Spurs out of the UEFA Cup?

Which trophies, if any, has Campbell lifted as Tottenham captain?

Which manager brought Sol into the Spurs team?

What is Sol's middle name?

Which number shirt does Sol wear at Tottenham?

When was Sol first given the captaincy of England?

In which position did Campbell begin his Spurs career?

What injury kept Sol out of the England World Cup qualifiers in October 2000?

Against which London club did Sol score a winning header in October 2000?

The 70s (see Quiz 63)
1 George Best. **2** Gordon Banks. **3** Salonika. **4** Rangers. **5** 1977.
6 Liverpool. **7** Jim Montgomery. **8** Frank Worthington. **9** Celtic.
10 1971. **11** Liverpool. **12** Bill Nicholson. **13** Two. **14** 1973.
15 Jan Tomaszewski. **16** Terry Paine. **17** Liverpool's Ian Callaghan.
18 Bobby Moore. **19** Chris Nicholl. **20** £400,000.

Quiz 62 Scandinavia

Answers – see page 272   **LEVEL 3**

1   Which Scandinavian team knocked Inter Milan out of the 2000-2001 Champions League qualifying rounds?

2   What nationality is Munich 1860's Erik Mykland?

3   Which club does Bent Skammelsrud play for?

4   How many footballing brothers are there in the Flo family?

5   Which country does Watford's Heidar Helguson come from?

6   Between which months does the Norwegian league season run?

7   In which city do Swedish club AIK play?

8   Which English club did Helsingborgs beat in the 1996 UEFA Cup?

9   For which Danish club did Brian Laudrup first play league football?

10   Which country knocked England out of the 1994 World Cup?

11   Who was the England manager at the time?

12   From which club did Chelsea buy Icelandic midfielder Eidur Gudjohnsen?

13   Which was the last Scandinavian club to reach the European Cup final?

14   From which club did Valencia buy striker John Carew?

15   Which country do Helsingborgs come from?

16   What is the Trippeligaen?

17   What is Helsingborgs stadium called?

18   Against which Norwegian team did Chelsea's Gianluca Vialli hit five goals in two matches in 1998?

19   In which country do Trelleborgs play?

20   Which Tottenham striker was born in Norway?

Answers

Alex Ferguson (see Quiz 64)
1 Arsenal. 2 Inter Milan. 3 David Elleray. 4 May 2002.
5 Queens Park. 6 East Stirlingshire. 7 1999. 8 1986. 9 Necaxa
10 None. 11 Rest of the World. 12 Five. 13 St. Mirren. 14 Two.
15 1990 FA Cup. 16 Managing My Life. 17 Glasgow.
18 Ron Atkinson. 19 1997-98. 20 David Beckham.

LEVEL 3

1   Who scored six goals for Manchester United against Northampton in an FA Cup match in Feburary 1970?

2   Who was voted Footballer of the Year in 1972?

3   Where did Leeds lose to AC Milan in the 1973 ECW Cup final?

4   Who won the Scottish treble in 1976?

5   In which year did Kevin Keegan leave Liverpool for Hamburg?

6   Who won the First Division title after a 3-1 win at Molineux in May 1976, consigning Wolves to relegation at the same time?

7   Whose double save helped to win Sunderland the FA Cup in 1973?

8   Who was the First Division's top scorer in 1979?

9   Who beat Leeds in the semi-final of the European Cup in 1970?

10   In which year did Jimmy Greaves retire from football?

11   Which club provided six players for England against Switzerland in 1977?

12   Who resigned as Spurs manager in 1974?

13   How many replays did it take to settle the League Cup final of 1977 between Aston Villa and Everton?

14   When was league football first played on Sundays?

15   Of whom did Alf Ramsey say 'I have never seen a better performance at Wembley by a visiting goalkeeper'?

16   Which ex-England winger retired in 1977 after 824 league games for Southampton and Hereford?

17   Who was voted Footballer of the Year in 1974?

18   Who saved a penalty for West Ham in a League Cup semi-final against Stoke in 1972?

19   Which Aston Villa defender scored all four goals in a 2-2 draw with Leicester in March 1976?

20   How much did Liverpool pay for Celtic's Kenny Dalglish in 1977?

1   In 1999 of which team did Alex Ferguson say 'the players are belligerent and like a scrap?'

2   What Champions League opponents did Alex expect to be 'scheming, cheating and ref-baiting?'

3   Which referee did Ferguson accuse of trying to rob United of the 1999 championship?

4   Which month and year has Ferguson set for his retirement?

5   At which Scottish club was Ferguson a teenage apprentice?

6   At which club did Ferguson begin his management career?

7   In which year did he become Sir Alex?

8   In which year did Ferguson take over as manager of Scotland?

9   Against which team in January 2000 was Alex Ferguson sent off?

10 How many Scotland caps did Ferguson win?

11 Who did United play in Ferguson's record-breaking 1999 testimonial?

12 How many times did Alex win the Manager of the Year award in the 90s?

13 Which club did Sir Alex win the Scottish First Division with in 1977?

14 How many times have Alex Ferguson's teams won the European Cup Winners Cup?

15 What was the first trophy Ferguson won with Manchester United?

16 What was the name of Ferguson's 1999 autobiography?

17 In which city was Ferguson born?

18 Who did Ferguson take over from at Manchester United?

19 Which was the only season of the 90s that Ferguson's team failed to pick up a trophy?

20 Who said: 'Alex Ferguson is the best manager I've ever had at this level. Well, he's the only manager I've actually had at this level. But he's the best manager I've ever had.'

Answers

Scandinavia (see Quiz 62)
1 Helsingborg. 2 Norwegian. 3 Rosenborg. 4 Five. 5 Iceland.
6 April to October. 7 Stockholm. 8 Aston Villa. 9 Brondby.
10 Holland. 11 Graham Taylor. 12 Bolton. 13 Malmo of Sweden in 1979. 14 Rosenborg. 15 Sweden. 16 The Norwegian Premier League. 17 Räsunda Stadium, Stockholm. 18 Tromso.
19 Sweden. 20 Steffen Iversen.

Quiz 65 Premiership Stars

Answers – see page 275

1 Which young Aston Villa and England defender was born in Hastings?

2 Which Saint went on as a second half sub and scored twice in a 3-3 draw at Old Trafford in September 1999?

3 Who top scored for Liverpool during 1999-2000?

4 Who scored twice as Chelsea beat Sunderland 4-0 on the opening day of the 1999-2000 season?

5 Which forward did West Ham buy from QPR in 1997?

6 Who made most appearances for Newcastle during 1998-99?

7 Who is Reg Vardy?

8 Which Manchester United defender missed every game but two through injury in 1999-2000?

9 Which Bradford City star does somersaults when he's celebrating?

10 For which Premiership club does youngster Ashley Cole play?

11 Who loaned midfielder John Eustace to Dundee United for 1999-2000?

12 Who signed Steven Hughes from Arsenal in 1999-2000?

13 Who signed Marcus Stewart for £2.5m in summer 2000?

14 Of which club is Peter Ridsdale the chairman?

15 For which club does Eidur Gudjohnsen play?

16 Which club might have Dyer, Hughes, Speed and Lee as the midfield?

17 From whom did Tottenham sign Mauricio Taricco?

18 For whom does Peruvian Ysrael Zuniga play?

19 Who was Middlesbrough's Player of the Season in 1999-2000?

20 Where does Norwegian Jo Tessam play?

Ful-Back/Wing-Back (see Quiz 67)
1 Sir Alf Ramsey. 2 Gianluca Zambrotta. 3 Sampdoria. 4 Roma.
5 Winston Bogarde. 6 Nicky Summerbee. 7 Eddie Gray.
8 Lee Martin. 9 Stuart Pearce. 10 Sparta Prague. 11 Anderlecht.
12 1991. 13 Tarhar El Khalej. 14 Inter Milan. 15 Paul Breitner.
16 Antonio Cabrini. 17 Cyril Knowles. 18 Roberto Carlos.
19 Tony Dorigo. 20 Keith Newton.

Quiz 66 Paul Scholes

Answers – see page 276   **LEVEL 3**

1   In which year was Paul Scholes born?

2   Where was he born?

3   In which year did he sign trainee forms for Manchester United?

4   Against whom did he make his league debut?

5   How many goals did he score in that game?

6   In which season did he become a first-team regular at Old Trafford?

7   What is his squad number?

8   Who did Paul support as a youngster?

9   Which club award did Paul win in 1993?

10   Against whom did Paul make his full England debut?

11   What was significant about Paul's goal against Inter in March 1999?

12   Why did Paul not go to Brazil in January 1999?

13   What is the name of Paul Scholes's son?

14   Against whom did Paul score a hat-trick for England at Wembley?

15   How tall is Paul?

16   Why did Paul miss the Champions League final in 1999?

17   Paul scored in his first England match at Wembley. Who were the opposition that day?

18   Against whom did Paul score in an FA Cup final?

19   Who were the opposition when Paul was sent off in an England international in June 1999?

20   Who did Paul score against in the opening game of the 1998 World Cup

Answers

Old Football 2 (see Quiz 68)
1 Alf Common. 2 Lord Alfred Kinnaird, 9. 3 1938. 4 John Thomson. 5 Arsenal. 6 1901. 7 Leeds City's. 8 1930. 9 Spain. 10 Arsenal v Sheffield United, 1927. 11 George V. 12 Pongo Waring. 13 Manchester City. 14 Italy. 15 Hampden Park, Glasgow 16 Hughie Gallacher. 17 Preston North End. 18 Millwall. 19 Sheffield United and Chelsea. 20 Frank Swift.

1 Who was the last former full-back to manage England?

2 Which Italian full-back was sent off in a Euro 2000 semi-final?

3 With which club side is Yugoslavia's Nenad Sakic a wing-back?

4 Where does French wing back Vincent Candela play his club football?

5 Which Chelsea wing-back was signed from Barcelona?

6 Which full-back was sent off in 1999-2000 for elbowing Sunderland's

7 Which Leeds United's forward became the team's full back in the 1980-81 season?

8 Which Manchester United full-back scored in the 1990 FA Cup final replay?

9 Who was the last full-back to score in an FA Cup final?

10 Against which opposition did Arsenal's Silvinho score a wonder goal in their opening 2000 Champions League match?

11 From which club did Chelsea sign Celestine Babayaro?

12 In which year did Dennis Irwin make his Republic of Ireland debut?

13 What is the name of Southampton's Moroccan full-back?

14 From which club did Manchester United sign Mickael Silvestre?

15 Which full-back scored in the 1974 World Cup final?

16 Which Italian full-back missed a penalty in the 1982 World Cup final?

17 Which former England full-back died in 1991while manager of Darlington?

18 Which wing-back scored four goals in Real Madrid's triumphant 1999-2000 Champions League campaign?

19 Which Australian-born full-back won a Championship medal with Leeds United in 1992?

20 Which Everton full-back made his last appearance for England against West Germany in the 1970 World Cup?

---

1   Who was English football's first £1000 player?

2   Which player holds the record number of appearances in the FA Cup final?

3   In which year were numbered shirts first worn for league games?

4   Which Celtic keeper died after a collision with a Rangers player in 1931?

5   Of which team was Herbert Chapman manager when he died in 1934?

6   In which year did Spurs first win the FA Cup?

7   Whose players were auctioned off when the team was expelled from the league in 1919?

8   In which year did the first World Cup take place?

9   In May 1929 England lost to a foreign team for the first time. Which team?

10 What was the first match broadcast live on radio?

11 Who became the first reigning monarch to attend the Cup final, in 1914?

12 Which Aston Villa player top scored in the First Division in 1932?

13 In 1926 who became the first club to reach the FA Cup final and be relegated from the First Division in the same season?

14 Who won the World Cup in 1934?

15 Which British ground held a world record crowd of 149,547 for an international in 1937?

16 Who scored five goals for Scotland in a 7-3 victory against Ireland in 1929?

17 Who became the first English league and cup double winners, in 1888-89?

18 Who became the first Third Division side to reach the FA Cup semi final, in 1937?

19 Who contested the 'Khaki Cup final' in 1915?

20 Which Manchester City keeper was so overcome at winning the FA Cup in 1934 that he fainted?

Answers

Paul Scholes (see Quiz 66)
1 1974. 2 Salford. 3 1991. 4 Ipswich Town. 5 Two in a 2-3 defeat. 6 1994-95. 7 18. 8 Oldham Athletic. 9 Young Player of the Year. 10 Italy. 11 First United player since Norman Whiteside to score on Italian soil. 12 Hernia operation. 13 Aaron Jake. 14 Poland. 15 5 ft 7 in (170c m). 16 Suspension. 17 Moldova. 18 Newcastle. 19 Sweden. 20 Tunisia.

Quiz 69 World Cup 1998

Answers – see page 279 **LEVEL 3**

1   Who did Scotland play in their opening game?

2   Who scored an own goal in that game?

3   Who did South African play in their first match?

4   Italy drew 2-2 in their opening match of the tournament – against which other nation?

5   Who did France defeat 4-0 in a group stage match?

6   Despite beating Bulgaria 6-1 in their last group game, who was eliminated from the tournament?

7   Who won the group stage game between Germany and the USA?

8   Who topped England's Group G?

9   Which country scored their first World Cup goal, in a group stage match against Croatia?

10 Who came back from 2-0 down against Holland to get a draw and qualify for the second round?

11 What was the score in the group match between Holland and Belgium?

12 Which Mexican performed the famous 'Bounce' during the tournament?

13 Which African country beat Spain 3-2 in a group stage match?

14 Who did Brazil beat 4-1 in a second round match?

15 Who did Denis Bergkamp score a sensational winner against in the quarter-finals?

16 Who did the hosts defeat to secure a semi-final place?

17 Where was the Brazil v Holland semi-final played?

18 Who won the third place play-off?

19 Who did they beat to claim their place?

20 Who scored France's third goal in the final?

Transfers (see Quiz 71)
1 Gianluigi Lentini. 2 Clive Allen. 3 Steve Simonson. 4 Michael Hughes. 5 Trevor Steven. 6 Rushden and Diamonds. 7 Bill Nicholson. 8 Udinese. 9 Allan Clarke. 10 Edu. 11 John Hartson. 12 Highest tribunal set fee. 13 Crystal Palace. 14 John Jensen. 15 £6 million. 16 Christian Vieri. 17 Duncan Ferguson. 18 Steve Bould. 19 Keith Gillespie. 20 Matt Jansen.

Answers

1   What was the score in the group match between Germany and Romania?

2   Who defeated Spain 1-0 in a group stage match?

3   Who went 3-0 down to Slovenia and got back for a 3-3 draw in their opening match of the tournament?

4   Who scored Italy's winner against Turkey in their group stage match?

5   Who beat Yugoslavia with a 90th-minute penalty in the last game of their group?

6   Who scored twice for the Czech Republic in a group match against Denmark?

7   What was the score in the group match between Holland and France?

8   Who topped England's Group A?

9   How many teams failed to win a single game in the tournament?

10 How many penalties were awarded during the tournament?

11 Which player scored the fastest goal in the competition?

12 Which was the only team beaten by co-hosts Belgium?

13 Who scored for Sweden against Italy in their group stage match?

14 Which country conceded most goals in the tournament?

15 Which Spurs player scored for Norway against Spain in a group stage game?

16 Who did Turkey play in the quarter-finals?

17 Who were the lowest scorers in the tournement?

18 Who scored Spain's goal from the penalty spot in their quarter-final match against France?

19 Who did Italy beat in the semi-final?

20 Who scored France's 90th-minute equaliser in the final?

Answers

Non-League (see Quiz 72)
1 Justin Jackson. 2 Dave McEwan. 3 Peterhead. 4 Kingstonian.
5 Hereford. 6 Dagenham and Redbridge. 7 Altrincham.
8 Stevenage Borough. 9 Nuneaton Borough. 10 Rushden and
Diamonds. 11 Nigel Clough. 12 Barry Hayles. 13 Colwyn Bay.
14 Eintracht Trier. 15 WBA. 16 Ian Wright. 17 Stan Collymore.
18 Surrey. 19 Edgar Street. 20 Andy Townsend.

Quiz 71 Transfers

Answers – see page 277

1 Whose transfer from Torino to Milan in 1992 set a world record fee that was unbroken for four years?

2 Which £1.25 million signing played only three friendlies for Arsenal before joining Crystal Palace in 1980?

3 Which Tranmere player cost Everton the record fee for a goalkeeper in 1998?

4 Who was the first British player to be transferred under the Bosman ruling?

5 Which Englishman moved for the highest fee paid to a Scottish club?

6 Which club did Morecambe's Justin Jackson join in 2000, creating a record fee between non-league clubs?

7 Which championship player and manager won just one England cup?

8 Amoroso and Appiah joined Parma from which club in June 1999?

9 Which player was the subject of a record transfer fee in 1968 and 1969?

10 Whose £6 million transfer to Arsenal collapsed after a passport fiasco?

11 Medicals stopped whose moves to Rangers and Tottenham in 2000?

12 Which transfer record does Chris Bart-Williams hold?

13 Which club sold Gareth Southgate and Chris Armstrong in 1994?

14 Which Dane was one of George Graham's 'bung' transfer deals?

15 West Ham bought Marc Vivien Foe for £3.5 million in 1999. How much did they receive for him six months later?

16 Who was transferred three times from 1997-2000 for over £60 million?

17 Who is the most expensive Scotsman ever?

18 Which player did not receive a free transfer in 2000: Steve Bould, Peter Atherton or John Scales?

19 Who went to Newcastle as part of Andy Cole's move to Manchester Utd?

20 Who is the most expensive player to be bought by a First Division club?

Quiz 72 Non-League

Answers – see page 278

LEVEL 3

1 Who was the Nationwide Conference's leading scorer in 1999-2000?

2 Who did Tottenham sign from Dulwich Hamlet in 1999?

3 Who won the Scottish Highfield League in 1999-2000?

4 Who won the 2000 FA Challenge Trophy?

5 Who drew 0-0 with Leicester City in the 1999-2000 FA Cup?

6 Which Essex team were the 1999-2000 Ryman League winners?

7 Which 80s Conference champions were relegated to the Unibond League in 1999-2000?

8 Who are the only Conference winners since 1986 not to have played League football?

9 From which non-league club did Derby County sign Malcolm Christie?

10 Which non-league team held Sheffield United to a draw in the 1999-2000 FA Cup?

11 Who is Burton Albion's manager?

12 Which 2000-2001 Fulham goalscorer played for Stevenage Borough?

13 Which Welsh team play in the Unibond League?

14 Which German non-league team beat Schalke 04 and Borussia Dortmund in the 1996-97 German Cup?

15 Which League team went out of the third round of the FA Cup in 1991 to Woking?

16 Which 90s England international joined Crystal Palace from Greenwich Borough in 1985?

17 Which 90s England international joined Crystal Palace from Stafford Rangers in 1990?

18 In which county do Corinthian Casuals play home games?

19 What is the name of Hereford's United ground?

20 Which Irish captain started his career at Welling and then Weymouth?

Answers

Euro 2000 (see Quiz 70)
1 1-1. 2 Norway. 3 Yugoslavia. 4 Inzaghi. 5 Spain. 6 Vladimir Smicer. 7 3-2 to Holland. 8 Portugal. 9 Four. 10 13 (8 were scored). 11 Paul Scholes. 12 Sweden. 13 Henrik Larsson. 14 Yugoslavia, nine goals. 15 Steffen Iversen. 16 Portugal. 17 Denmark, no goals. 18 Mendieta. 19 Holland. 20 Sylvain Wiltord.

Quiz 73 Who Did What? 4
LEVEL 3

1 Who said 'I know Tony Adams is playing because he is the only name I know. All these Viallis, Vieiras and Viagras'?

2 Which Portuguese player signed for Spurs from Sporting Lisbon?

3 Which club completed post-war record of 12 successive home league wins in April 1999?

4 Who is the longest-serving club chaplain?

5 Which club scored seven goals in 25 minutes in an FA Cup match against Southport in 1932?

6 Which Leyton Orient player played for France against England in 1992?

7 Who scored five goals for Gillingham in a league game at Burnley in February 1999?

8 Who was the first English league club to tour South America?

9 Who set a club record of 28 games undefeated in 1984-85?

10 Who won their first match at Villa Park for 63 years in February 1999?

11 Who scored a hat-trick on his debut for Bristol Rovers in 1977?

12 What did Aston Villa do in a match against Celta Vigo in October 1998?

13 Who was the top scorer in Portuguese football from 1997 to 2000?

14 Who scored a hat-trick for Portugal against Germany at Euro 2000?

15 Who left Dortmund for Schalke in summer 2000?

16 Who scored twice for Vasco Da Gama against Manchester United in the FIFA World Club Championship in January 2000?

17 Who won the Portuguese championship for five years in a row between 1995 and 1999?

18 With which club did Brazilian captain Dunga begin his career?

19 Which keeper joined Brescia in summer 2000?

20 Who were Brazilian champions in 1999?

1   Who introduced *catenaccio* defending to Italian football during the 1960s?

2   Which Italian defender was known as the Emperor of Milan?

3   Which Spanish player was known as 'The Vulture'?

4   Who scored the winner for AC Milan in the 1990 European Cup final?

5   Which Romanian midfielder plies his trade in Turkey with Galatasaray?

6   Complete the great 1970s French midfield line-up: Giresse, Platini and...?

7   Which legendary German team won three European Cups in a row?

8   Which Dutchman scored the winner for Barcelona in the 1992 European Cup final aganst Sampdoria?

9   Of which Argentinian-born player was it said that 'He is the greatest player I have ever seen. The things he does in a match will never be equalled'?

10 Whose legendary forward line of the 1950s was known as *La Maquina*?

11 Whose life story was told in a film entitled *Sua Majestade o Rei*?

12 Who captained Bayern Munich to victory in the 1967 ECWC?

13 Which Belgian midfielder holds the record for international appearances for the country?

14 Which Italian legend was known as *Il Bambino D'Oro*?

15 Which Mexican of the 1980s was legendary for somersaulting after he had scored?

16 Apart from Pele, who is the only other player to score in four World Cups?

17 Who inspired Barcelona to a 5-0 victory against rivals Real Madrid in his first season as manager?

18 Which Italian player was voted Man of the Match in the 1982 World Cup final defeat of West Germany?

19 Which Colombian is well known for his frizzy hairstyle?

20 Who top scored in the 1978 World Cup finals, including two goals in the final for Argentina against Holland?

Quiz 75 Dennis Bergkamp
Answers – see page 281 **LEVEL 3**

1 In which competition did Bergkamp become Holland's highest scorer?

2 Which club did Dennis support as a boy?

3 How many goals did Bergkamp score against England at Wembley in 1993?

4 Who did Bergkamp replace at Inter Milan?

5 How many championships did Bergkamp win at Ajax?

6 Which English team did Bergkamp score, then at Inter, against in both UEFA Cup legs in 1993?

7 How much did Bergkamp cost Arsenal?

8 Against whom did Bergkamp score a hat-trick in his first season at Arsenal?

9 A goal against which team earned Bergkamp the 1998 World Cup Goal of the Tournament?

10 For how many years running was Bergkamp the Dutch league's top scorer?

11 Which trophies did Bergkamp win with Inter Milan?

12 What is Bergkamp's phobia?

13 Apart from the final, what was the only round of the 1999-2000 UEFA Cup in which Bergkamp failed to score?

14 Which substitute replaced Bergkamp in the 1999-2000 UEFA Cup final?

15 Which footballer is Bergkamp named after?

16 How many goals did Dennis score in Euro 2000?

17 In what year was Bergkamp voted the World and PFA Footballer of the Year?

18 When was Bergkamp given first, second and third places in *Match Of The Day*'s goal of the month competition?

19 Which Ajax team-mate signed with Bergkamp for Inter Milan?

20 In which year did Bergkamp make his international debut?

Quiz 76 Who Did What? 5
LEVEL 3

Answers – see page 282

1. Who was Nigeria's top scorer in the 1994 World Cup?

2. Which Japanese team did Ossie Ardiles manage in 1996?

3. Who was the last amateur to play in an FA Cup Final?

4. Which Nationwide team had two players in England's 2000 European Under 21championship squad?

5. Who were the first team to be automatically relegated from the league?

6. Men's magazine Loaded sponsored which Nationwide League team?

7. The 69er is a fanzine of which Nationwide League club?

8. Who beat West Ham in the 1976 Cup Winners Cup final?

9. Darko Pancev's penalty won the European Cup for which team?

10. Which Liverpool player helped develop the 'Predator' football boot?

11. Which England international was sold four times in the 90s for fees amounting to over £21 million?

12. Which Rochdale player received the PFA merit award in 1999?

13. Which Sunderland player was transfer-listed after wearing a 'sad Mackem b******s' t-shirt to Wembley?

14. Which Peruvian international played for Fort Lauderdale Strikers?

15. Who was Poland's goalkeeper in their 1973 match against England at Wembley?

16. Who were runners-up to Kidderminster Harriers in the 1999-2000 Vauxhall Conference?

17. Which club used to play at Pink Bank Lane and Reddish Lane?

18. Who were ranked higher by FIFA in January 2000, Nigeria or Peru?

19. Who made a return to the Premiership for Bradford City against Leeds in March 2000?

20. Who made his England debut in a 2-0 defeat by Chile at Wembley in 1998?

Quiz 77 Glenn Hoddle

Answers – see page 287

LEVEL 3

1 Which Tottenham legend has been credited with 'discovering' Hoddle?
2 Which England keeper did Hoddle beat for his first League goal?
3 Which trophy did Hoddle help win in 1975?
4 Against which team did Hoddle score the 1980 *Match of the Day* Goal of the Season?
5 Which Arsenal player was Hoddle's England roommate?
6 Which player was preferred to Hoddle in most of England's 1982 World Cup games?
7 A defeat against which country in 1988 marked the end of Hoddle's international career?
8 Which Cups did Hoddle win with Tottenham?
9 Which manager took Hoddle to Monaco?
10 Who did Hoddle replace as manager of Swindon Town?
11 Which team did Hoddle's Swindon Town beat in the 1993 play-offs?
12 In which season did Hoddle join Chelsea as player manager?
13 Which club defeated Hoddle's Chelsea in the Cup-winners Cup semi-final?
14 Who did Hoddle appoint as England's assistant manager?
15 Which Hoddle brother played for Barnet?
16 What was the name of Hoddle's controversial faith healer?
17 How old was Hoddle when he was appointed England manager?
18 Which creative player was given one last chance for England by Hoddle?
19 Which striker did Hoddle sign for Chelsea for £1.25 million?
20 Who were England's last opposition under Hoddle's management?
   Who did Hoddle sell to Everton a month after taking over at Southampton?

Quiz 78 True or False?

Answers – see page 288

LEVEL 3

1 Reigning champions Leeds United failed to win an away match in 1992-93.

2 'Dixie' Dean's real name was Albert.

3 Ferenc Puskas scored hat-tricks in two European Cup finals.

4 Preston North End have the biggest pitch in the Football League.

5 Bobby Robson was sacked by PSV after taking them to the 1993 UEFA Cup final.

6 Gheorghe Hagi has played for Barcelona and Real Madrid.

7 Pierre van Hooijdonk left Nottingham Forest on a free transfer.

8 Alan Hansen captained Scotland in the 1986 World Cup.

9 Chelsea signed Gabriele Ambrosetti from Vicenza.

10 George Cohen and Ray Wilson are the only 1966 England World Cup heroes not to have been decorated.

11 Jeff Winter is on the 2000-2001 FIFA refereeing list.

12 Spartak, Dynamo and Lokomotiv Moscow all took part in the 2000-2001 Champions League.

13 Opel have sponsored AC Milan, Bayern Munich, PSG and Eire.

14 Steve Stone scored twice on his first two full appearances for England

15 1999-2000 relegated Blackpool had three players in the PFA Divisional Team of the Season.

16 Arsenal paid less to bring Thierry Henry to Highbury than Juventus pa PSV for him in 1999.

17 Fabien Barthez moved to Manchester United for a world record fee fo a goalkeeper.

18 Clydebank and Greenock Morton shared grounds in 1999-2000.

19 Roy Keane was sent off twice in Ireland's 2000 Nike Cup in the USA

20 Davor Suker and Patrik Vieira both missed in the penalty shoot-out ir the 2000 UEFA Cup final.

Answers

Team Colours (see Quiz 80)
1 Light and dark blue quarters. 2 Blue. 3 Sheffield United.
4 Red and white. 5 Liberia 6 Green. 7 Barcelona. 8 South Afri
9 Yellow. 10 Red. 11 Claret and sky blue. 12 The Dell. 13 Whi
14 All white. 15 Dark Blue. 16 Indigo blue (grey). 17 Jimmy Hil
18 Greece. 19 Atletico Madrid. 20 Inter Milan.

Quiz 79 Penalty!

Answers – see page 285

LEVEL 3

1 Who saved Gary Lineker's penalty in the 1991 FA Cup final?

2 Who scored Romania's last-minute penalty against England in Euro 2000?

3 Which England star missed a penalty in his first match in the Italian league?

4 A converted penalty by Tayfur in the play-offs helped which team to Euro 2000?

5 Who scored a penalty against Leeds United at Elland Road in the 2000 EUFA Cup semi-final?

6 Miroslav Djukic's missed penalty in 1994 cost which team the title?

7 A foul on which player earned a penalty for West Germany in the 1990 World Cup final?

8 Which keeper scored a hat-trick of penalties in Argentina in 1999?

9 Whose penalty won Czechoslovakia the 1976 European Championship?

10 Who scored a penalty in the play-offs to send Blackburn to the Premiership in 1992?

11 Who scored a penalty in the Euro '96 final?

12 Which Barnsley player missed a penalty in the 2000 play-offs?

13 Who was the only person in the Twentieth Century to score two penalties in an FA Cup final?

14 Who scored Cameroon's penalty against England in the 1990 World Cup?

15 Which Kilmarnock player's only goal in 1999-2000 came from a penalty?

16 Whose converted penalty set off a mass brawl at Highbury in 1990?

17 Who has scored the most penalties in a English league season?

18 Whose cheeky penalty knocked Sheffield United out of the 1996 FA Cup?

19 Who earned a controversial penalty for Chelsea against Leicester City in the FA Cup in 1997?

20 Who scored Holland's penalty against the Czech Republic in Euro 2000?

1. What colour are Wycombe Wanderers shirts?
2. What colour shirts did Manchester United wear in the 1968 European Cup final?
3. Which Division One club's 2000-2001 away kit was gold and lilac?
4. What colours do Kidderminster Harriers play in?
5. Which country's entire squad wore red boots in the 1996 African Cup of Nations?
6. Which colour shirts do Slovenia wear?
7. Which major European club refuse to have a sponsorship name on their shirts?
8. Which African team play in gold and black shirts?
9. What colour are Celtic's 2000-2001 away shirts?
10. What is the colour of the sash on River Plate's shirts?
11. What colours did Crystal Palace play in before Malcolm Allison changed them?
12. At which ground did Manchester United wear grey shirts for the first half before changing them for the second half because they were 'bad luck'?
13. In what colour shirts do Russia play?
14. What is the least successful FA Cup final colour combination?
15. What colour are Tottenham Hotspur's 2000-2001 away shirts?
16. In which colour shirts did England play Germany in the Euro '96 semi-final?
17. Which Coventry manager changed their colours to Sky Blue?
18. Lazio's colours are based on which country's flag?
19. Which Spanish club's nickname Los Colchomeros (mattress makers) derives from their shirt colours?
20. Which Italian club's nickname Negrazzurri derives from their shirt colours

---

Answers

True or False? (see Quiz 78)
1 True. 2 False. 3 True. 4 False. 5 False. 6 True. 7 False.
8 False. 9 True. 10 False. 11 False. 12 False. 13 True.
14 True. 15 False. 16 True. 17 False. 18 True. 19 False.
20 True.

Quiz 81 Strikers

LEVEL 3

Answers – see page 291

1 Who scored twice for Liverpool against Wimbledon in April 2000?

2 Who top scored for Charlton as they won promotion from the First Division in 1999-2000?

3 Who scored a sensational goal for Rangers in Monaco in a 2001 Champions League group match?

4 Who leads the Huddersfield Town attack?

5 Against whom did Sergei Rebrov score his first goals for Spurs?

6 From which country does Southampton's Marian Pahars come?

7 Who scored a spectacular 20-yarder for Fiorentina against Manchester United in the Champions League in November 1999?

8 Who scored for England in a friendly match in Paris in September 2000?

9 Who scored 30 goals for Sunderland in his first season of Premier League football in 1999-2000?

10 How many goals did Flo and Zola get between them for Chelsea in 1999-2000?

11 From which country does Coventry's Cedric Roussel hail?

12 Where does the much travelled striker Lee Bradbury currently play?

13 Which Villa striker broke his neck in a freak accident in 1999?

14 Who scored twice for Newcastle against Man United in February 2000?

15 Which Everton striker was sent off in the Merseyside derby in September 1999?

16 Who top scored for Norwich City in 1999-2000?

17 Who lines up with Belgium's Branco Strupar in Derby's strike force?

18 Who was the 1999-2000 Scottish Golden Boot winner?

19 For which team did Cameroonian stiker Patrick Suffo sign in summer 2000?

20 Which former Manchester United apprentice scored 25 goals for Preston during 1999-2000?

Novices (see Quiz 83)
1 Steve Moran. 2 Gareth Barry. 3 Lee Bowyer. 4 Ashley Cole.
5 Roque Santa Cruz. 6 David Nish. 7 Jimmy Greaves.
8 Seventeen. 9 Eighteen. 10 Twenty-one. 11 Francis Jeffers.
12 Three. 13 Shaun Wright-Phillips. 14 Titus Bramble.
15 Fowler and Giggs. 16 Jermaine Defoe. 17 Andy Gray.
18 Kenny Miller. 19 Seth Johnson. 20 Lee Sharpe.

Answers

Quiz 82 Politics

Answers – see page 292

1 Which manager reacted with disgust when compared to Margaret Thatcher?

2 Who was West Germany's 1970s Marxist defender?

3 Which Arsenal star appeared at an 80s Conservative party rally at Wembley?

4 Which manager sent a congratulations message to John Major from his sick bed in 1992?

5 Which of Sunderland's 1973 FA Cup winning team later went into politics?

6 Which country's referees went on strike in 1997?

7 Which political issue contributed to England's lowest crowd, against Chile in 1989?

8 Politicians Michael Foot and David Owen support which club?

9 Which former Premier League manager insisted he was a communist?

10 Which Scottish team is supported by two 2000 cabinet ministers?

11 Who was the 80s Minister of Sport who tried to introduce identity cards?

12 Who links the Green Party to Coventry City?

13 Which apartheid apologist MP was a chairman at Luton Town?

14 Which politician was behind the dubious success of Marseilles in the early 1990s?

15 Why was Barcelona able to revert to its Catalan name in 1975?

16 Who wore a slogan under his West Ham shirt supporting striking Essex firemen in 1998?

17 Which club were forced to add Ambrosiana to their name to dilute its Leninist connotations?

18 Which football figure started the Forza Italia political party?

19 Which country withdrew from 1996 African Cup of Nations for political reasons?

20 Who dedicated his World and European Footballer of the Year awards Nelson Mandela?

Answers

Veterans (see Quiz 84)
1 Mark Walters. 2 Dragan Stojkovic. 3 David Watson.
4 David Seaman. 5 Swansea City. 6 Blackpool. 7 Tony Parks.
8 Barry Horne. 9 Peter Davenport. 10 Bobby Mimms.
11 Chris Fairclough. 12 Peter Schmeichel. 13 McCall and Saunder
14 Tony Cottee. 15 Gascoigne. 16 Stuart Pearce. 17 47.
18 John Burridge. 19 Pat Bonner. 20 Lothar Matthaus.

1   Which Southampton forward, a PFA Young Player of the Year, never won an international cap?

2   Who was the youngest member of England's Euro 2000 squad?

3   Who left Charlton in a then record British fee for a teenager?

4   Which 19-year-old scored his first goal for Arsenal in September 2000?

5   Which Bayern Munich signing was the world record fee for a 17-year-old?

6   Who was the youngest FA Cup final captain?

7   Who is the youngest player to score 100 League goals?

8   How old was Pele when he played in the 1958 World Cup finals?

9   How old was Michael Owen when he scored his first England goal?

10   How old was Duncan Edwards when he died in the Munich air disaster?

11   Who is the youngest: Alan Smith, Michael Owen or Francis Jeffers?

12   How many players in Leeds United's 2000 semi-final matches against Galatasaray were under 21?

13   Which 17-year-old made his Manchester City debut in 1999-2000?

14   Which 19-year-old Ipswich Town defender scored his first Premier League goal in 2000-2001?

15   Which two players have won the PFA Young Player of the Year award on two occasions?

16   Which 17- year-old scored his first goal for West Ham in September 2000?

17   Who won the PFA Player and Young Player of the Year awards in the same season?

18   Who was the Scotland's 2000 Young Player of the Year?

19   Which Derby County player was booked in England's opening two fixtures of the under 21 Euro 2000?

20   Which 2000-2001 Premier League player won all eight of his England caps before he was 24?

Quiz 84 Veterans

Answers – see page 290

LEVEL 3

1 Which former Rangers, Liverpool and England player was at Bristol Rovers in 2000-2001?

2 Which Euro 2000 captain played in Euro 84?

3 Who was the eldest defender in Everton's 2000-2001 squad?

4 Which member of England's Euro 2000 squad was born before the 1966 World Cup victory?

5 For which team is Nick Cusack a veteran midfielder?

6 For which team were over 35s Paul Beesley and Mike Newell playing in 2000-2001?

7 Which 2000 Halifax player won a UEFA Cup winners medal?

8 Which former Everton FA Cup winner joined League newcomers Kidderminster Harriers?

9 Which Macclesfield Town player won his only England cap in 1985?

10 Which Mansfield Town player has two League Championship medals?

11 Which 37-year-old 2000-2001 York City defender has a League champions medal?

12 Which goalkeeper played in both a 1985 and a 2000 League Championship winning side, in different countries?

13 Who are Bradford City's 2000-2001 two over 35-year-old internationals?

14 Who last played for England in 1989, but scored 13 goals in the Premier League in 1999-2000?

15 Which is the oldest player: Paul Gascoigne, Paul Ince or Brian Deane?

16 Which 2000 England player was first capped in 1987?

17 How old was Peter Shilton when he made his last League appearance?

18 Who is the oldest player to have played in the Premier League?

19 Who spent 19 seasons at Celtic between 1978 and 1997?

20 Who played in the 1987 and 1999 European Cup finals?

Answers

Politics (see Quiz 82)
1 Alex Ferguson. 2 Paul Breitner. 3 Charlie Nicholas.
4 Graeme Souness. 5 Vic Hallom. 6 Spain. 7 Underground strike.
8 Plymouth Argyle. 9 Egil Olsen. 10 Raith Rovers.
11 Colin Moynihan. 12 David Icke. 13 David Evans.
14 Bernard Tapie. 15 Franco died. 16 Ian Wright. 17 Inter Milan.
18 Silvio Berlusconi. 19 Nigeria. 20 Ruud Gullit.

Quiz 85 Who Played For?

Answers – see page 295 LEVEL 3

1 Liverpool, Wrexham, Chelsea, Huddersfield Town and Wales?
2 Arsenal, Manchester United, Ajax, Derby, Le Havre, Blackburn Rovers and Republic of Ireland?
3 Spurs, Watford, Real Mallorca, WBA and Northern Ireland?
4 Newcastle, Nottingham Forest, Reading, Manchester City and Northern Ireland?
5 CSKA Sofia, Barcelona, Parma and Bulgaria?
6 Tonnerre Yaounde, St Denis, Monaco, Bastia, Montpelier and Cameroon?
7 Montpelier, Everton, Marseille and Nigeria?
8 Orient, WBA, Real Madrid and England?
9 Sampdoria, Juventus, Chelsea and Italy?
10 Manchester United, Newcastle, Blackburn Rovers and Northern Ireland?
11 Coventry City, Manchester United, Aston Villa and England?
12 Southampton, Blackburn Rovers, Leicester City and England?
13 Auxerre, Newcastle, Rangers and France?
14 Borussia Monchengladbach, Inter Milan and Germany?
15 Feyenoord, PSV, AC Milan, Sampdoria, Chelsea and Holland?
16 Borussia Monchengladbach, Barcelona, Charlton and Denmark?
17 Crystal Palace, Arsenal, Luton Town, Aberdeen, Chelsea and Wales?
18 Crystal Palace, Leeds United, Bradford City and Scotland?
19 Flamengo, Deportivo La Coruna, Botafogo, Cruzeiro, Vitoria and Brazil?
20 West Ham, Spurs, Norwich City, Sheffield United and England?

Rovers & Rangers (see Quiz 87)
1 Tranmere. 2 Blackburn. 3 QPR. 4 Glasgow. 5 Bristol.
6 Blackburn. 7 QPR. 8 Bristol. 9 Raith. 10 Berwick. 11 QPR.
12 Tranmere. 13 QPR. 14 Bristol. 15 QPR. 16 Blackburn.
17 Doncaster. 18 Bristol. 19 Glasgow. 20 Tranmere.

293

Quiz 86 Managers

Answers – see page 296

LEVEL 3

1 Which former Coventry City player took over as manager of Solihull Borough in January 2000?

2 Which Ajax coach gave a debut to Marco Van Basten?

3 Which wartime England goalscorer managed Leeds United in their 1955-56 promotion season?

4 At which League club did Ian Atkins take over as manager in June 2000?

5 Who is the 2000-2001 Inter Milan manager?

6 In 1995 who was the last non-Celtic or Rangers Scottish Manager of the Year?

7 Which Italian club has Graeme Souness managed?

8 Which Irish club did Geoff Hurst manage after leaving WBA?

9 Who became the first black manager of an English club, in 1993?

10 Who was Belgium's Euro 2000 manager?

11 Which manager was fined by the FA after indiscretions at the 2000 Worthington Cup final?

12 Bela Guttmann steered which club to European success in the 60s?

13 Which former Arsenal and England striker led Chelsea to their 1954-5 League title?

14 Which club did Malcolm Crosby manage for 27 days in 1998?

15 At which club was Craig Brown assistant manager from 1972-77?

16 Who was Cameroon's coach in the 2000 African Cup of Nations?

17 Which former England striker was sacked by Doncaster Rovers 12 days into the 1997-8 season?

18 For how many games did John Toshack manage Wales in 1994?

19 How much compensation did Tottenham pay Leeds United for George Graham?

20 Which two relegated clubs did Billy McNeill manage in 1986-87?

Answers

Many Clubbed Players (see Quiz 88)
1 10. 2 Burnley. 3 Eric Nixon in 1986-87. 4 Seven.
5 Gordon Cowans. 6 Marco Branca. 7 Dean Saunders.
8 Benito Carbone. 9 12. 10 Chester, Liverpool, Juventus, Leeds, Newcastle, Sheffield Utd and Wrexham. 11 Three. 12 Eight.
13 Brian Laudrup. 14 Eric Cantona. 15 Paolo Di Canio.
16 Derek Mountfield. 17 Paul Ince. 18 Mark Hateley. 19 Nine.
20 Peter Davenport.

1   Which Rovers play in Birkenhead?
2   For which Rovers does Derek Fazackerley hold the appearances record?
3   For which Rangers does Chris Kiwomya lead the line?
4   Of which Rangers is Dick Advocaat the manager?
5   Which Rovers play at the memorial ground?
6   Which Rovers are managed by Graeme Souness?
7   For which Rangers is Alan McDonald the most capped player?
8   Malcolm Allison managed which Rovers between 1992 and 1993?
9   Which Rovers play at Stark's Park?
10   Which Rangers beat Rangers in a Scottish Cup match in 1966-67?
11   That year another Rangers won the League Cup in England. Who was it?
12   Which Rovers won the Leyland Daf trophy in 1990?
3   Which Rangers were originally called St Jude's?
4   Which Rovers used to play at Eastville?
5   Which Rangers beat Partizan Belgrade 6-2 in the 1984-85 UEFA Cup?
6   Which Rovers played West Ham in the League War Cup final in 1940?
7   Which Rovers lost their place in the football league in 1998?
8   Which Rovers finished bottom of Division One in 1992-93?
9   Which Rangers lost twice to Ajax in the 1996-97 European Cup competition?
)   Which Rovers were originally called Belmont AFC?

Quiz 88 Men of Many Clubs
LEVEL 3

Answers – see page 294

1	For how many clubs has striker Steve Claridge played?
2	Where did Arsenal's Lee Dixon begin his career?
3	Which keeper played for five clubs in four divisions in one season?
4	For how many clubs did David Platt play for during his career?
5	Which player had three spells at Aston Villa?
6	Which forward played for eight Italian clubs before joining Middlesbrough?
7	Which Welsh striker started his career in Wales, played in England, Turkey and Portugal, then returned to play for Bradford City?
8	Who played for Torino, Napoli and Inter before joining Sheff Wed?
9	For how many clubs has keeper Les Sealey played?
10	Name Ian Rush's seven clubs.
11	For how many countries did Ladislao Kubala play?
12	Striker Marco Gabbiadini has played for how many clubs?
13	Which great Danish striker played only seven games for Chelsea before leaving for FC Copenhagen in 1998?
14	Who won championship medals with different clubs in two seasons at the beginning of the 1990s?
15	Who went fron Juventus to AC Milan to Celtic to Sheff Wed to West Ham
16	Who played 108 games for Everton, 90 games for Villa, 83 games for Wolves and ended his career at Scarborough?
17	Who started his career at West Ham, moved to Man Utd, then to Inter then to Liverpool and then to Middlesbrough?
18	Which striker started his career at Coventry, then played in Italy, France and Scotland before finishing his career at Hull City?
19	For how many teams has defender Noel Blake played?
20	Which striker played for Forest, Man Utd, Middlesbrough, Sunderland Airdrie, St Johnstone, Stockport and Macclesfield?

Answers

Managers (see Quiz 86)
1 David Busst. 2 Johan Cruyff. 3 Raich Carter. 4 Carlisle United.
5 Marcello Lippi. 6 Jimmy Nicholl. 7 Torino. 8 Cork City. 9 Viv
Anderson. 10 Robert Waseige. 11 John Aldridge. 12 Benfica.
13 Ted Drake. 14 Oxford United. 15 Motherwell. 16 Pierre
Lechantre. 17 Kerry Dixon. 18 One. 19 £3 million.
20 Manchester City and Aston Villa.

In which year did Rangers win their only European trophy?

Who did Dick Advocaat take over from as manager at Ibrox?

Who holds the league appearances record for Rangers?

How many times have Rangers won the Scottish League?

Who beat Rangers in the European Cup Winners' Cup final in 1967?

Who scored a hat-trick for Rangers in the 1996 Scottish Cup final?

In which year did the nine-in-a-row series of league championships for Rangers begin?

In which year was the Rangers centenary?

Where was the 1972 European Cup Winners' Cup final played?

Which Rangers player was voted Footballer of the Year in 1975?

How many times have Rangers won the treble?

How many replays were needed before Rangers won the Scottish FA Cup aganst Hibs in 1979?

Who joined Rangers as player/manager from Sampdoria in 1985?

Who did Rangers play in their first match under Graeme Souness?

Who is the club's all-time top scorer?

Which Englishman scored twice for the Gers in the 1996 League Cup final?

In which year did winger Davie Cooper win his first Scottish Cup winner's medal with Rangers?

Who is the chairman of Rangers?

Who top scored for Rangers during 1998-99?

Who was the first black player to play for the Gers?

Town & County (see Quiz 91)
1 Ipswich. 2 Mansfield. 3 Notts. 4 Huddersfield. 5 Halifax.
6 Stockport. 7 Derby. 8 Swindon. 9 Northampton. 10 Stockport.
11 Shrewsbury. 12 Cheltenham. 13 Derby. 14 Luton. 15 Grimsby.
16 Swindon. 17 Macclesfield. 18 Cheltenham. 19 Grimsby.
20 Derby.

Quiz 90 David Seaman
LEVEL 3

Answers – see page 300

1 In which county was David Seaman born?

2 Which club released him before he had played a first-team match?

3 With which club was he playing when he won England under 21 honours

4 In which year did Seaman make his first full England appearance?

5 In which year did he make his second full England appearance?

6 Who did he replace as Arsenal goalkeeper?

7 The song by rock group Lush 'And Seaman will be disappointed with that…' refers to which match?

8 How many clean sheets did Seaman keep during Arsenal's triumphant 1994 Cup Winners' Cup run?

9 Whose penalty did he save to put England in the semi-finals of Euro '96

10 How many penalties did Seaman save in the 1995 Cup Winners Cup semi-final shootout against Sampdoria?

11 What change did David Seaman make to his appearance at the start of the 2000-2001 season?

12 Which of England's Euro 2000 games did Seaman miss?

13 How much did Arsenal pay QPR for him?

14 What injury kept Seaman out of the Arsenal team in the first 12 matches of the 1999-2000 season?

15 How many clean sheets did Seaman keep in the league in 1999-2000

16 Which team-mate helped pull Seaman from a car crash in April 2000

17 What is Seaman's short and enigmatic nickname?

18 Which Italian international's penalty did Seaman save to win the 199 Cup Winners' Cup semi-final shootout against Sampdoria?

19 Which TV presenter was Seaman's best man at his wedding?

20 How many of Galatasary's penalties did Seaman save in the 2000 U Cup Final?

Quiz 91 Town & County
Answers – see page 297 **LEVEL 3**

1 Which Town play in Suffolk?

2 Which Town are nicknamed 'The Stags'?

3 Which County play local derbies against Forest?

4 Which Town used to play at Leeds Road?

5 Which Town did Jim McCalliog manage in 1990 and 1991?

6 Which County play at Edgeley Park?

7 Who are the only County in the Premier League?

8 Which Town won the Anglo-Italian Cup in 1970?

9 Which Town play in claret with white shirts?

10 For which County does Tony Dinning play?

11 Which Town play at Gay Meadow?

12 Which Town play in the county of Gloucester?

13 For which County does Mart Poom keep goal?

14 For which Town did Joe Payne hit 10 goals in one game in 1936?

15 Which Town only 'sing when they're fishing'?

16 Which Town won the League Cup in 1969?

17 Which Town play at the Moss Rose Ground?

18 For which Town does striker Martin Devaney score goals?

19 Which Town play in Cleethorpes?

20 Which County did Burnley beat in the 2000 FA Cup?

Quiz 92 Who's the Slaphead?
Answers – see page 298
LEVEL 3

1   Steve's balding gracefully in the Sunderland defence?

2   The smallest and baldest full-back in the Premier League?

3   Z-Z (thinning on) Top?

4   Henry showed some cheek as a Gunner?

5   There's nothing butch about this domehead?

6   Poland's follically-challenged 1974 World Cup Golden Boot?

7   Dundee and Tottenham striker who used his shining pate to great effect?

8   Walsall manager who thinned in his Villa days?

9   Middlesbrough's late 70s 'lighthouse brothers'?

10 Danny is an England under 21 moonhead?

11 Bulgarian as a coot, he destroyed Germany's 1990 World Cup?

12 Southampton's 2000 signing is a former Leicester and Villa baldie?

13 Burnley and Tottenham star who copied Sir Bobby's hairstyle?

14 Reading's toupee-wearing Bulgarian keeper?

15 Derby midfielder who gave Scotland a goal to remember?

16 Bayern and Germany's shaven-headed striker?

17 Top Italian shinehead referee?

18 Birmingham, Forest, Derby and Wales 60s bald solid defender?

19 The last balding England captain since Bobby Charlton?

20 Chelsea's flash 70s winger?

Who scored twice for Chelsea in a league game at Old Trafford in September 2000?

Who scored seven goals in the first seven games of the 2000-01 Premiership season?

Who top scored for champions Manchester United in the 1999-2000 season?

Who is Newcastle United's all-time top league scorer?

Who is regarded as the all-time top scorer in world football?

Who is the top scorer in a single World Cup match?

Who holds the record for most international goals in a career?

Who holds the record for most goals in FA Cup finals?

Who scored the only FA Cup final hat-trick?

What is the record number of goals scored by one player in a Premier League season?

What is the record number of goals scored by one player in a League Cup final?

Who were joint top scorers in the First Division in 1984-85?

How many goals did England score v Yugoslavia in a European Championship qualifier in Belgrade in 1988?

What was the score in the 1990 FA Cup semi-final between Liverpool and Crystal Palace?

Which player top scored in the first Premier League season?

Who is Liverpool's all-time leading league goalscorer?

What was the score in the league game that marked John Aldridge's last appearance for Liverpool?

What record was set in that match?

Who is Leeds United's all-time leading league goalscorer?

Who did Arsenal beat 7-0 in the 1993-94 European Cup Winners' Cup?

Losers (see Quiz 95)
1 Chelsea. 2 Sheffield Wednesday. 3 Arsenal. 4 West Ham.
5 18. 6 Holland. 7 Sunderland in 1992. 8 Arsenal in the 1980 European Cup Winners' Cup. 9 Hamburg. 10 7-0.
11 Seven games. 12 Arsenal. 13 QPR. 14 Hearts.
15 Manchester City. 16 Leeds United. 17 Ayr United. 18 England.
19 Germany. 20 Germany.

Quiz 94 Hard Men

Answers – see page 304

LEVEL 3

1 Who left George McCluskey needing nine stitches in a knee in 1986?

2 Who was banned five times between 1964 and 1967?

3 Who, in 1994, became the first player to accumulate 61 points since the disciplinary system began in 1972-73?

4 What is the nickname of hard man Andoni Goicoechea?

5 Which Spurs' hard man spat out two teeth during the 1981 FA Cup Final?

6 How many England caps did Tommy Smith win?

7 Who stamped on Gareth Southgate in the 1994 FA Cup semi-final?

8 Which Sunderland player received 14 bookings in 1998-99?

9 Who broke Southampton's Glen Cockerill's jaw in 1988?

10 Who was sent off for the 13th time, against Chelsea, in January 2000?

11 Which defender was booked for the 64th time in ten seasons in 198?

12 Who was booked within five seconds of a league match in '91 and '9?

13 How many times had Mark Hughes been sent off by the end of the 1999-2000 season?

14 Which Scottish international was sent off 21 times in his career?

15 For how many matches was Andoni Goicoechea banned after breaking Maradona's ankle?

16 How many times had Dennis Wise been sent off by the end of the 1999-2000 season?

17 Which hard man scored for Brighton against his old team in their 19 FA Cup run?

18 Which Bristol-born defender stamped on John Spencer's head in 19?

19 Which Italian marked and kicked Maradona out of a 1982 World Cup?

20 Which hard man's tackle on French star Jacky Simon led to the FA demanding his omission from the England team?

True or False? 2 (see Quiz 96)

Answers

1 True. 2 True, at Bramall Lane, the Oval and in Birmingham.
3 False, it was after 3 seconds. 4 True. 5 False, it was Watford.
6 False, it was in 1996. 7 True. 8 True. 9 True. 10 False, it w
Torquay. 11 True. 12 True. 13 False, it was Scarborough.
14 False, he scored their second goal of three. 15 False, it was 6
16 True, they won 2-0. 17 True. 18 False, it was three.
19 False, Italy beat them in the final. 20 True.

Quiz 95 Losers

Answers – see page 301

LEVEL 3

1 Who lost on penalties in the 1997 Charity Shield?

2 Who lost to Arsenal in both FA Cup and League Cup finals in 1993?

3 Who lost to AC Milan in the 1994 European Super Cup?

4 Who lost 4-2 and 7-1 to Manchester United in the 1999-2000 league season?

5 How many league teams have lost to non-league Yeovil Town?

6 Who lost in the 1978 World Cup final?

7 Who were the first FA Cup final losers to go up the Wembley steps first to collect their medals?

8 Who were the first team to lose a major European final on penalties?

9 Who did Nottingham Forest beat to retain the European Cup in 1980?

10 What was the score in Manchester United's worst league defeat?

11 What is Chelsea's longest sequence of league defeats?

12 Who finished second in the Premier League in 1999-2000?

13 Who did Spurs beat in a replay to win the FA Cup in 1982?

14 Who lost 5-1 in the 1996 Scottish Cup final?

15 Who lost 5-2 to Leeds in the FA Cup fourth round in 2000?

16 Who lost to Coventry in the 1987 FA Cup semi-final?

17 Who lost 7-0 to Rangers in the Tennent's Scottish Cup semi-final in 2000?

18 Who did Brazil beat in the final match of le Tournoi in Paris in 1997?

19 Who lost to Denmark in the European Championship final in 1992?

20 Who did England beat, for the first time in 34 years, in Charleroi in Euro 2000?

1   Liverpool's Titi Camara is the first player from Guinea to play in the Premiership?

2   The first floodlit matches took place in 1878?

3   Chelsea's Vinnie Jones was booked after four seconds of a match against Sheffield United in 1992?

4   Celtic's Jimmy McGrory scored 410 goals in 408 matches before the war?

5   Bristol City won the Second Division championship in 1997-98?

6   Eric Cantona scored the winning goal in the FA Cup final in 1995?

7   Ali Fakih, a Lebanese goalkeeper, did not concede a goal for 1516 minutes?

8   Steve Bull scored 100 goals in two seasons for Wolves between 1987 and 1989?

9   Germany did not win a single game during the Euro 2000 finals?

10   Blackpool became the first team to win promotion on penalties, in 1991?

11   Chris Waddle was voted Player of the Season in 1993?

12   The first football pools coupons were issued in 1920?

13   Kidderminster Harriers became the first team automatically promoted to the football league in 1987?

14   Keith Houchen scored the winner for Coventry against Spurs in the 1987 FA Cup final?

15   The greatest number of clubs that have contested the FA Cup is 676?

16   Bournemouth knocked Manchester United out of the FA Cup in 1984?

17   Bobby Moore saved a penalty for West Ham in the 1972 League Cup semi-final against Stoke?

18   Ladislao Kubala played in internationals for four different countries just after the war?

19   Czechoslovakia won the World Cup in 1934?

20   The Jules Rimet trophy was stolen in Brazil and was never recovered?

Answers

Hard Men (see Quiz 94)
1 Graeme Souness. 2 Billy Bremner. 3 Terry Hurlock.
4   The Butcher of Bilbao. 5 Graham Roberts. 6 One. 7 Roy Keane
8 Kevin Ball. 9 Paul Davis. 10 Steve Walsh. 11 Mark Dennis.
12 Vinnie Jones. 13 Eight. 14 Willie Johnston. 15 21. 16 11.
17 Jimmy Case. 18 Julian Dicks. 19 Claudio Gentile.
20 Nobby Stiles.

Quiz 97 Sackings

Answers – see page 307

LEVEL 3

1 Who was sacked as manager of Chelsea in September 2000?

2 Who was sacked October 2000 as manager of Brazil?

3 Who was sacked by Newcastle in 1992 to make way for Kevin Keegan?

4 Whose contract as England manager was terminated in February 1999 following his controversial comments on disabled people?

5 Who was sacked as manager of Newcastle after just two matches of the 1998-99 season?

6 Whose is the quickest managerial dismissal in English football?

7 Which England manager was sacked in 1974 after 11 years in charge?

8 Who was sacked as manager of Manchester United for breaking the 'moral code'?

9 Who was dismissed as manager of Arsenal for illegal transfer payments?

10 Which legendary player was sacked by Spanish club Seville in 1993 for his disappointing performances?

11 Who was sacked by Everton in November 1994 after 305 days in charge?

12 Who was sacked as manager of Manchester United in November 1986?

13 Who was sacked by Spurs in May 1993 but managed to get himself reinstated by means of a court order?

14 Which World Cup winner was sacked as manager of Chelsea in April 1981?

15 Who was sacked as Wolves manager in 1995 after 18 months for failing to bring Premiership football to Molineux?

16 Who was sacked as boss of Nottingham Forest boss in Janaury 1999?

17 By which two clubs was Ruud Gullit sacked as manager?

18 Who was sacked as Manchester City boss in 1980 after two spells with them?

19 Who was sacked as manager of Everton in 1990 only to return as assistant manager six days later?

20 Who was sacked as manger of Leeds United in 1997?

Answers

Wales (see Quiz 99)
1 Ian Rush. 2 Mark Hughes. 3 1-0 to Argentina. 4 1988.
5 Wales 4 England 1. 6 M Thomas, Walsh, L James and an o.g.
7 Gary Speed. 8 Scotland. 9 1936-37. 10 John Hartson.
11 Paul Jones. 12 Wales lost 4-6. 13 Two, Barry Town and
Cwmbran. 14 Italy, Denmark, Switzerland and Belarus. 15 Fourth.
16 Anfield, Liverpool. 17 Neville Southall. 18 John Toshack.
19 Norwich City. 20 Northern Ireland.

305

Quiz 98 Memorable Matches 2
LEVEL 3

Answers – see page 308

1   Who did Leeds beat to win the Centenary FA Cup final in 1972?
2   What happened in the Division Two match at Maine Road between Manchester City and Huddersfield in November 1987?
3   By how many goals did Rangers beat Aberdeen to win the Tennent's Scottish Cup final in May 2000?
4   What was the score in the World Cup qualifier between Italy and England in Rome in October 1997?
5   In which year did Roger Osborne score the winning goal for Ipswich in the FA Cup final?
6   Liverpool played Celtic in which competition in 1997-98?
7   Which team scored nine goals in two local derbies against Fulham in 1983-84?
8   Which two teams drew 4-4 in the Division 1 play-off final at Wembley in 1998 before the match was decided on penalties?
9   Which was the first Wembley FA Cup final to go to a replay?
10 Who beat Rangers 1-0 in the 1994 Scottish Cup final?
11 What was the score in the first FA Cup final, in 1872?
12 What did the Republic of Ireland do to Northern Ireland in Belfast in 1994?
13 What was significant about the 1983 European Cup final?
14 Where was the 1983 FA Cup final replay played?
15 Which English team were knocked out of the UEFA Cup by Atletico Madrid in 1997-98?
16 Who won the 1982 World Cup match between England and France?
17 Who scored England's second goal against Scotland in Euro 96?
18 Which non-league team beat Coventry City in the FA Cup in 1989?
19 What happened at the UEFA cup match between Moscow Spartak and Haarlem in Moscow in 1992?
20 Who won the all-Merseyside FA Cup final of 1989?

Answers

Kevin Keegan (see Quiz 100)
1 Arthur Cox in 1984. 2 Southampton. 3 49. 4 Scunthorpe.
5 John Toshack. 6 Newcastle United. 7 321. 8 Hamburg. 9 Lawrie McMenemy. 10 Two years. 11 63. 12 1982. 13 1992.
14 1951. 15 QRR 16 Terry McDermott. 17 Fulham. 18 'Mighty Mouse'. 19 1999. 20 Three to Scotland, Portugal and Romania.

LEVEL 3

1   Who has scored most goals as a Welsh international?

2   Who took over from Bobby Gould as manager of Wales?

3   Wales played Argentina in Tokyo in 1992. What was the score?

4   In which year was Wales' only victory against Italy?

5   What was the score of the Wales v England match at Wrexham in 1980?

6   Who scored the Welsh goals that day?

7   Who scored Wales' winner against Moldova in Cardiff in September 1995?

8   Who were Wales' first international opponents?

9   When did Wales last win the Home International Championship outright?

10 Who scored Wales' winner against Scotland in May 1997?

11 Who kept goal for Wales against Jamaica in March 1998?

12 What was the score when Wales played Turkey in Istanbul in 1997?

13 How many Welsh clubs have contested the European Cup?

14 Who were in Wales' qualifying group for Euro 2000 ?

15 Where did Wales finish in the group?

16 Where did Wales play their home match against Denmark in that competition?

17 Who is Wales's most capped player?

18 Who acted as Wales's manager for one match in 1994?

19 Where does Welsh international Craig Bellamy play his club football?

20 Against whom did keeper Neville Southall make his debut for Wales in 1982?

1   Who said of Wor Kev 'No other player in the world could have had such a dramatic effect on the club and its supporters'?

2   From which club did Newcastle sign Kevin Keegan in 1984?

3   How many goals did Keegan score during his playing days with the Magpies?

4   For which club did Keegan make his league debut?

5   Who was Keegan's main strike partner at Liverpool?

6   Who did Keegan and Liverpool beat in the 1974 FA Cup final?

7   How many appearances did Keegan notch up for the Reds?

8   Who did Keegan join when he left Liverpool in 1977?

9   Who was manager at Southampton when he returned to England in 1980?

10   How long did Keegan stay on the south coast?

11   How many England caps did he win?

12   In which year did Keegan win his OBE?

13   When did Keegan become manager of Newcastle?

14   In which year was Keegan born?

15   Against whom did Keegan make his playing debut for Newcastle?

16   Who was Keegan's assistant manager at Newcastle?

17   Where did Keegan go after his term as manager of Newcastle?

18   What was Keegan's nickname at Liverpool?

19   When did Keegan take over as England manager?

20   Up to the end of Euro 2000, how many matches had England lost under Keegan's leadership?

Answers

Memorable Matches 2 (see Quiz 98)
1 Arsenal. **2** Manchester City won 10-1. **3** 4-0. **4** 0-0.
5 1978. **6** UEFA Cup. **7** Chelsea. **8** Charlton and Sunderland.
9 Chelsea v Leeds, 1970. **10** Dundee United. **11** Wanderers 1
Royal Engineers 0. **12** Beat them 4-0. **13** First time for seven years
without an English club. **14** Wembley. **15** Aston Villa.
16 England won 3-1. **17** Paul Gascoigne. **18** Sutton United.
19 340 crushed to death on stairway. **20** Liverpool.

1. Who captained Charlton when they returned to the Premier League in 2000?
2. Who left Man City in 1989 for West Ham, then returned to City in 1998?
3. Which Barnsley midfielder was voted Division One Player of the Year in 1999-2000 and was then sold to Blackburn?
4. Which French midfield great of the 1980s is now manager of Fulham?
5. Which legendary hard man leads the midfield for both Manchester United and the Republic of Ireland?
6. Who made his Anfield debut for Liverpool v Sunderland in September 2000?
7. Which midfielder arrived at Highbury from Marseille during summer 2000?
8. Which Rangers midfielder was born in Kirograd in the Ukraine?
9. Which former Arsenal midfielder went on to coach at Stamford Bridge?
10. Which midfielder had success with Aberdeen, Manchester United and Leeds before going into management with Coventry City?
11. Who scored the winner for Man City in the 1981 FA Cup semi-final v Ipswich?
12. Which former Burnley and Everton midfielder appeared in the FA Cup final in 1984, 1985 and 1986?
13. Which club's colours did Manchester United adopt as their away kit in 1992-93?
14. Which current Leeds United midfielder was born in Llanelli?
15. Which midfielder is player-coach at Gillingham?
16. Which midfielder, born in Maidstone, played for Southampton, Norwich, Chelsea, Aston Villa and Middlesbrough during his career?
17. Whose midfield might read: Powell, Burley, Johnson, Kinkladze in 2000-01?
18. Which Leeds midfielder missed the whole of the 1999-2000 season and seems unlikely to play again until 2001?
19. For whom does young Michael Carrick patrol the midfield?
20. Who is the inspirational midfielder and skipper of Preston North End?

1   Chris Kelly became which non-league team's 'Lip' on their 1975 FA Cup run?

2   What do West Brom, West Ham, Southampton and Sunderland have in common?

3   Who were the 'lucky losers' in 2000?

4   What have the Wanderers, Blackburn, Newcastle and Tottenham (twice) achieved?

5   At what age did Bergkamp play his first match in a European competition?

6   What do Mark Hughes, John Barnes and Roy Keane have in common?

7   Who were the last team to win the FA Cup with an all-English side?

8   Which team did Arsenal beat 2-1 twice in the 1999 FA Cup?

9   Who since 1900 has won the most FA Cup winner's medals?

10   Who since 1900 has been the winning FA Cup captain on three occasions?

11   What FA Cup fact ties Tom Finney, Johnny Haynes and George Best?

12   Who were the last team to win the FA Cup without an international player?

13   Who knocked champions Arsenal out of the FA Cup in 1992?

14   What was the last year that both semi-finals were local derbies?

15   Who won the first FA Cup tie to be decided on a penalty shoot-out?

16   What 'double' did West Bromwich Albion win in 1931?

17   In the 70s who became the first substitute to score in an FA Cup final

18   In which way did Manchester United win the FA Cup against the odds in 1990?

19   Which Hertfordshire team's cup run ended in an acrimonious match against Newcastle in 1998?

20   Manchester City, Leicester, Brighton and Middlesbrough all were what?

Answers

Last-gasp Goals   (see Quiz 104)
1 Spain. 2 Gary Stevens. 3 David Hopkin. 4 Gillingham. 5 Dani.
6 Dwight Yorke. 7 Poland. 8 Stuart Pearce. 9 Paul Gascoigne.
10 117th. 11 Roberto Baggio. 12 Andy Linighan. 13 Motherwell.
14 Julius Aghahowa of Nigeria. 15 Luis Hernandez. 16 Alan Smith
17 France. 18 Paul Scholes 19 Republic of Ireland.
20 Martin Keown.

Quiz 103 Injuries

Answers – see page 309   **LEVEL 3**

1   Which Republic of Ireland striker ruptured a knee cartilage in 1998 by stretching to pick up his TV remote control?

2   Whose knee gave out a few days after failing a medical in 2000?

3   Which injured player did Geoff Hurst replace in England's 1966 team?

4   What kept Gordon Banks out of England's 1970 tie with West Germany?

5   Which player had ten facial stitches during half-time of England's 1990 World Cup qualifier in Sweden?

6   Who missed the rest of the tournament after an injury in England's first Euro 2000 match?

7   Which captain missed the 1983 Wembley Cup Final due to injury?

8   Which international broke Gazza's leg in a training session in 1994?

9   Which Premier League full-back needed treatment for a knee strain caused by stretching to reach the accelerator in his new Ferrari?

10   Who drew Gazza into a career-threatening tackle in the '91 FA Cup final?

11   Which Arsenal player needed treatment after hitting himself in the face with the corner flag in a goal celebration?

12   Which substitute was injured in England's Euro '96 tie with Scotland?

13   Who was taken to court for a tackle that ended Paul Elliott's career?

14   Which star's injury was put back when he was run over by a tricycle?

15   Which injury kept Michael Owen out of much of the 1999-2000 season?

16   How did Man United keeper Alex Stepney break his jaw in 1975?

17   Which two injured players came on in a double substitution in England's last 1982 World Cup match?

18   Which Arsenal legend never fully recovered from cutting off a big toe with a lawnmower?

19   Injuries to what part of his body ended Marco Van Basten's career?

20   Which Polish hero missed the 1974 World Cup because of injury?

Answers

Midfielders   (see Quiz 101)
1 Mark Kinsella. 2 Ian Bishop. 3 Craig Hignett. 4 Jean Tigana.
5 Roy Keane. 6 Bernard Diomede. 7 Robert Pires.
8 Andrei Kanchelskis. 9 Graham Rix. 10 Gordon Strachan.
11 Paul Power. 12 Trevor Steven. 13 Newton Heath. 14 Matthew Jones. 15 Andy Hessenthaler. 16 Andy Townsend. 17 Derby County's. 18 David Batty. 19 West Ham. 20 Sean Gregan.

1   Who scored two goals in the last minute to win a crucial Euro 2000 tie?

2   Who scored Brighton's 87th-minute equaliser in the 1984 FA Cup final?

3   Whose 1997 last-minute goal won the play-offs for Crystal Palace ?

4   Headers from Steve Butler and Andy Thomson in the last six minutes of extra time won the 2000 play-offs for which side?

5   Whose goal seven minutes from time against Chelsea rescued his team in the 2000 Champions League quarter-final?

6   Who scored an 81st-minute goal to salvage a point in Manchetser United's World Club championship tie with Necaxa in 2000?

7   Against whom did Ian Wright score his first England goal, in the 84th minute?

8   Whose last-minute free-kick goal was disallowed in England's 1990 World Cup match with Holland?

9   Whose first England goal came in the 88th minute against Albania in '89?

10   In which minute did Zidane score to win the Euro 2000 tie with Portugal?

11   Who hit Italy's last-gasp equaliser in the '94 World Cup tie with Nigeria?

12   Who headed Arsenal's last-minute goal in the 1993 FA Cup final?

13   Who won the Scottish FA Cup in 1991 with a last-minute goal by Kirk?

14   Who scored three goals in as many games as a very late substitute in the 2000 African Cup of Nations?

15   Who scored Mexico's stoppage-time goal against Holland in World Cup '98?

16   Who passed to Michael Thomas for his 1989 title-winning last-gasp goal?

17   Bellone scored a last-minute winner for which Euro '84 team?

18   Whose last-gasp goal against Inter Milan took Manchester United through to the Champions League semi-finals in 1999?

19   A late goal by Stavrevski put paid to whose Euro 2000 group qualification?

20   Who scored Arsenal's last-gasp winner in their 2000 Champions League match against Shakhtar Donetsk?

Answers

FA Cup   (see Quiz 102)
1 Leatherhead. **2** Won Cup when in Division Two.   **3** Darlington.
4 Won Cup in successive years. **5** 17. **6** They are the last three of nine men to have played in five finals. **7** West Ham. **8** Sheffield Utd. **9** Mark Hughes, four. **10** Bryan Robson. **11** Never won Cup.
12 Sunderland. **13** Wrexham. **14** 1993. **15** Aston Villa.
16 Cup and promotion. **17** Eddie Kelly. **18** Every game was away.
19 Stevenage Town. **20** Relegated Cup finalists.

HOW TO SET UP YOUR OWN
PUB QUIZ

It isn't easy, get that right from the start. This isn't going to be easy. Think instead of words like; 'difficult', 'taxing' and 'infuriating'. A bit like a Wednesday night cup-tie against Yeovil. Consider yourself with damp palms and a dry throat and then, when you have concentrated on that, put it out of your mind and think of the recognition you will receive at your local, imagine all the regulars lifting you high upon their shoulders dancing and weaving their way around the pub. Just like they did in '66. It won't help but it's good to dream every once in a while.

What you will need:

A good selection of Biros (never be tempted to give your own pen up, not even to family members)

A copy of *The Best Football Pub Quiz Book Ever!* *(Volume 2)*

A set of answer sheets photocopied from the back of the book

A good speaking voice and possibly a microphone and an amp

A pub

At least one pint inside you

At least one more on your table

A table

What to do:

Choose your local to start with, there is no need to get halfway through your first quiz and decide you weren't cut out for all this and then find yourself in the roughest pub in Christendom 30 miles and a long run from home.

Chat it through with the landlord and agree on whether you will be charging or not, if you don't then there is little chance of a prize for the winners other than a free pint each and this is obviously at the landlord's discretion – if you pack his pub to bursting then five free pints won't worry him, but if it's only you and a two others then he may be less than unwilling, as publicans tend to be.

If you decide on a payment entry keep it reasonable, you don't want to take the fun out of the quiz; some people will be well aware that they have very little hope of winning and will be reluctant to celebrate the fact by mortgaging their house.

Once location and prize are all sorted, then advertising the event is paramount. Get people's attention – sell sell, sell or, alternatively, stick up a gaudy looking poster on the door of the bogs. Be sure to specify all the details, time, prize and so on – remember you are selling to people whose tiny attention span is being whittled down to nothing by alcohol.

After this it is time for the big night, if you are holding the event in the 'snug' which seats ten or so you can rely on your voice, if not you should get hold of a good microphone and an amplifier so that you can boom out your questions and enunciate the length and breadth of the pub – once again, clear this with the landlord and don't let liquid anywhere near the electrical equipment. Make sure to practice, and get comfortable with the sound of your own voice and relax as much as possible, try not to rely on alcohol too much or "round one" will be followed by "rown' too" which will eventually give way to "runfree". Relax with your voice so that you can handle any queries from the teams, and any venomous abuse from the 'lively' bar area.

When you enter the pub make sure you take everything listed above. Also, make sure you have a set of tie-break questions and that you instruct everybody who is taking part of the rules – and be firm. It will only upset people if you start handing out impromptu solutions and let's face it the wisdom of Solomon is not needed when you are talking pub quiz rules; 'no cheating' is a perfectly healthy stance to start with.

Finally, keep the teams to a maximum of five members, hand out your answer papers and pens and, when everybody is good and settled, start the quiz. It might not be easy and it might not propel you to international stardom or pay for a life of luxury but you will enjoy yourself. No, really.

ANSWERS

1 _____

2 _____

3 _____

4 _____

5 _____

6 _____

7 _____

8 _____

9 _____

10 _____

11 _____

12 _____

13 _____

14 _____

15 _____

16 _____

17 _____

18 _____

19 _____

20 _____

ANSWERS

Part Two

1 _____   11 _____

2 _____   12 _____

3 _____   13 _____

4 _____   14 _____

5 _____   15 _____

6 _____   16 _____

_____   17 _____

_____   18 _____

_____   19 _____

0 _____   20 _____

ANSWERS

Part Three

1 _____

2 _____

3 _____

4 _____

5 _____

6 _____

7 _____

8 _____

9 _____

10 _____

11 _____

12 _____

13 _____

14 _____

15 _____

16 _____

17 _____

18 _____

19 _____

20 _____

Useful Notes

Useful Notes